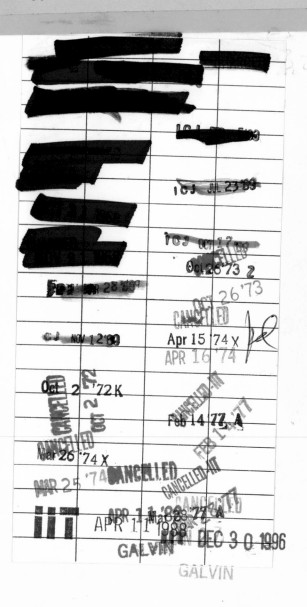

The Physics of Engineering Solids

The Physics of

Royal Military College of Canada

New York and London

Engineering Solids

T. S. Hutchison and D. C. Baird

John Wiley and Sons, Inc.

Library of Congress Catalog Card Number: 63-12281
Printed in the United States of America

Preface

The invasion of engineering practice by the methods, discoveries, and man-power of the physical sciences which has occurred over the last two decades is now being reflected in the teaching curricula of most engineering schools. The most spectacular aspects of this invasion lie in the introduction of nuclear power and the ever-growing use of electronic devices of a solid state nature. There is no doubt that the engineering students now in our schools and universities will, throughout their professional lives, make almost exclusive use of such devices for the measurement and control of nuclear and electrical power, radiation, heat, liquid and gas flow, temperature, acceleration, strain, etc., in the engineering systems with which they are associated.

To assist in the discovery and development of solid state instruments, it is necessary in most cases to have a knowledge and working familiarity with quantum mechanics to a greater degree than that usually acquired at the undergraduate level. This applies to students of physics and chemistry as well as engineering. In order, however, to make intelligent use of existing devices and to forecast new uses this is not so. A sound grasp of the fundamental principles on which the physics of the solid state is based should suffice. This is also true of the current use of electronic tubes which can be intelligently employed without a specialist's knowledge of electron ballistics and thermionic emission. Familiarity with the fundamental principles of these latter two topics is, however, essential.

Therefore, the purpose of this textbook is to acquaint the undergraduate engineer with the fundamental properties of the solid state. These properties fall into two categories. One aspect is purely geometrical and

v

deals with the packing characteristics of atoms in a solid. These packing characteristics and the defects from perfection which occur govern to a great extent the mechanical properties of the solid. They also govern the possible types of alloying of several elements. In addition, the interaction of defects and electrons are responsible for many of the characteristics of semiconductors and luminescent solids. The second fundamental aspect of the physics of the solid state concerns the allowed energies of electrons in solids. An understanding of this aspect requires a knowledge of quantum mechanics. The book then falls into two parts. Chapters 1 to 5 are concerned with the consequences of the periodic nature of atomic packing in solids. Chapters 6 to 8 introduce the quantum principles, and Chapters 9 to 13 introduce the consequences of these principles when applied to electrons in solids.

We have made no attempt to avoid a certain amount of repetition in the chapters introducing wave mechanics, since it is here that the imagination of the student will be most severely taxed. In the chapters that follow, we introduce a number of solid state devices in current use and discuss these in terms of simple physical models that depend on the energy band structure. We have, of course, omitted from our discussion a number of types of engineering solids. For instance, we have made no reference to ceramics, organic solids, agglomerated solids, and a number of others that are undoubtedly of technical importance. We have also omitted descriptions of a number of important physical phenomena. Examples of these are dipole relaxation, internal friction, corrosion, and radiation damage. Throughout we have limited our selection to the aspects of solids that are of technical importance, and for which there exists a relatively simple physical model.

A group of problems follow each of the chapters, these being for the most part exercises on the topics of the chapters. An attempt has been made to introduce into the problems some association of theory with practice. As far as possible, however, the problems have been kept elementary, in keeping with the intention that this is a second- or third-year book and will be studied in a busy curriculum.

Courses in mathematics and physics at the level given in the first and second years of most engineering schools should suffice as introductory material to most of this work.

In a book of this nature, which is not original, we owe a great deal to the books already published. In particular we would like to record our special indebtedness to the books by Professors Barrett, Sproull, Kittel, and Dekker.

T. S. Hutchison
D. C. Baird

Kingston, Ontario, Canada
February, 1963

Contents

Introduction

It is our intention in this introduction to summarize the topics to be discussed in subsequent sections. The introduction can be read to give a more detailed estimate of the scope of the book than appeared in the Preface. It should be read at the conclusion of detailed work on the chapters to enable the reader to fit this work into the overall study of solids which has been attempted.

Chapter 1 concerns the nature of crystal structure. The complete determination of crystal structure is a highly specialized art that involves a detailed knowledge of and familiarity with the subjects of symmetry and space groups. Since it is impossible within the present framework to do justice to these topics, we have restricted their discussion to a superficial description of the nature of the problems. This chapter is principally concerned, therefore, with a description of some of the easier structures found in metals, ionic crystals, and semiconducting compounds.

Chapter 2 deals with the diffraction techniques used in the examination of the atomic pattern of solids. The measurement of lattice parameters, orientation, grain size, stress, etc., in crystals is a part of the work of the development as well as the research laboratory. Without an acquaintance with the nature of the techniques involved in these measurements, the engineer will lack a sense of familiarity with crystal structure. Furthermore, many laboratories are concerned with crystal structures but lack the services of a crystal structure analyst. We have therefore included a discussion of more of these procedures than might at first sight seem necessary.

Chapter 3 deals with a few of the common types of alloy, and it is chiefly metallurgical in nature. So many of the recent advances in solid-state physics and technology depend on the new availability of pure materials and controlled alloys and compounds that the omission of a chapter on alloys in a book on solids would be completely misleading. Transistor technology is a case in point. Without the knowledge of the purification techniques involved, the world would still await the practical realization of the physics of semiconductors. In Chapter 3 we have very briefly dealt with the concept of free energy and have omitted a thermodynamic analysis of phase diagrams. We have done this because, although the free-energy diagrams are fundamental, it is often not yet possible to predict the equilibrium diagram from the free-energy diagram, and the study is still largely phenomenological. We have therefore given only the composition-temperature equilibrium diagrams.

In Chapter 4 we introduce the concept of defects in solids and describe the Schottky and Frenkel types. The equilibrium number of Schottky defects at a certain temperature is obtained in full, partly because of its intrinsic importance, and also because the mathematical technique is similar to that encountered in the problem of the entropy of mixing in alloys. The central topic of Chapter 4 is the discussion of diffusion. The mechanisms of solid-state diffusion are related to the presence of defects. Quite simple derivations of Fick's laws are given. In the development the concept of atom movements is used since this is more meaningful to the less mathematically sophisticated student. It is hoped that the ideas connected with the movement of atoms down a concentration gradient will be carried over into the study of the movement of charge carriers as in semiconductor junctions.

Chapter 5 deals with the elastic and plastic properties of solids. Following definitions of stress and strain, Hooke's law is given for isotropic solids. Anisotropy is then discussed, and the elastic constants for single crystals introduced. The purpose of the book unfortunately prevents inclusion of a full discussion of changes of axes, a topic that is so useful to the practising researcher on single crystals. After elasticity, a phenomenological discussion is given of plastic deformation. The effects of temperature, purity, prior deformation, and rate of strain are qualitatively described. After this introduction to plastic flow the mechanisms are discussed. Dislocation theory is introduced and a number of the mathematical properties of dislocations are deduced. To end the chapter the evidence for the presence of dislocations is presented. We hope that at this point the student will have before him the qualitative picture of deformation and the properties of the defects which give rise to deformation. We have been unable to give sufficient space to show adequately the correspondence between these two topics, but we hope that the reader, thus equipped, will have a basis for future study of the dislocation picture.

At this point in the text further discussion of the geometrical aspects of solids is postponed. We must now pave the way for presentation of the nature of charge transfer in solids. Chapter 6 therefore provides an introduction to wave mechanics. The particle and wave properties of the electron are discussed and the time-dependent and time-independent Schroedinger equations obtained. Two examples are given at this point to illustrate the solutions of the Schroedinger equation in the free and bound cases. The problems chosen are also of a type that will be useful in later work. This is the physicist's approach to the subject and it does not often appear in books for engineers. We believe, however, that it is realistic to include it here since further study of quantum mechanics is necessary in solid-state physics and is possible only on an adequate foundation.

Chapter 7 contains the discussion of the energy levels of a single electron. The solution of the Schroedinger equation for the hydrogen atom is sketched out, the purpose being to give plausibility to the introduction of the quantum numbers. The significance of these numbers is then discussed. To work toward the conditions of an electron in a solid, we introduce the splitting of the energy level which results from bringing first two and then more hydrogen nuclei close together. This topic enables the nature and significance of sharp, tightly bound levels and of energy bands to be presented. From this point on in Chapter 7 the emphasis is on the properties and available energies of the loosely bound valence electrons. The pace of presentation of new ideas has been deliberately slowed in this part of the book, because it takes time for the student at his first meeting with the subject to appreciate the relationships and differences between electron energy levels in isolated atoms and in solids. The chapter closes with the Kronig-Penney model of the electron in a periodic lattice and the introduction of the ideas of boundary values of allowed energies. The nature of Brillouin zones is discussed, and the form of the zone boundaries given in some simple cases. It is emphasized that many of the properties of electrons in solids will be governed by the closeness of the electron energy to the value at the boundary of the Brillouin zone.

Chapter 8 shifts the emphasis from the properties of a single electron to the distribution of an assembly of electrons among the available energies. The nature of distribution functions is discussed, the Pauli Exclusion Principle stated and the Fermi function presented. We can then combine the expression for the density of available states with the expression for the probability of occupation in order to obtain the actual number of electrons in any energy interval. Since the problem has resolved itself into the calculation of the state density function for each problem, examples are given for a number of systems. The first example concerns the distribution of electrons in atoms. The quantum numbers are recalled and the electrons in multi-electron atoms are allotted their quantum numbers in accordance with the Exclusion Principle. The elements at the beginning of the Periodic Table are used as examples, and the connection between the energies of the various electrons and the chemical nature of the elements is emphasized.

The second example of a distribution function is that of the relatively free electron in a broadened energy band. Through this we can come to the concept of the Fermi surface and the importance of the role of the Fermi energy in solid state electronics. We hope, then, in Chapters 6, 7, and 8 to have brought the reader to an appreciation of the nature of electronic energy levels in atoms and solids and of the characteristic parameters of the population by electrons of these levels.

Chapter 9 discusses the first practical uses that are made of the concepts of electron distribution. In our description of the electronic properties of metals, we first divide these properties into two groups. In the first group, dealt with in Chapter 9, we concern ourselves mostly with the electron emission phenomena. These generally involve relatively high-energy excitation, and the free electron theory is adequate for the present purpose. The second group, treated in Chapter 10, concerns the conduction properties in which the perturbation of the electron distribution is generally small and consequently more sensitive to band structure. Our examples in the first group, which we have called the static electron properties (in contrast to the transport mechanisms of conduction phenomena), include photoelectric phenomena, some aspects of X-ray emission, thermionic emission, and field emission, and a study of contact potentials. Chapter 9 concludes with a short discussion of the specific heat of electrons in a metal. This topic is of historical interest since it constituted one of the earliest triumphs of the quantum theory. It is also likely to be of increasing technical importance with the introduction of new solid-state devices working at the very low temperatures at which the electronic specific heat becomes significant.

Chapter 10 concerns electrical conductivity in metals. It is first emphasized that we are here concerned with the electrons at the Fermi surface only. The relative configurations of the Fermi surface and the Brillouin zone boundaries strongly govern the effect that an accelerating electric field has on the conduction electron. This effect is partially taken into account by assigning to the electron an "effective mass." This modification to the Kronig-Penney treatment is considered in some detail because of its central importance to the whole of conductivity theory. After a computation of the value of the conductivity, we summarize the sources of electrical resistance which exist in metals. The temperature-dependent contribution is discussed at greater length than the residual resistance because of the inadequacies of theory which still exist when dealing with the scattering of electrons by defects. High-frequency conduction is discussed and related briefly to the optical properties of metals. The research tool of cyclotron resonance, which is treated next, is invaluable because of its power in the measurement of effective masses. The chapter continues with a discussion of the conduction of heat by electrons and the law of Wiedemann and Franz which relates the conduction of heat and of electricity in metals. The chapter closes with a description of the phenomenon of superconductivity. Until a very few years ago this was purely a research topic and little understood. Today many of the fundamental questions have been answered and the application of superconducting devices in technology has made the topic one of widespread and growing interest.

Chapter 11 moves the discussion of electrical conductivity to the case of semiconducting materials. Here the band structure, in contrast to metals, is characterized by an energy gap between the filled valence band and the empty conduction band. The number of charge carriers is greatly influenced by temperature and by the presence of impurity atoms which can contribute a surplus or deficit of electrons when combined with the pure semiconductor matrix. The position of the Fermi level in intrinsic or pure semiconductors and in extrinsic or impure semiconductors is established. With this knowledge we can then apply the theory that was discussed in the previous two chapters to compute the number of charge carriers and hence the conductivity. The distinction between a metal and a semiconductor is examined in some detail so that the reader may see clearly the essential difference between ohmic and rectifying contacts. Following this the $p - n$ junction and the $n - p - n$ transistor are discussed from the fundamental point of view, but the circuitry of junctions and transistors is omitted completely. The chapter concludes with a brief description of a number of semiconducting devices.

Two classes of solid-state phenomenon—the magnetic and dielectric properties—remain to be discussed. They have been treated in the last two chapters. In the chapter on magnetism we begin by reminding the reader of the quantities induction, field intensity, and dipole moment, because of the widely differing interpretations of these quantities which are apparent in the books on magnetism. These macroscopic quantities are then related to the atomic quantity of magnetic susceptibility. The solids are then characterized both by the magnitude of their susceptibility and by its temperature dependence, which is less confusing than a classification by magnitude alone. The rest of the chapter relates the nature of the atom to the magnetic susceptibility. Diamagnetism is discussed from a greatly simplified electron orbit model. The existence of permanent spin dipole moments oriented in a magnetic field according to Boltzmann statistics is used to give the paramagnetic dipole moment. The susceptibility is thus obtained as a function of temperature, and consequently Curie's law is derived.

The nature of the enormous internal fields which give rise to ferromagnetism is discussed from the point of view of band theory, following the analyses of Slater and Stoner. No attempt is made here to account rigorously for the exchange integral. The energy terms which give rise to domains and the factors which influence the growth of domains related to the existence of hard and soft magnetic materials are briefly mentioned. The chapter concludes with a very brief discussion of antiferromagnetism and ferrimagnetism in MnO and magnetite respectively.

The concluding chapter of the book concerns the solids in which an energy gap exists between the valence and conduction bands that is too large for the conductivity to be markedly affected by temperature. First the quantities electric displacement, field strength, and dipole moment are defined, as were the analogous quantities in magnetism. The relation between the quantities is found and the polarizability defined. The remainder of the discussion of dielectrics relates the polarizability to the atomic characteristics of the solid. The polarization of a molecule in a solid is effected by the local field to which it is subjected, and we discuss therefore the terms that make up the local field. The electronic, ionic, and orientational polarizability are defined, and the method of separating them by the use of alternating fields is given. We have omitted a discussion of dipole relaxation and absorption because of the difficulties of adequate mathematical presentation in a book of this nature, and because, with few exceptions, the techniques involved are still those of the research scientist. Ferroelectricity is discussed, using the best known example of barium titanate. A greatly simplified order-of-magnitude calculation is given of the polarization, and the polarization catastrophe which characterizes such phenomena is briefly mentioned. The discussion of polarization closes with a description of the related phenomenon of piezoelectricity in which we have again used a greatly simplified model.

The remaining properties of solids which we discuss result from the presence of impurities in dielectric solids. The difference between such solids and semiconductors arises only from the magnitude of the energy gap between the valence and conduction bands. Localized energy levels associated with the impurities or defects give rise to a number of optical phenomena which are described. We have reminded the reader of the nature of optical absorption and have dealt briefly with the re-emission of absorbed energy. The time between excitation and re-emission is dependent on the presence of electron-trapping centers. We have therefore discussed traps in simple phosphors and the phenomena of phosphorescence and fluorescence. To conclude the chapter we have devoted a section to the mechanism of stimulated emission which differentiates laser action from normal fluorescence. We have used only one example, that of the ruby laser, to point out the difference, and we have chosen this example because of its popular interest and great number of potential applications.

1

Crystal Structures

1.1 The Properties of Crystals

Most solids exist naturally in crystalline form. By this is meant that the atoms of which the solid is composed are arranged in a regular pattern, the regularity or order extending over distances many times the diameter of the atoms. The crystalline form is characterized by a number of physical properties, some of which will be briefly discussed.

X-rays, electrons, and neutrons are scattered by the regular planes of atoms in crystalline solids, the scattered beam leaving the crystal in certain preferred directions. A highly developed technique exists for deducing the arrangement of the atoms in the solid from measurements of the scattering angles and intensities. This technique, known as diffraction, has contributed most of the recent crystallographic information. We shall give consideration to diffraction in Chapter 2.

Mineral crystals sometimes reveal well-defined planes of growth, which give an external appearance of symmetry. The significant feature is that the angles between corresponding faces are constant. The crystal can often be cleaved along these planes, a familiar example being diamond, which cleaves along planes parallel to the eight faces of an octahedron.

Since the atoms of the crystal are arranged in a regular pattern, it follows that particular directions are characterized by their unique periodicity of atomic spacing. It is not surprising, therefore, to find that a number of physical properties depend markedly on the direction in the crystal in which the property is measured. Such properties reveal the *anisotropy* of the crystal. Examples of physical properties which in many crystals are direction dependent, are the refractive index, the electrical conductivity, the Hall coefficient, the magnetic susceptibility, and many others.

Most solid materials as they occur in their usual form are composed of very large numbers of small crystals of various sizes, packed together in an irregular way. The boundaries between the individual crystals are called *grain boundaries*. The presence of these grain boundaries affects many of the physical properties of the solid. Materials with many crystals are said to be *polycrystalline*. If the crystals composing the polycrystalline aggregate are randomly oriented with respect to one another, a physical property dependent on direction in a single crystal will not show anisotropy in the polycrystalline solid.

Before we describe some of the crystal structures associated with the technologically important metals, ionic crystals, and semiconductors, it is necessary to have a reference scheme to which the atomic positions may be referred. For every crystal there is a unit of pattern called the *unit cell* which, when repeated many times with the cells stacked against one another, constitute a lattice for the crystal. The method of choosing such a unit cell will now be given.

1.2   The Unit Cell

Suppose we have an arrangement of atoms depicted by the circles in Fig. 1.1*a*. We first choose a point *P* and then every other point which has the same environment as *P*. These equivalent points form a *space lattice*. In three-dimensional space, it is obvious that the connecting lines form an arrangement of identical parallelepipeds. Each elementary parallelepiped is called a *unit cell*. The points of the space lattice need not be atomic sites, although in some crystals, particularly metals where a single atom is the unit of pattern, it is obviously convenient to make the points of the space lattice and the atomic sites coincide. Figure 1.1*b* shows that the space lattice of *a* is also a good choice to describe the atomic pattern of *b* in which the atom is the unit of pattern. It is obvious that many space lattices and unit cells can be chosen as reference networks for a particular atomic arrangement. For example, in Fig. 1.1*c*, which has an identical atomic arrangement to *b*, a different choice of unit cell has been made. It should be noted that there is in *a*, *b*, and *c* a one-to-one correspondence between lattice points, that is, points where the space lattice lines cross, and unit cells. Unit cells with this property are called *primitive*.

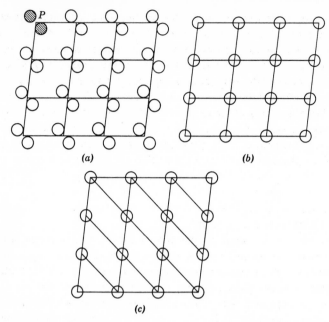

Figure 1.1 Space lattices. Identical unit cells are shown in (*a*) and (*b*) with a different choice in (*c*).

Let us now illustrate in Fig. 1.2 a unit cell of the most general type. The edges *OA*, *OB*, and *OC* are called the *axial lengths* or *lattice param-eters* and are designated *a*, *b*, and *c* respectively, whereas the angles $\widehat{BOC}$, $\widehat{AOC}$, and $\widehat{AOB}$ are α, β, and γ respectively. For any point in the lattice having the coordinates *x y z* measured parallel to the axes, there will be a

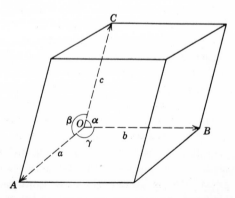

Figure 1.2 Unit cell of the most general type.

similar point at $(x + pa, y + qb, z + rc)$ where p, q, and r are whole numbers.

Let us refer again to Fig. 1.1a. The unit assembly of atoms is the pair such as are shaded in the diagram. The individual atoms of the pair are related in position to one another and to the point P by a very simple symmetry operation or *element*, (in this illustration rotation through 180°

Table 1.1

(In this table $\neq$ means "not necessarily equal to, and generally different from")

SYSTEM	AXES AND INTERAXIAL ANGLES	EXAMPLES
Triclinic	Three axes not at right angles, of any lengths	K_2CrO_7
	$a \neq b \neq c \qquad \alpha \neq \beta \neq \gamma \neq 90°$	
Monoclinic	Three axes, one pair not at right angles, of any lengths	β-S $CaSO_4 \cdot 2H_2O$
	$a \neq b \neq c \qquad \alpha = \gamma = 90° \neq \beta$	(gypsum)
Orthorhombic (rhombic)	Three axes at right angles; all unequal	α-S
	$a \neq b \neq c \qquad \alpha = \beta = \gamma = 90°$	Ga
		Fe_3C (cementite)
Tetragonal	Three axes at right angles; two equal	β-Sn (white)
	$a = b \neq c \qquad \alpha = \beta = \gamma = 90°$	TiO_2
Cubic	Three axes at right angles; all equal	Cu, Ag, Au
	$a = b = c \qquad \alpha = \beta = \gamma = 90°$	Fe
		NaCl
Hexagonal	Three axes coplanar at 120°, equal	Zn, Cd
	Fourth axis at right angles to these	NiAs
	$a_1 = a_2 = a_2 \neq c \quad \alpha = \beta = 90°, \gamma = 120°$	
Rhombohedral (trigonal)	Three axes equally inclined, not at right angles; all equal	As, Sb, Bi Calcite
	$a = b = c \qquad \alpha = \beta = \gamma \neq 90°$	

about P). In three dimensions and with more complex unit assemblies, the symmetry elements may be less simple. A group of symmetry elements about a point such as P is called a *point group*. There are thirty-two possible point groups, the restriction in number being a consequence of the restricted number of symmetry operations. This restriction also limits the number of possible space lattices to just fourteen. The fourteen space lattices are illustrated in Fig. 1.3 by a unit cell of each. Note that all of the unit cells are not primitive. There are two kinds of lattice called monoclinic, three kinds of orthorhombic space lattice, only one kind of hexagonal, and so on. There are, in fact, seven different classifications known as the *crystal systems*. Table 1.1 gives the seven crystal systems

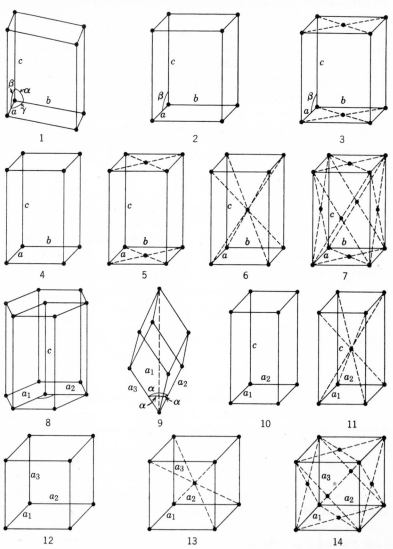

Figure 1.3   Possible space lattices of the seven crystal systems. 1. Triclinic, simple; 2. Monoclinic, simple; 3. Monoclinic, base-centered; 4. Orthorhombic, simple; 5. Orthorhombic, base-centered; 6. Orthorhombic, body-centered; 7. Ortho-rhombic, face-centered; 8. Hexagonal; 9. Rhombohedral; 10. Tetragonal, simple; 11. Tetragonal, body-centered; 12. Cubic, simple; 13. Cubic, body-centered; 14. Cubic, face-centered.

with the relationships between the *lattice parameters* and the *angles* between the axes.

Finally, if a point group symmetry is arrayed on every point of a space lattice, we have a *space group*. The number of possible space groups is limited to 230. Thus the positions of the atoms in all crystal structures can be referred to the 230 space groups, that is to the basically different repetitive patterns in which symmetry elements can be arranged. The study of space groups is fundamental to the subject of crystallography, but will not be discussed further in this text.

1.3　Some Simple Crystal Structures

We will now illustrate some of the simplest crystal structures found in technologically important solids. For each structure a *conventional* unit cell of the space lattice is drawn with the *primitive* unit cell outlined. The choice of conventional unit cell is one of convenience. For instance, when we come to study the face-centered cubic structure, it will be seen that the conventional cell has cube axes whereas the primitive cell does not. It should be noted that, since there is a one-to-one correspondence between primitive unit cells and space lattice points, then if each unit assembly of atoms at each lattice point is a single atom, there must be just one atom per unit cell. The conventional unit cells, however, often contain more than one atom.

Body-Centered Cubic. The simplest crystal structure commonly found (see Fig. 1.4) is called body-centered cubic. In Fig. 1.4 the conventional unit cell is shown and the three axes of the primitive unit cell are marked by dotted lines. Completion of the dotted line cube gives the primitive unit cell, which has one atom. The conventional unit cell, on the other hand, contains two atoms. This can readily be seen since the eight corner atoms are each shared by eight neighboring cells whereas the central atom is uniquely associated with the cell drawn. If a corner of the conventional unit cell is regarded as an origin of axes, the coordinates of the atoms are 000 and $\frac{1}{2}\frac{1}{2}\frac{1}{2}$ when written as fractions of the lattice parameters. It is readily seen that this is a rather open structure. The greatest number of atoms per unit length lie along the cube diagonal. There are, however, no planes of atoms where the packing is as close as possible.

Face-Centered Cubic. Figure 1.5 shows the unit cell of the face-centered cubic structure. The coordinates of the atoms are 000 and $0\frac{1}{2}\frac{1}{2}$. The eight corner atoms of the conventional unit cell are each shared by the eight neighboring unit cells whereas the six atoms at the middle of the cube faces are each shared by two unit cells. Thus there are one plus

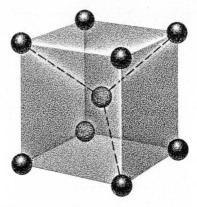

Figure 1.4 Conventional unit cell of body-centered cubic structure. Dotted lines show edges of primitive cell. Examples: Fe(α), Li, Na, K, Rb, Cs.

three, that is, four atoms per conventional unit cell. This structure can be considered to be constructed in the following way. Suppose atoms are closely packed in a single first layer, their positions being marked ○ in Fig. 1.6a. A second layer can then be laid down on top of the first layer in two ways. Once one of the hollows in the first layer marked + has been chosen for the first of the second layer atoms, then all other hollows marked + must be used. There is, of course, another set of hollows in the

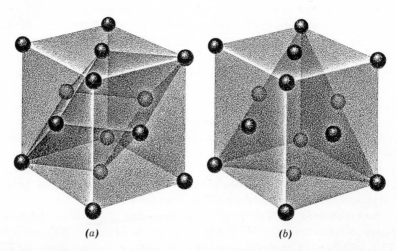

(a)   (b)

Figure 1.5 (a) The face-centered cubic unit cell with the primitive cell inside. (b) Close-packed plane shown. Examples: Ag, Al, Au, Cu, Co(β), Fe(γ), Ir, Ni(β), Pb, Pt, Sr, Th.

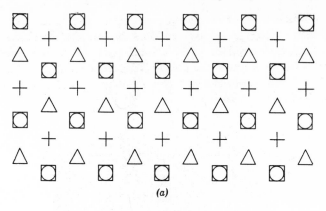

(a)

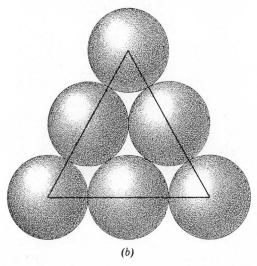

(b)

Figure 1.6   Illustration of close packing of atoms. (a) ○ First-layer atoms. + Second-layer atoms, first choice. □ Third-layer atoms in hexagonal close-packed structure. △ Third-layer atoms in face-centered cubic structure. (b) Close-packed octahedral plane of Fig. 1.5b.

first layer which can be utilized instead of the + hollows. The size of the atom, however, precludes the second layer atoms from going into a mixture of the two sets of hollows. The two-layered structures with the second layer atoms in either position are identical. When we look for possible positions for the atoms of the third layer, two nonidentical choices are available. First, we may select hollows in the second layer, marked □, which are directly above the first-layer atoms. This gives rise to a crystal

structure which is called *hexagonal close-packed* and which will be considered later. Second, we may envisage the third-layer atoms in the
positions marked △. This latter choice forms the *face-centered cubic
structure*. The portion of the close-packed octahedral plane shown in
Fig. 1.5*b* is again shown in Fig. 1.6*b*. The close-packed direction in this
plane is the face diagonal.

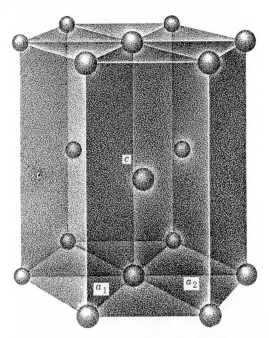

Figure 1.7   Hexagonal close-packed unit cell. The
darker shading shows the primitive cell within the
conventional cell. Examples: Be, Cd, Mg, Nd, P, Re,
Ru, Ti, Zn.

Hexagonal Close-Packed Structure.   This structure is shown in Fig.
1.7. As has been previously described, it consists of close-packed layers
of atoms placed one above the other with the atoms of each layer nestling
in the hollows of the lower layer. The conventional unit cell consists of
two hexagons with atoms at each corner and one in the middle. Separating
the layers are three atoms in the allowed spaces between the top and bottom
layers. The atoms of the cell have the coordinates 000 and $\frac{2}{3}\frac{1}{3}\frac{1}{2}$ when
referred to the axes a_1, a_2, and c. Whereas the primitive unit cell contains
two atoms, the conventional cell contains six atoms.

The foregoing structures are those of highest symmetry commonly
found in crystalline solids. There are, however, a number of modifications

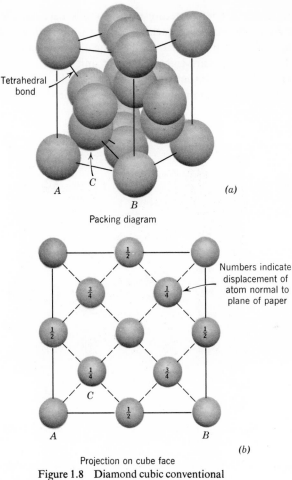

Figure 1.8   Diamond cubic conventional unit cell. In (b) the displacement of the atoms normal to the plane of the paper is given in fractions of the unit cell edge. Examples: Si, Ge, Sn (gray). (After Wykoff)

of both the cubic and hexagonal structures which occur in solids of technological importance and these will now be described.

Diamond Cubic Structure. The atoms of certain elements are held together in the solid by tetrahedral bonds at angles of $109\frac{1}{2}°$ to one another. Each atom has four nearest neighbors, which is a consequence of each atom sharing one of its outer electrons with each of four neighbors. The typical crystal structure so formed is that of diamond which is shown in Fig. 1.8a and b. As can be seen from the figure, this is not a close-packed

structure, the directional nature of the bonds between the atoms over-
weighing considerations of packing economy. Figure 1.8*b* gives the displacement of the atoms normal to the plane of the paper as fractions of the
unit cell edge. There are eight atoms per unit cell.

Sodium Chloride Structure. The sodium chloride structure, shown
in Fig. 1.9, is a typical ionic structure in which the ions occupy the corners

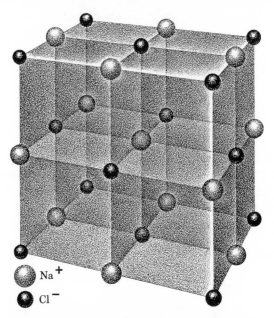

Figure 1.9   Sodium chloride unit cell. Examples: NaCl,
KCl, BaO, MgO, NiO, MnO, PbS, PbTe.

of a simple cubic lattice in such a way that each kind of ion occupies
alternate positions along the cube edges. The ions are in the positions

$$\text{Na:}\quad 000;\quad \tfrac{1}{2}\tfrac{1}{2}0;\quad \tfrac{1}{2}0\tfrac{1}{2};\quad 0\tfrac{1}{2}\tfrac{1}{2}.$$

$$\text{Cl:}\quad \tfrac{1}{2}\tfrac{1}{2}\tfrac{1}{2};\quad 00\tfrac{1}{2};\quad 0\tfrac{1}{2}0;\quad \tfrac{1}{2}00.$$

The structure may be looked on as formed by the interpenetration of two
face-centered cubic lattices. The unit cell shown contains four sodium
ions and four chlorine ions. The sodium chloride type of structure is
produced with ions of equal and opposite charge, the chemical formula
being of the type AX.

Zinc Blende Structure. We have already seen that the diamond cubic
structure is a consequence of the carbon valency of four. We may quite
well expect to find the same structure in compounds where one atom has
more than four electrons and the other the same number less than four,

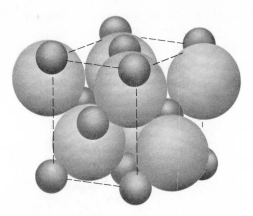

Figure 1.10   The zinc blende structure. Examples:
αZnS, αCdS, βAgI, SiC. (After Azaroff)

so that a total of four valency electrons to each atom is maintained. If
the compound is of the form AX, this structure can be produced in two
ways. The first is the cubic zinc-blende structure shown in Fig. 1.10 with
four zinc and four sulfur atoms per conventional unit cell.

Wurtzite Structure. The second method by which a structure is
formed where each atom of one kind, in a compound AX, is surrounded
by four of another, is shown in Fig. 1.11. This is the hexagonal βZnS or

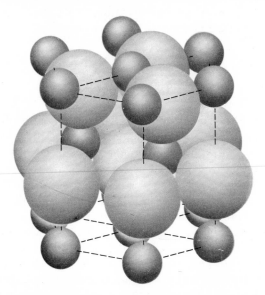

Figure 1.11   The wurtzite structure. Example;
βZnS, βCdS, MgTe, CdSe. (After Azaroff)

wurtzite structure, which differs only from the zinc blende structure in the stacking sequence of the sulfur layers.

Selenium Structure.   The important materials selenium and tellurium have crystal structures that can also be described as hexagonal.   Here the

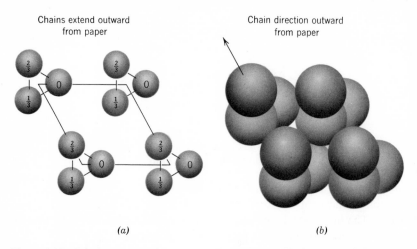

(a)   (b)

Figure 1.12   Selenium conventional unit cell.   In (a) the displacement of the atoms normal to the plane of the paper is given in fractions of the appropriate unit cell parameter.   (After Wykoff)

covalent bonds between neighboring atoms hold the atoms in spirals around the long hexagonal axes.   The crystal structure is shown in Fig. 1.12a and b.

1.4   Nomenclature of Crystal Directions

It is necessary in crystallography to have a system of notation for directions in a crystal.   The standard notation will now be described.   Suppose in Fig. 1.13a that we wish to indicate the direction OP.   The translation from O to P can be accomplished by going along the X-axis a distance u times the unit distance a, then in the Y direction a distance v times the unit distance b, then in the Z direction a distance w times the unit distance c.   If u, v, and w are the smallest integers that will accomplish the desired translation, the direction OP is written [uvw] with the square brackets shown being widely adopted.   Figure 1.13b gives the notation for some important directions and also indicates the method of dealing with negative directions.   A full set of equivalent directions are indicated by carets: $\langle uvw \rangle$.

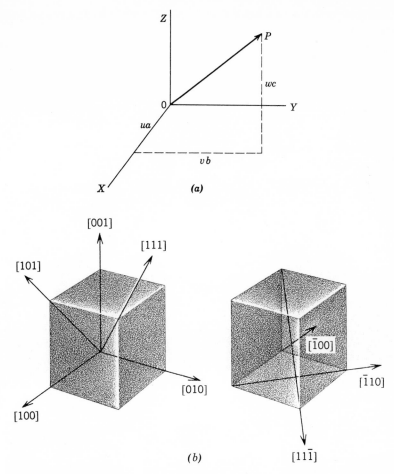

Figure 1.13   Notation for directions in crystals. (*a*) *OP* is the direction *uvw* if *u*, *v*, and *w* are the smallest integers. (*b*) Some important directions in crystals.

1.5   Nomenclature of Crystal Planes: Miller Indices

It is also necessary to have a system of notation for crystallographic planes. The use of *Miller indices* for this purpose is universal. Suppose that in Fig. 1.14*a* we wish to refer to the shaded plane. This plane cuts the three crystallographic axes in the three intercept lengths x, y, and z. First express the intercepts as fractions x/a, y/b, and z/c of the unit distances a, b, c along the respective axes. Next take the reciprocals of the fractions just found. After this has been done and the reciprocals reduced to the

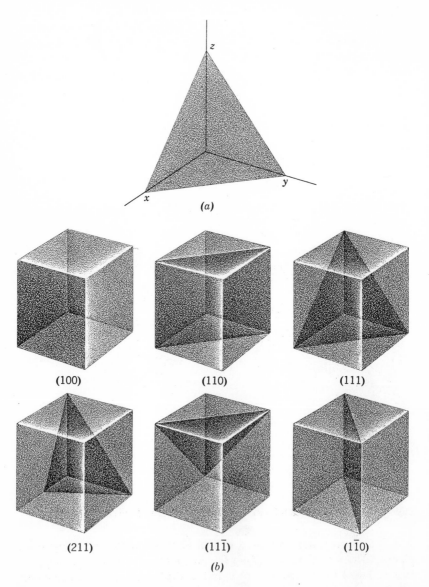

Figure 1.14   Miller index nomenclature for crystal planes. In (b) some important planes are indexed.

smallest integers h, k, l, having the same ratios, then (hkl) are the Miller indices of the plane. They are always shown in parenthesis. Fig. 1.14b shows some important planes and also indicates how to deal with planes that cut an axis on the negative side of the origin. Braces $\{hkl\}$ signify all the planes that are equivalent in a crystal, such as the cube faces of a cubic crystal: that is, $\{100\} \equiv (100) + (010) + (001) + (\bar{1}00) + (0\bar{1}0) + (00\bar{1})$.

REFERENCES

F. C. Phillips, *An Introduction to Crystallography*, Longmans, London, 1946.
R. W. G. Wyckoff, *Crystal Structures*, Interscience Publishers, New York, 1948.
W. Hume-Rothery, *The structure of Metals and Alloys*, Institute of Metals, London, 1947.
Many texts on X-ray Crystallography give material on crystal structures.

EXERCISES

1. Show that the ratio: volume of atoms: volume available, is given for the various structures by:

   (a) Simple cubic
   $$\frac{\pi}{6} \ (52\%)$$

   (b) Body-centered cubic
   $$\frac{\pi 3^{1/2}}{8} \ (68\%)$$

   (c) Face-centered cubic
   $$\frac{\pi 2^{1/2}}{6} \ (74\%)$$

   (d) Hexagonal close-packed
   $$\frac{\pi 2^{1/2}}{6} \ (74\%)$$

   (e) Diamond cubic
   $$\frac{\pi 3^{1/2}}{16} \ (34\%)$$

2. From the following table of atomic weights and lattice parameters, calculate the densities of the elements in solid form. Compare with measured values.

   αFe: Atomic weight $= 55.85$; $a = 2.861$ Å.
   Cu: atomic weight $= 63.57$; $a = 3.608$ Å.
   Zn: atomic weight $= 65.38$; $a = 2.659$ Å: $c = 4.934$ Å.
   Diamond: atomic weight (carbon) $= 12.01$; $a = 3.560$ Å.

3. Show that in an ideal hexagonal close-packed structure that

   $$\frac{c}{a} = \frac{8^{1/2}}{3^{1/2}} = 1.633.$$

   Using the data of exercise 2, compare with the measured ratio in zinc.

4. Give the coordinates of the principal voids in the body-centered cubic structure and compute the radii of the interstitial atoms which can fit into these voids.

5. Calculate the density of packing, in atoms per square meter, for the following planes:

   (a) (110) plane in αFe

   (b) (111) plane in Cu

   (110) plane in Cu

   (c) (001) plane in Zn.

2

The Examination of Crystals by X-Rays, Electrons, and Neutrons

The external symmetry shown by many crystals, particularly those naturally grown, led investigators many centuries ago to postulate that the fundamental atoms of which the crystals were composed must be arranged in a characteristic pattern. The direct exploration of the atomic arrangement, however, had to await the discovery of waves which would interact with atoms and have wavelengths comparable to the atomic spacing in crystals. Such waves, called X-rays and of wavelength of the order of 1 Å (10^{-10} m), were first used in this connection about 1912 in the pioneer X-ray diffraction experiments of von Laue and W. H. and W. L. Bragg.

Some fifteen years later the first experiments on diffraction of electrons by crystals were carried out. Electrons penetrate crystals to only small depths, and as a consequence the technique of electron diffraction has had its greatest use in the examination of surfaces and thin films.

With the availability of sources of neutrons from the chain-reacting atomic pile, the investigation of crystals by neutron diffraction has become possible. The penetration depth is great for neutrons, and moreover, differences between the neutron and X-ray scattering powers of atoms has led to the growth of the technique of neutron diffraction as a useful supplement to X-ray diffraction.

This chapter will contain a brief outline of some of the properties of X-rays, electrons, and neutrons which are of significance in diffraction, followed by a description of the diffraction techniques currently used in the study of solids.

25

2.1 Emission of X-Rays

X-rays are electromagnetic radiation with wavelengths of the order of 1 Å. If a beam of electrons, emitted usually from a hot filament, are accelerated on to a positive metallic electrode by a high voltage, the loss of energy is in two important ways, (*a*) by emission of *white* X-

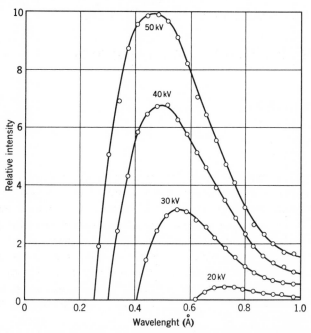

Figure 2.1   Relative intensity of white X-radiation as a function of wavelength for different applied accelerating voltages.

radiation, and (*b*) if the voltage is sufficiently high, by the emission of X-radiation *characteristic* of the target material.

White Radiation.   White radiation, as the name implies, is of continuously varying wavelength from one end of the allowed spectrum to the other. The maximum energy which the electron can impart to an atom of the target is eV, where e is the electronic charge and V the accelerating voltage. If this energy is completely converted into X-radiation, the shortest wavelength which will be emitted from the target will be given by the Einstein conversion formula

$$eV = \frac{hc}{\lambda} \tag{2.1}$$

where λ is the wavelength of the emitted X-rays, c is speed of light, and h is Planck's constant. Substitution of numerical values in (2.1) gives

$$\lambda = \frac{12.4}{V}$$

with λ in Angstroms and V in kilovolts.

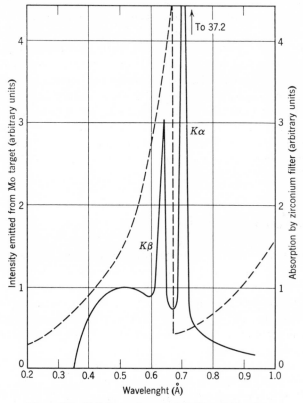

Figure 2.2   Full line: characteristic X-radiation from a Mo target with 35 kV applied voltage. Dotted line: absorption of X-radiation by a zirconium filter.

Figure 2.1 shows the distribution of intensity of white X-radiation as a function of wavelength for different applied accelerating voltages. As can be seen, the point of sharp cutoff on the short wavelength end of the spectrum depends on the accelerating potential. High-voltage machines give shorter possible wavelengths.

White X-radiation has its principal use in medical and industrial radiography. X-rays from the target are made to penetrate the specimen under investigation. Behind the specimen is a fluorescent screen or photographic film to record the intensity. Variations in density of the specimen give corresponding variations in density on the photographic film, enabling the operator to detect, for example, bone fractures in the medical application or porosity in castings in the metal industry.

Characteristic Radiation. If the accelerating voltage applied to the electrons is raised above that necessary to produce white radiation, the X-radiation characteristic of the element of which the target is composed may be emitted. Such radiation depends on the electron energy levels of the target atom. A discussion of such levels in many-electron atoms is given on page 176. It will be seen that these levels are sharply defined in energy. Transitions of electrons between the atomic levels results in absorption or emission of energy. Energy emitted is in the form of electromagnetic radiation which is also sharply defined in wavelength. The characteristic wavelengths used in X-ray diffraction techniques are called the Kα and Kβ. The distribution of intensity in the X-ray spectrum from a molybdenum target with an accelerating voltage of 35 kV is shown in Fig. 2.2.

2.2   Absorption of X-Rays

If X-radiation irradiates a specimen, absorption of energy may be brought about by the electrons of the atoms of the specimen being excited from one set of energy levels to other levels. The apparent absorption of incident X-rays increases abruptly at the critical wavelength for absorption. The dotted line in Fig. 2.2 shows the absorption of radiation by the element zirconium. The abrupt rise in absorption is called an *absorption edge*.

These considerations affect the choice of X-radiation for a particular diffraction analysis. For instance, the choice of an X-radiation, whose Kα wavelength is just under an absorption edge of the specimen irradiated, would result in a good deal of absorption of the X-radiation by the specimen. The electrons of the atoms of the specimen then rearrange among the available energy levels resulting in most cases in unwelcome re-emission from the specimen of *secondary X-radiation*. This is precisely what happens where an iron specimen is irradiated by characteristic radiation from a copper target. On the other hand, a beam of X-rays containing Kα and Kβ may be made much more monochromatic by passing the beam through a thin filter of a material whose absorption edge lies between the Kα and Kβ wavelengths. It is obvious from Fig. 2.2 that zirconium would filter out much of molybdenum Kβ radiation without affecting the intensity of the Kα to the same extent. Table 2.1 lists the characteristics of several filters for the production of monochromatic X-rays.

Table 2.1

TARGET	FILTER	THICKNESS IN mm	% Kβ ABSORBED
Mo	Zr	0.063	96%
Cu	Ni	0.016	98%
Co	Fe	0.015	99%
Cr	V	0.015	99%

2.3   X-Ray Diffraction

The Atomic Scattering Factor f.   An X-ray beam passing over an atom of a solid sets each electron of the atom into oscillation because of the oscillating electric field of the beam. The atomic electrons then scatter the beam in all directions without change in wavelength. These statements are reasonably true for most solids if the type of X-radiation has been chosen so that absorption is not great. The electrons of the atom are not concentrated at a single point, and if the wavelength of the X-rays is commensurate with the distance apart of the electrons in the atom, the scattered rays from the electrons will interfere with one another, and the atom will scatter less efficiently than would a similar number of electrons concentrated at a single point. The efficiency of cooperation among the scattering electrons of the atom is expressed by the *atomic scattering factor f* which may be defined as the ratio of the X-ray amplitude scattered by an atom at rest to that scattered by a single electron. If θ measures the angle between the incident and scattered X-rays, then at $\theta = 0$ the electrons are scattering in phase and f is equal to the atomic number Z of the atom. The scattered amplitude rapidly decreases with increasing $\sin \theta / \lambda$ where λ is the incident wavelength. Tables of atomic scattering factors at different values of $\sin \theta / \lambda$ are listed for the elements in *International Tables for the Determination of Crystal Structure*, Vol. 2, Borntraeger, Berlin, 1935. A satisfactory interpretation of atomic scattering can be made on the basis of wave mechanics and measured intensities used as a test of atomic models.

The Bragg Equation.   The superposition of X-rays scattered by individual atoms in a crystal results in diffraction. The amplitude of the scattered wave is a maximum in a direction such that the contributions from each atom of the crystal structure differ in phase only by integral multiples of 2π. The separate scattered amplitudes add up constructively for this condition, and the intensity is a maximum in the diffracted beam. The Laue and Bragg equations give the conditions for the formation of diffracted beams of maximum intensity. They relate the atomic spacing d of a particular plane (hkl) with the X-ray wavelength λ and the angle θ between the incident X-ray beam and the atomic plane. We will use the Bragg model to derive the required relation. This model gives the position of the diffracted beam produced by a crystal on the assumption that X-rays are reflected specularly from the various planes in the crystal.

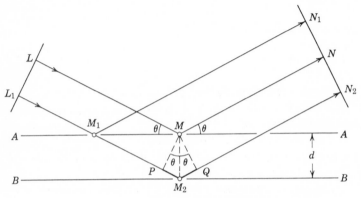

Figure 2.3   Geometry of X-ray reflection from atomic planes.

Suppose that in Fig. 2.3 the horizontal parallel lines AA and BB represent planes of atoms which partly reflect incident X-radiation. The path difference for rays LMN and $L_1M_2N_2$, reflected from adjacent planes, is the length PM_2Q which is equal to $2d \sin \theta$. The reflected rays from adjacent planes will be in phase, and their amplitudes will reinforce if this path difference is equal to an integral number of wavelengths. Thus the Bragg condition for diffraction is

$$n\lambda = 2d \sin \theta \tag{2.2}$$

with n an integer.

This is similar to the familiar equation for the optical diffraction grating in experiments on visible spectra. There n was the order of the spectra. In equation 2.2, if the diffracted beam arises from the nth-order reflection from a set of atomic planes of true spacing d, we may think of the beam as a first-order reflection from a set of planes parallel to the true lattice planes but with a spacing which is $1/n$ of the true spacing. This device leads to great simplification in interpretation.

From equation 2.2 it is seen that λ, d, and θ must have simultaneous specific values to satisfy the diffraction condition. In practice, this matching of the parameters is accomplished in three standard ways.

X-Ray Diffraction Methods.   In the *Laue method*, Fig. 2.4, a single crystal specimen is held stationary while irradiated with *white X-radiation*. A photographic film is placed to receive the rays diffracted through the crystal or (see Fig. 2.9) those diffracted in a back reflection direction. Because the crystal is fixed in position the angles θ are also fixed. The Bragg condition (equation 2.2) can be satisfied since a range of wavelengths is present. If the photographic film is at a distance D from the crystal, it will show reflection spots at various distances R from the direct beam. Here

$$R = D \tan 2\theta \qquad (2.3)$$

Each spot will be due to all the orders of reflection $n = 1, 2, 3, \ldots$ superimposed from a single plane. This can be considered as reflections from

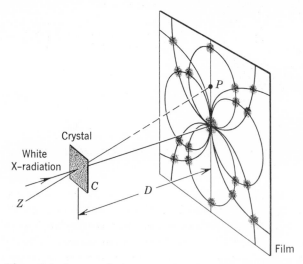

Figure 2.4   Laue method.   A set of planes lying parallel to a common zone axis ZCP give rise to a series of spots on a given ellipse.

planes with spacing d, $d/2$, $d/3$, ... The Laue photograph gives a series of values of θ for different crystal planes, together with the orientation of each R relative to horizontal and vertical directions on the photograph. The Laue method gives only the symmetry, the axial ratios a/b, c/b, and the axial angles α, β, and γ. The method does not give the size of the unit cell, only its shape, because it gives a measure of angles only, not of spacings.

In the *rotating crystal* method a single crystal is rotated in a beam of monochromatic X-rays. The rotation makes it possible for the Bragg law to be satisfied. Not every plane can reflect; for example, a plane which always contains the incident beam during the whole rotation cannot reflect, nor could one whose spacing is so small that $\lambda/2d > 1$. The reflected spots, on a cylindrical film whose axis is the rotation axis of the crystal, lie on parallel lines. Since the wavelength is known, the spacing d may be calculated from equation 2.2. Reflections from planes in different orientations may overlap on the film, and to make the identification of the spots less ambiguous, two modifications of the apparatus are often employed—the *oscillation* method and the *Weissenberg* method. In the

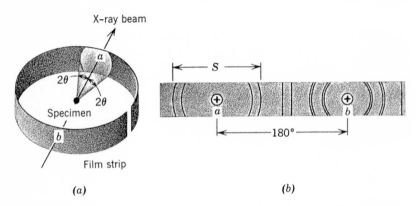

(a)   (b)

Figure 2.5   (a) Schematic diagram of use of powder camera. (b) diffraction pattern recorded on film strip.

oscillation method the number of planes which can reflect is restricted by oscillating the crystal through a small angle. In the Weissenberg method, while the crystal rotates, the film is translated parallel to the axis of rotation, the two motions being synchronized.

The oscillation and Weissenberg methods are used in complete crystal structure analysis.

In the *powder method* a finely powdered specimen is placed in a mono-chromatic beam. The specimen is often rotated. Certain of the many crystallites are correctly oriented to satisfy equation 2.2. The powder method, convenient because single crystals are not required, is used for accurate determination of lattice parameters in crystals of known structure and for the identification of elements and compounds.

Figure 2.5a shows a small cylindrical powder specimen mounted at the centre of a cylindrical camera. A narrow incident beam of monochroma-tic X-rays, often Kα radiation, irradiates the sample. Each type of atomic plane with its characteristic spacing d produces a diffracted cone of X-rays of vertex angle 4θ. The cone of X-rays is intercepted by a narrow strip of film which is fitted inside the circular camera. Development of the film after exposure will reveal a diffraction pattern shown in Fig. 2.5b. The distance S on the film between diffraction lines corresponding to a particular plane is related to the Bragg angle by the equation

$$S = 4\theta R \tag{2.4}$$

where R is the known radius of the camera. A list of θ values can thus be obtained from the measured values of S. Since the wavelength is known, substitution in equation 2.2 gives a list of spacings d. Each spacing d is the distance between neighboring planes (hkl).

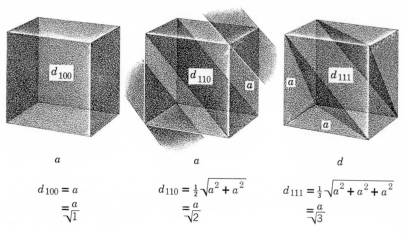

$$d_{100} = a$$
$$= \frac{a}{\sqrt{1}}$$

$$d_{110} = \tfrac{1}{2}\sqrt{a^2 + a^2}$$
$$= \frac{a}{\sqrt{2}}$$

$$d_{111} = \tfrac{1}{3}\sqrt{a^2 + a^2 + a^2}$$
$$= \frac{a}{\sqrt{3}}$$

Figure 2.6   Spacings in a cubic crystal calculated from equation 2.5.

In the simple case of a *cubic* structure the relationship between d and the lattice parameter a is given by the equation

$$d = \frac{a}{\sqrt{h^2 + k^2 + l^2}} \tag{2.5}$$

Some simple examples of this relationship are shown in Fig. 2.6.
   Combined with the Bragg law equation 2.5 gives for the *cubic* system

$$\sin^2 \theta_{hkl} = \frac{\lambda^2}{4a^2}(h^2 + k^2 + l^2) \tag{2.6}$$

The corresponding relation for the hexagonal system is

$$\sin^2 \theta_{hkl} = \frac{\lambda^2}{4}\left[\frac{4(h^2 + k^2 + hk)}{3a^2} + \frac{l^2}{c^2}\right] \tag{2.7}$$

Clearly if the values of θ for which diffracted beams exist can be measured and associated with particular planes, substitution in these equations will give a number of values of the lattice spacings. With systems of lower symmetry than hexagonal, it is rarely possible to carry out a structure analysis by the powder method alone.

The values of spacing given by measurement of the higher angle lines, that is, greatest θ, are the most accurate. This can be shown by differentiating the Bragg relationship with respect to θ.

We have

$$\frac{d}{d\theta}(n\lambda) = 2\frac{\Delta d}{\Delta\theta}\sin\theta + 2d\cos\theta$$

and for monochromatic radiation when the left-hand side is zero

$$\frac{\Delta\theta}{\Delta d} = -\frac{1}{d}\tan\theta \qquad (2.8)$$

Equation 2.8 shows that the variation in θ for a small change in d becomes very large as θ, the Bragg angle, approaches $90°$. Accurate determinations of parameters are thus best made by back reflection methods.

The Intensity of the Lines in a Diffraction Pattern. The Geometrical Structure Factor. We have seen that the angles through which a beam of X-rays is diffracted depend on the spacings of the atomic planes. The relative intensities of the various reflections from a crystal depend on the contents of the unit cell, that is, the number, type, and distribution of atoms in the cell. The amplitude of reflection is determined by the phase relationship between the waves scattered by the individual atoms of the cell. The factor that gives the reflected amplitude as a multiple of the amplitude scattered by a single electron is the *geometrical structure factor* $|F(hkl)|$. Determinations of structure factors for diffraction from each plane (*hkl*) finally determines the actual positions of atoms in a particular structure. The technique is highly developed and has led to the complete elucidation of complex structures. The principles will be illustrated by reference to a very simple example.

Let us consider the intensity of an X-ray beam reflected by the (001) planes in a body-centered cubic structure. Figure 2.7 shows the unit cell and phase relationships in the emergent beam. The diffracted beams XX and ZZ differ in phase by one wavelength and therefore reinforce. Now consider the effect of the presence of atoms on the central dotted plane. The diffracted beam YY must be exactly out of phase with XX and ZZ and will reduce the intensity of the total emergent beam at this angle to zero if the scattering power of the atoms on the central plane is equal to that of the atoms on the upper or lower plane. If this is not so, the (001) diffracted intensity will not be exactly equal to zero but will of course be reduced.

Thus for a body-centered cubic element we would not expect to find (001) X-ray reflections. In fact, when dealing with a body-centered structure, the intensity of a diffracted beam is always zero if $(h + k + l)$ is an odd number. In the diffraction pattern from α-iron, for example, we will find lines from the following planes in order of increasing θ: (110), (200), (211), (220), (310), (222), (321), (400), (411) or (330), (420), etc.

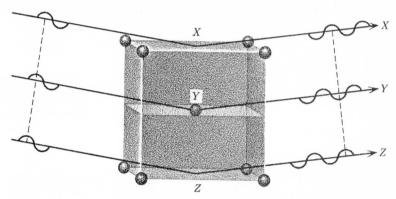

Figure 2.7   Body-centered cubic unit cell with reflected X-ray beams from top, middle, and bottom planes. The phase relationships in the reflected beams are shown on the right.

2.4   The Uses of X-Ray Diffraction Techniques

So far we have dealt with the principles of X-ray diffraction only and have made little mention of its practical uses. This section discusses a number of such uses of importance to the solid-state engineer and metallurgist. The intention will be to show the types of investigation of solids made possible by X-ray diffraction, and no attempt will be made to give the individual steps in detail. The reader is referred to the texts listed at the end of the chapter for such detail. Complete structure analysis will not be discussed since this subject is one that must be treated by the specialist.

Identification of Elements and Compounds by Examination of X-ray Powder Patterns.   The X-ray powder pattern of a crystalline substance is uniquely characteristic of the substance. The investigator can identify the elements and compounds in a specimen whose chemical nature is unknown by comparing the powder pattern of the specimen to standard diffraction patterns of known substances. The powder method is preferred because it is easy to prepare.

First the values of spacings are obtained, and then the relative intensities of the lines are estimated. It is best to estimate them photometrically, but visual estimate is accurate enough in most cases. The intensities will depend on the type of X-radiation used, but here again corrections are usually unnecessary. The *d* values for the strongest three lines are then specially noted.

2829 *d* 1–1069	2.69	1.89	1.19	3.11	KF
*I/I*₁ 1–1056	100	80	25	15	Potassium fluoride

Rad. λ 0.709 Filter		*d*Å	*I/I*₁	*hkl*	*d*Å	*I/I*₁	*hkl*
Dia. Cut-off Coll.							
*I/I*₁ *d* corr. abs.?		3.11	15				
Ref. Davey, *Phys. Rev.*, **21**, 143 (1923)		2.69	100				
		1.89	80				
		1.61	10				
Sys. Cubic** S.G. O$_H^5$ FM3M		1.54	20				
a_0 2.664 b_0 c_0 A C							
α β γ Z 4		1.33	10				
Ref. Wy		1.22	8				
		1.19	25				
		1.09	15				
	Sign	1.02	5				
2V D2.534 mp 857 Color							
	Colorless	0.94	5				
Ref. C.C.		0.90	5				
		0.89	8				
		0.84	8				
B.P. 1502		0.80	8				
** NaCl type							
Stock		0.71	8				

Figure 2.8   A.S.T.M. Index card showing diffraction pattern data for KF.

Sets of American Society for Testing Materials index cards have been prepared for several thousand diffraction patterns of known substances. Figure 2.8 shows a typical card. The eight boxes in the top left-hand corner show the spacings of the strongest three lines and the largest spacing found. Accompanying the 1950 card file are two indexes, (*a*) the alphabetical index in three parts—general inorganic and organic index, organic index, mineral index—and (*b*) the numerical index in which the cards are filed in order of spacing magnitude. The pattern card of each substance is entered three times in file positions corresponding to the spacings of the three strongest lines. A reference at the end of the chapter gives details of the standardized procedure recommended for specimen preparation and identification by manual or machine sorting methods.

The Estimation of Grain Size by X-ray Diffraction. The size of the crystals in a polycrystalline aggregate has an influence on many of its mechanical properties. For instance the ultimate tensile strength and hardness of iron is approximately doubled by reducing the grain size from

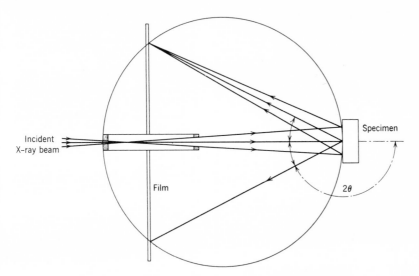

Figure 2.9   Back reflection X-ray diffraction technique.

1 cm to 10^{-3} cm. A decrease in grain size will also improve the attainable surface finish on pressed sheet metal and other metal products.

Optical methods making use of microscope examination for the estimation of grain size are used when the grain size is greater than 10^{-2} cm. The A.S.T.M. index charts find widespread use in this connection. These charts employ a series of micrographs of equiaxed grains at a magnification of $\times 100$. The charts carry the grain diameters and are compared directly with $\times 100$ micrographs of the material whose grain size is desired.

For smaller grain sizes the nature of the diffraction rings in a back reflection powder picture gives an indication of the size of the individual crystallites in the specimen. Figure 2.9 shows the method of preparing back reflection powder photographs and Fig. 2.10 shows X-ray patterns of powdered quartz of different particle size. The X-ray image on the film from a particular grain is related in size and shape to the diffracting crystallite. An approximately linear relationship exists between the size of the X-ray image and the grain size measured by the microscope in the range in which the two methods overlap. The best method of making use

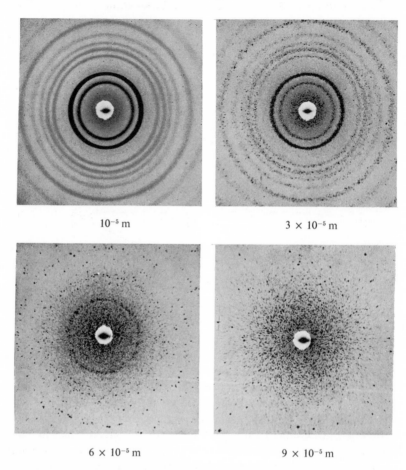

10^{-5} m 3×10^{-5} m

6×10^{-5} m 9×10^{-5} m

Figure 2.10   X-ray diffraction patterns of powdered quartz crystals of different particle size. (H. P. Rooksby, Cantor Lectures, Royal Society of Arts, London).

of the X-ray technique is to first prepare a set of X-ray photographs calibrated by means of the microscope method. The grain size of further specimens may then be quickly determined by comparison of the X-ray photographs. The advantage of the X-ray method is that it is non-destructive and no surface polishing is necessary.

When the grain size is of the order or less than 10^{-6} m, the rings of the X-ray pattern begin to grow diffuse. This effect is identical to the imperfect resolution of spectral lines by an optical grating that has an insufficient number of rulings. If we consider a diffraction line that has increased in half-peak width from b corresponding to "particles of infinite size," that is, larger than 10^{-6} m, to a new value B when the crystallite size has fallen below 10^{-6} m, the extent of the angular broadening β derived from B and b is related to the grain size ϵ by the formula

$$\beta = \frac{K\lambda}{\epsilon \cos \theta} \tag{2.9}$$

Here K is a constant of value close to unity, θ is the Bragg angle, and λ the wavelength. The relation between β, B, and b is often taken as

$$\beta = \sqrt{B^2 - b^2} \tag{2.10}$$

The success with which β can be deduced from the experimentally measured B limits the accuracy of estimate of ϵ.

The Detection of the Presence of Micro-Stress by X-ray Diffraction. Diffraction lines in monochromatic X-ray diffraction photographs may also be broadened by the presence of micro-stress in the crystal. Diffuse patterns are typical of cold-worked metals where variations in interplanar spacing results in the line broadening. It is a complicated task to relate the broadening to a definite stress pattern within the material, and the results are often unsatisfactory.

Asterism in X-ray Patterns. Asterism is the name given to the appearance of Laue X-ray diffraction photographs of a material containing bent crystal planes. The streaks in Fig. 2.11 arise from curved diffracting atomic planes. The spots are usually elongated in a radial or nearly radial direction, the length of elongation being obviously related to the degree of curvature of the atomic plane. A little consideration will show that a number of small crystallites arranged in a particular orientation could give overlapping diffraction spots very similar in appearance to asterism.

The Determination of the Orientation of a Single Crystal by the X-ray Method. Many physical properties are dependent on the crystallographic direction in which they are measured. It is therefore of importance to be able to determine the orientation of a single crystal or an individual crystal in a polycrystalline aggregate. The most convenient method is to employ the X-ray back-reflection Laue technique. The apparatus is similar to that shown in Fig. 2.9. White radiation is used, usually from a tungsten or molybdenum target. A back-reflection Laue pattern of iron is shown in Fig. 2.12. It will be seen that the Laue spots lie on hyperbolas. The spots on each of these rows are reflections from various planes of a given zone, that is, planes parallel to a line that is the zone axis. A cone of reflected rays is formed for each zone of planes in the crystal,

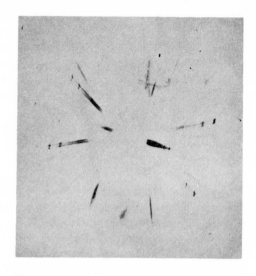

Figure 2.11   Asterism from a bent thin crystal of ferrite.   Mo radiation unfiltered.   (After Barrett)

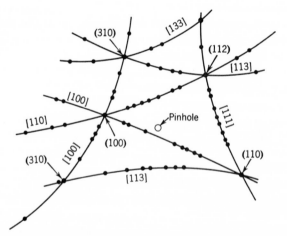

Figure 2.12   Back reflection Laue pattern from an iron single crystal.   The main diffraction spots and zone axes are indexed. (After Barrett)

the cone intersecting the flat film in a hyperbola. It follows that if the proper Miller indices can be assigned to the zones, the orientation of the single crystal can be deduced. There are standard methods and charts to carry out the procedure.

Detection of X-rays by the Geiger-Müller Tube. So far we have limited the discussion of X-ray diffraction equipment to that using photographic film as a means of detection. With the photographic film an entire pattern may be recorded at once, and thus all the reflections are on a strictly comparable basis.

In certain instances, however, particularly in commercial X-ray powder techniques, it is more convenient to use the Geiger-Müller tube as a detector. With this tube the inherent sensitivity to X-rays is much greater than with film. When X-ray quanta of sufficient energy enter the Geiger tube, voltage pulses are produced that may be shaped and counted by electronic circuits. The tube is automatically scanned around the specimen to give all θ values, and the integrated intensity is automatically drawn as a function of angle by a chart recorder.

2.5 Electron Diffraction

The relationship between the momentum of a particle and its associated wavelength is dealt with in Chapter 6. It is sufficient at this stage to note that electrons of mass m and velocity v have a momentum mv and an associated de Broglie wavelength λ given by

$$\lambda = \frac{h}{mv} \tag{2.11}$$

where h is Planck's constant.

If a stream of electrons is accelerated by an applied electrical potential, the kinetic energy of the electrons $\frac{1}{2}mv^2$ is given by

$$\frac{1}{2}mv^2 = eV \tag{2.12}$$

where V is the electrical potential and e the electron charge.

From equations 2.11 and 2.12 we have

$$\lambda = \sqrt{\frac{150}{V}}$$

with λ expressed in Angstroms and V in volts.

For example, for $V = 50$ kV, $\lambda = 0.05$ Å.

In contrast with X-rays, a beam of electrons is scattered by the atomic nuclei as well as by the outer atomic electrons. The scattering factor f_0 again decreases with increasing angle of incidence θ, as in X-rays.

But the scattering efficiency by atoms of electrons is considerably greater than of X-rays, and although the penetration depth of electrons in most solids is small, say 500 Å for 50 kV electrons, sufficient material exists in the thin layer to efficiently scatter the incident electron beam.

Figure 2.13   Electron diffraction pattern of gold foil.

Diffraction pictures like those of X-rays are produced by electrons. Figure 2.13 shows the rings in an electron diffraction study of thin gold foil. The type of problem that has been successfully attempted by electron diffraction is illustrated by the following examples.

1. Investigation of the surface oxides in iron and aluminum.

2. Determination of the orientation and lattice parameter in a deposited metallic film.

3. Studies of the nature of the thin amorphous layer produced on solid surfaces by the process of polishing.

2.6 Neutron Diffraction

The relationship between wavelength and momentum of a neutron is similar to that for electrons given in equation 2.11. The mass of the neutron, however is about 2000 times that of the electron. Thus a wavelength of about 1 Å is associated with neutrons of energy only 0.1 eV.

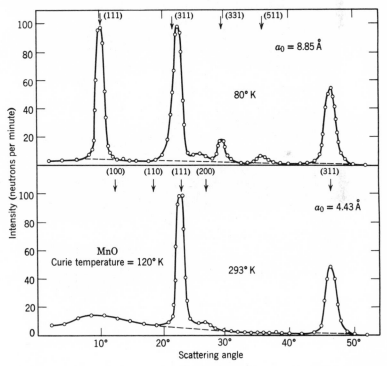

Figure 2.14   Neutron diffraction patterns of MnO at temperatures below and above the Curie temperature. (After Shull et al.)

Neutrons are chiefly scattered by the nuclei of atoms and since the wavelength of the neutron is much greater than the dimension of the scattering nucleus ($\simeq 10^{-15}$ m) the atomic scattering factor is practically independent of the scattering angle.

The factors that make diffraction by neutrons a useful supplementary tool to solid studies by X-rays are twofold. First, the scattering of neutrons

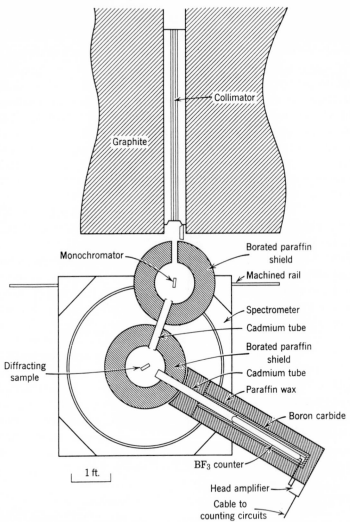

Figure 2.15   The technique of neutron diffraction. (After Shull et al.)

by light elements is, in contrast to X-rays, quite often relatively strong. Second, the magnetic moment of the neutron interacts with the magnetic moment of the scattering atom, modifying the diffraction pattern in a way that gives information about the number of atoms grouped in a common magnetic pattern.

The first factor has enabled the crystallographer to deduce the positions of hydrogen and carbon atoms in a number of organic crystals by the technique of neutron diffraction. The second factor has proved useful in the detection of antiferromagnetism (see Chapter 12). In an antiferromagnetic solid the magnetic moments of pairs of atoms are aligned antiparallel and hence appear different to an incident neutron. The neutron diffraction pattern of MnO is shown in Fig. 2.14 taken at two different temperatures. At room temperature, which is above the Curie temperature for MnO, the long-range magnetic ordering is destroyed by thermal agitation, and the pattern is typical of a structure of the NaCl type. At a temperature below the Curie temperature the *magnetic* unit cell is twice the size of the *chemical* one. This is because in antiferromagnetic MnO the Mn atoms at positions 000 and 100 have oppositely directed magnetic moments and thus appear to the neutrons to be different atoms; similarly the atoms at 010 and 001 have moments directed opposite to the one at 000. Thus if the MnO is held below the Curie temperature of 120°K, additional diffraction lines appear, typical of the larger cell.

Figure 2.15 shows apparatus for crystal structure investigation by neutron diffraction. Neutrons from the reactor are slowed down in the graphite thermal column. Very few are lost while their energy decreases to the equilibrium value equal to the thermal energy of the carbon atoms. A distribution of energies and consequently of wavelengths is present in the neutron beam. Neutrons of a suitable wavelength are then selected by the single crystal monochromator, which reflects according to the Bragg relation. The reflected monochromatic neutrons are then used to investigate the solid under test. The scattered neutron beam can be detected with a counter filled with boron trifluoride gas. The boron is often enriched in B^{10} for better absorption. The diffracted neutrons cause disintegration of the B^{10} into the lighter elements Li^7 and He^4. These move rapidly through the gas and the resulting ionization is recorded electronically as the counter is moved slowly through the range of diffraction angles θ.

REFERENCES

R. Beeching, *Electron Diffraction*, Methuen, London, 1946.

G. E. Bacon, *Neutron Diffraction*, Clarendon Press, Oxford, 1955.

N. F. M. Henry, H. Lipson, and W. A. Wooster, *The Interpretation of X-ray Diffraction Photographs*, The Macmillan Company Ltd., London, 1951.

H. P. Klug and L. E. Alexander, *X-ray Diffraction Procedures*, John Wiley and Sons, New York, 1954. (Contains A.S.T.M. identification procedures).

EXERCISES

1. (a) What is the wavelength associated with an electron of kinetic energy 10 keV?

   (b) What is the wavelength associated with a neutron of 300°K ($K.E. = \frac{1}{2}kT$)?

(c) What is the minimum wavelength in X-ray white radiation if the applied voltage on the tube is 30 kV?

2. The fraction of the incident radiation intensity transmitted by a shield of thickness x is $e^{-\mu x}$ where μ is the *absorption coefficient*. Calculate the thickness of lead shield to reduce the intensity to 50 per cent of its incident value for (a) neutrons of wavelength 1.08 Å for which μ for lead is $3 \times 10^{-1}\,\text{m}^{-1}$; (b) X-rays of wavelength 1.54 Å for which μ for lead is $2.4 \times 10^5\,\text{m}^{-1}$.

3. First-order X-ray diffraction from the (100) planes in NaCl occurs with MoKα radiation ($\lambda = 0.709$ Å) at a Bragg angle of 7.3°. If the density of the NaCl crystal is $2160\,\text{kg m}^{-3}$, calculate Avagadro's number. Atomic weight Na = 23; Cl = 35.5. (*Hint:* in Fig. 2.9 the cube of side d_{100} contains $\frac{1}{2}$ atom Na and $\frac{1}{2}$ atom Cl.)

4. X-ray back-reflection experiments with an aluminum specimen and CuKα_1 radiation ($\lambda = 1.5405$ Å) indicate that the Bragg angle of the (422) ring changes by 0.3° as the aluminum specimen is raised in temperature by 100°C. Calculate the mean coefficient of thermal expansion of aluminum. Lattice parameter a for aluminum = 4.041 Å.

5. The table shows the measured θ values in a tantalum powder diffraction pattern using CuKα_1 X-radiation:

Line	$\theta°$
1	19.611
2	28.136
3	35.156
4	41.564
5	47.769
6	54.119
7	60.876
8	68.912
9	81.520

(a) Calculate the spacings, d. (b) Index the lines with the indices (*hkl*). (c) Calculate the lattice parameter a from each d value. (d) Plot a against $\cos^2 \theta$ and extrapolate to $\theta = 90°$ to get a best value of the lattice parameter. This procedure eliminates a number of systematic errors.

3

Alloys

We have already seen that elements in the solid form possess a characteristic atomic arrangement (Chapter 1). It is now of interest to discuss the effect on this atomic arrangement of introducing atoms of a second element. We will first discuss the effect of the addition of small amounts of the second element before proceeding to a brief discussion of alloying in binary systems.

If, for example, we take pure copper, which has a face-centered cubic lattice, and introduce a small amount of zinc, we obtain a homogeneous solid called α brass. After the surface of this solid has been polished to a fine finish and etched, the microscopic appearance is little different from that of the pure copper. The X-ray diffraction powder photographs also show little difference from that of pure copper, although a calculation of lattice parameter would reveal that the parameter has slightly increased to accommodate the larger zinc atoms. Here we are dealing with a *substitutional* solid solution of zinc in copper in which some of the lattice positions occupied by copper atoms in the pure copper have now been taken by zinc atoms. The substitutional type of solid solution is by far the most common in alloys.

If, however, the second element is much smaller in atomic radius than the solvent atom, a type of alloy may be formed in which the solute atom fits into the interstices between the solvent atoms. Such a solid solution is called *interstitial*. Technologically, the most important of such alloys is austenitic steel in which carbon atoms are in interstitial solution in γ iron.

3.1   Hume-Rothery Rules for Solubility

The rules of Hume-Rothery identify the important factors which favour or oppose solid solubility. These rules are qualitative.

Size Factor.   If an element B is added to an element A, the lattice of A must be distorted to accommodate the atoms of B. It is not surprising to find that the extent to which A can dissolve B atoms depends on the difference in atomic radii. The effective atomic radius of an element is

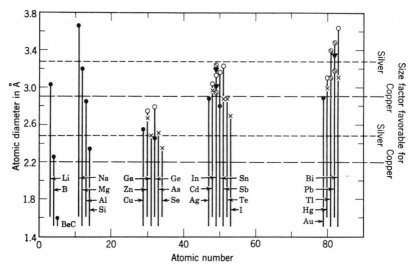

Figure 3.1   Atomic diameters of elements plotted against atomic number with size factors favorable for solution in copper and silver. (After Hume-Rothery)

often taken as one-half of the closest distance between the centers of atoms in the crystal of the pure material. If the other factors, yet to be discussed, are favorable, extensive solid solubility is expected if the atomic radii differ by less than 14 per cent. Silver and gold atoms, for example, have nearly identical radii and form a continuous series of solid solutions.

It is more difficult to assign a ratio between solute and solvent atomic radii to categorize interstitial solid solution. The common interstitial solids—carbon, hydrogen, nitrogen, boron, oxygen—may ionize in solution making uncertain the effective radius. We may in many cases, however, expect extensive interstitial solid solution if the radius of the solute atom is less than about 60 per cent of the solvent atom.

Figure 3.1 shows the atomic diameters of some of the elements plotted against atomic numbers with the size factors favorable for solution in copper and silver marked on the diagram. In explanation of the figure, it should be noted that when the crystal structure of the element is such that all the close neighbors of an atom are equidistant, the single atomic diameter is represented by ●. Where there are two sets of neighbors, the smaller interatomic distance is marked ×. Calculated atomic diameters by Goldschmidt are marked ○. Where the element is incompletely ionized in the solid state, the interatomic distance in the crystal of the element is marked ⊘, and an arrow is drawn to the estimated value of atomic diameter in the fully ionized state. It is this latter value which is usually important in connection with solid solutions in copper and silver.

Electronegative Valency Effect. We have next to discuss what other factors may prevent the formation of a solid solution even though the size factor is favorable. Sometimes stable intermediate compounds are formed at the expense of the primary solid solution. The general rule for the formation of such compounds is that the solute element be electronegative and the solvent be electropositive, or vice versa. For example, the elements of Group VIA sulfur, selenium, and tellurium (see Table 3.1) form stable sulfides, selenides, and tellurides, and consequently the solid solubility of these elements in metals is low. Group VA elements such as phosphorus, arsenic, and antimony are less electronegative and slight solubility in metals is possible. Group IVA elements, being still less electronegative, are able to enter into solid solution in some metals to a certain extent.

In most cases where formation of such compounds takes place, the solid solubility of one element in another increases with temperature. It is then possible to precipitate the compound out of solution by decreasing the temperature. This is also the case in some ternary alloys. For example the elements Mg and Si will remain in solution in Al at high temperatures, but will precipitate out as the stable compound Mg_2Si when the temperature is lowered. A critical dispersion of the precipitated particles of compound will often harden the alloy, making the process, known as "age hardening," one of industrial importance.

The Relative Valency Effect. The third important factor is the relative valency effect, according to which, other factors being equal, a metal of lower valency is more likely to dissolve one of higher valency than vice versa. Suppose we consider the system copper-silicon. The atom of higher valency, that is, silicon, crystallizes so that each atom has four nearest neighbors (see Chapter 1). If an atom of silicon is replaced by a copper atom, which has only one valence electron, there will be insufficient electrons to form the tetrahedral bonds, and the solid solution will be very restricted. On the other hand, the univalent elements copper, silver, and gold can dissolve elements of higher valency to a much greater degree.

So far in our discussion of the introduction of one element in solid

Table 3.1   Periodic Classification of the Elements

GROUP	IA	IIA	IIIB	IVB	VB	VIB	VIIB	VIIIB			IB	IIB	IIIA	IVA	VA	VIA	VIIA	VIIIA
1	H_1																	He_2
2	Li_3	Be_4											B_5	C_6	N_7	O_8	F_9	Ne_{10}
3	Na_{11}	Mg_{12}											Al_{13}	Si_{14}	P_{15}	S_{16}	Cl_{17}	Ar_{18}
4	K_{19}	Ca_{20}	Sc_{21}	Ti_{22}	V_{23}	Cr_{24}	Mn_{25}	Fe_{26}	Co_{27}	Ni_{28}	Cu_{29}	Zn_{30}	Ga_{31}	Ge_{32}	As_{33}	Se_{34}	Br_{35}	Kr_{36}
5	Rb_{37}	Sr_{38}	Y_{39}	Zr_{40}	Nb_{41}	Mo_{42}	Te_{43}	Ru_{44}	Rh_{45}	Pd_{46}	Ag_{47}	Cd_{48}	In_{49}	Sn_{50}	Sb_{51}	Te_{52}	I_{53}	Ne_{54}
6	Cs_{55}	Ba_{56}	La_{57}* Lu_{71}	Hf_{72}	Ta_{73}	W_{74}	Re_{75}	Os_{76}	Ir_{77}	Pt_{78}	Au_{79}	Hg_{80}	Tl_{81}	Pb_{82}	Bi_{83}	Po_{84}	At_{85}	Rn_{86}
7	Fr_{87}	Ra_{88}	Ac_{89}†	Th_{90}	Pa_{91}	U_{92}												

PERIODS

* Rare earth series: Ce_{58}, Pr_{59}, Nd_{60}, Pm_{61}, Sm_{62}, Eu_{63}, Gd_{64}, Tb_{65}, Dy_{66}, Ho_{67}, Er_{68}, Tm_{69}, Yb_{70}, Lu_{71}.

† Actinide Series: Th_{90}, Pa_{91}, U_{92}, Np_{93}, Pu_{94}, Am_{95}, Cm_{96}, Bk_{97}, Cf_{98}, E_{99}, Fm_{100}, Mv_{101}, No_{102}.

solution in another we have dealt only with the factors that limit solid solubility. We will now briefly describe the nature of alloys formed when elements are mixed in sizable proportions. The examples selected will be chiefly metallurgical, and the discussion will be limited to binary alloys.

3.2 Free Energy

In a binary alloy of a certain composition the *components*, which in this case are the two elements, may be liquid, if the temperature is high enough. The liquid mixture is called a liquid *phase*. On lowering the temperature partial solidification may take place and two phases—liquid and solid— coexist together. In the solid state one component may be in solution in the other, making a solid solution phase. Or an intermetallic compound phase may form. It is necessary at the outset of our discussion of binary alloys to try to define the conditions that govern the choice of phase in which an alloy of a certain composition will exist at a certain temperature. In many cases this is not known in detail. We can, however, give a thermodynamic condition that defines the equilibrium state of a solid state system.

Suppose that a system of volume V at a pressure p has internal energy E and entropy S. The internal energy is the sum of the kinetic and potential energies of the atoms present and in an isolated system would be constant. Suppose here that the system is not isolated but can exchange energy with its surroundings. In alloy formation heat can be absorbed or rejected in the melting or solidifying processes.

Then from the first law of thermodynamics, if dQ is the heat absorbed by the system from its surroundings, we have

$$dQ = dE + p \, dV \tag{3.1}$$

Here the term dE represents energy associated with the internal rearrangement and $p \, dV$ gives the external work done by the system. Both are a consequence of absorbing energy dQ.

Let dS_1 and dS_2 be the entropy change in the system and in its environment respectively. The second law of thermodynamics then ensures that whatever the nature of the change there is an entropy increase, that is, $dS_1 + dS_2 \geqslant 0$. The change in entropy of the environment dS_2 is associated with the heat transfer dQ at the temperature T. From the definition of entropy we have therefore

$$dS_2 = \frac{-dQ}{T} \tag{3.2}$$

Thus $dS_1 - dQ/T \geqslant 0$ and from (3.1) this reads

$$dE + p \, dV - T \, dS_1 \leqslant 0 \qquad (3.3)$$

This is the condition that defines, for the system itself, in which direction the physical-chemical change will proceed.

When the condition

$$dE + p \, dV - T \, dS_1 = 0 \qquad (3.4)$$

is reached, the system is in equilibrium and all further infinitesimal changes are reversible. In solid-state systems the term $p \, dV$ is very small and the condition (3.4) for equilibrium may be written, dropping the suffix and referring to the system itself

$$dE - T \, dS = 0 \qquad (3.5)$$

We may now define the equilibrium condition for a particular temperature T. Equation 3.5 may be written $d(E - TS) = 0$. This is equivalent to saying that the quantity $E - TS$ should be a minimum. The quantity $E - TS$ is called the Helmholtz *free energy* F or simply the *free energy*.

Solid-state systems are generally not in a state of equilibrium because of the slowness of rearrangement of atomic positions in a rigid solid. We can say, however, that as far as is possible under the conditions prevailing, the system will continually change in the direction of minimization of free energy.

3.3   The Rate of Approach to Equilibrium

We have defined the quantity F controlling the direction in which a system will undergo change. At this point we will briefly deal with a law which expresses for many systems the rate at which this change will take place.

Unless an atom in a particular atomic arrangement can pick up enough energy to change its position to one of lower free energy, it will remain confined to its original position. The amount of energy required to shift position is called the *activation energy* Q. The energy may be the energy per atom, when it is usually referred to as q, or the energy per mole or gram atomic weight, when Q is used. The particular process envisaged here of redistribution of atoms within the solid state system is one of diffusion. We will discuss diffusion in greater detail in Chapter 4. The intention at present is merely to introduce the concept of activation energy and activated processes of which a very large number indeed exist in nature.

The speed of change in a particular system will obviously depend on

1. the magnitude of the activation energy Q for the reaction in question, and
2. the number of atoms or molecules that possess energy q at any moment.

In almost all the systems in solid-state physics there is no restriction on the fundamental components of the systems, atoms in this case, taking up energy if it is available. In such cases the steady-state distribution of energy among the different atoms of the system is such that numbers have energies ranging from quite small to very high values. The fraction of atoms possessing energy greater than a certain value q is, according to the Maxwell-Boltzmann distribution law, proportional to $e^{-Q/RT}$.

Here R is the Boltzmann constant per mole with a value of 8.31 joules deg^{-1}. If q is the energy per atom, the fraction of atoms possessing energy greater than q is proportional to $e^{-q/kT}$ where k is the Boltzmann constant equal to 1.380×10^{-23} joule deg^{-1}. The relationship between R and k is, of course,

$$R = kN \tag{3.6}$$

where N is Avogadro's constant. Therefore, if we are dealing with an "activated" process, the rate of reaction r is given by

$$r = Ae^{-Q/RT} \tag{3.7}$$

with A a constant.

The obvious experimental test for such a process is to carry out the reaction at various temperatures, measuring in each case some quantity proportional to the rate. If a plot of $\log r$ vs. $1/T$ is linear, the process is specified by an activation energy whose value can be obtained from the slope of the linear plot.

3.4 Phase Diagrams

We have now considered both the direction in which a physical-chemical system will change toward equilibrium and the rate at which the change will take place. Ideally, if it were possible to calculate the internal energy and entropy for each of a number of possible atomic arrangements in a solid-state system, we could choose the arrangement of minimum free energy. This would be the atomic structure found in equilibrium at the particular temperature. Complete calculations are complicated, but some success along these lines has already been achieved. Discussions of the nature of the calculations in sufficient detail to be useful are too lengthy for inclusion in this book. The remainder of this section will simply contain examples of some of the simpler types of alloy equilibrium phase diagrams. As is common practice, the percentage by weight of the components of the system are plotted against the temperature. It must be emphasized again that these are equilibrium diagrams and will represent conditions actually found in practice only if sufficient time for diffusion has elapsed.

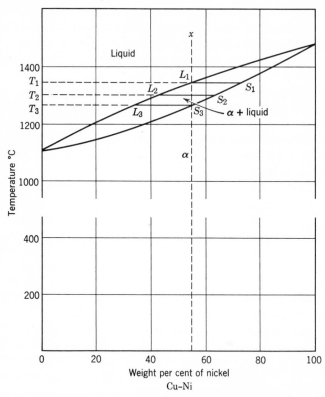

Figure 3.2   Binary phase diagram with complete miscibility.

Binary System with Complete Miscibility. The simplest type of binary phase diagram is one representing continuous solubility. In the example chosen and shown in Fig. 3.2, nickel forms a series of solid solutions in copper in all proportions from pure copper to pure nickel. In this type of phase diagram the upper curved line is called the *liquidus* line and represents the limit of the liquid phase, and the lower curved line is called the *solidus* and represents the limit of the solid phase. Points in the area between the lines represent composition-temperature combinations in the form of mixtures of solid and liquid phase. If an alloy of arbitrary composition, say about 55 per cent nickel, is cooled very slowly from the liquid phase (point x) and equilibrium is maintained, the solidification will take place in the following sequence. When the temperature has fallen to T_1 solidification begins, the solid first formed being of composition S_1 which is richer in nickel than 55 per cent. The remaining melt will thus be enriched in copper. At a lower temperature T_2 further solidification takes place, the composition of the solid in equilibrium with liquid being S_2. If the cooling is sufficiently slow, the original solid deposit will have time to absorb copper from the liquid to change its composition from S_1 to S_2. Finally at temperature T_3 no liquid remains, and the solid has attained the uniform composition of x.

It is readily understood that if the cooling is too rapid to permit diffusion of copper from the liquid into the forming solid, each layer of solid that is deposited differs in composition from the preceding layer. This is called "*coring.*" Coring is often found in practice and may be removed by suitable annealing at a high enough temperature and for sufficient time to allow diffusion of atoms to homogenize the solid.

Binary Eutectic. It is rare to find in the solid state two elements completely soluble in one another as in the last example. Partial solubility is much more common. We will now discuss the other extreme in which two elements, ordinarily solid, are completely soluble in one another in the liquid state and only partially soluble in the solid state. The lead-antimony system will serve as an example. The equilibrium phase diagram is shown in Fig. 3.3.

In this system the liquidus line *DEF* is in two branches intersecting at a point E called the *eutectic* point. The eutectic temperature in this example is 247°C. The region on the left marked α is the solid solution of antimony in lead, and the region on the right marked β is the solid solution of lead in antimony. The limit of solubility of antimony in lead is represented by the point A (about 2 per cent antimony) and that of lead in antimony by the point B (about 6 per cent lead). We can see from the natures of the low-temperature α and β boundary lines that the solubilities decrease as the temperature is lowered, and the compositions of the two solid solutions tend to approach those of the pure solvent metals. For compositions between A and B, the final structure of the solid will consist of either a eutectic mixture of α and β crystals if the composition corresponded to E or an excess of α or β crystals dispersed in the α-β eutectic.

Let us again consider the solidification of an alloy of arbitrary composition, say 55 per cent by weight of antimony. When the temperature has fallen to T_1, first crystals of β will begin to precipitate at the point C. Further cooling results in precipitation of β crystals, whose composition

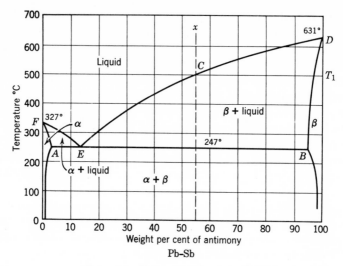

Figure 3.3   Binary eutectic phase diagram.

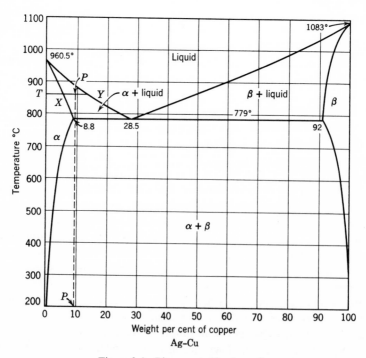

Figure 3.4   Binary eutectic phase diagram.

varies along the solidus line *DB*. The composition of the remaining liquid varies along the liquidus line *DE*. Once the eutectic temperature has been reached, further heat removal results in the eutectic liquid solidifying in the intimate mixture of α and β crystals which is called the eutectic solid. Further cooling to room temperature does not result in great change since diffusion in the solid is slow.

Figure 3.4 shows the silver-copper phase diagram which is similar in nature to the lead-antimony just discussed.

Binary Phase Diagram with Intermediate Phases. We have already seen that one of the factors limiting the solubility of one solid element in

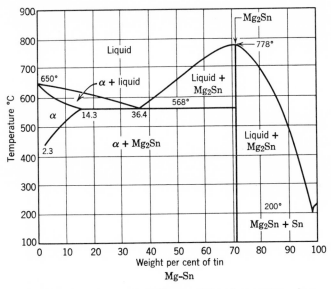

Figure 3.5   Binary phase diagram with an intermediate phase.

another is a tendency in some instances toward formation of a chemical compound. Thus magnesium, for example, forms compounds of the type MgX with S, Se or Te, of the type Mg_2X with Si, Ge, Sn or Pb, and of the type Mg_3X with As_2, Sb_2, or Bi_2. The nature of an equilibrium diagram which contains an intermediate compound is illustrated by the magnesium-tin system shown in Fig. 3.5. The compound Mg_2Sn contains 29.08 per cent by weight of magnesium. The complete phase diagram consists of two eutectic diagrams placed together, the dividing line coming at the compound composition.

Binary Peritectic Phase Diagram. Sometimes as solidification proceeds a reaction may take place at a definite temperature between the solid already deposited and a definite proportion of the remaining melt.

This can result in the formation of another solid solution or compound, the composition of which is intermediate between the first solid and the liquid. This is known as a *peritectic* reaction. The example shown in Fig. 3.6 is from the copper–tin binary system.

The peritectic reaction affects the solidification of alloys with weight per cent of tin between 13.2 and 25.5, that is, points A and P. Alloys with tin composition outside these limits solidify as solid solutions in a manner already described. Suppose we examine the solidification of an alloy of

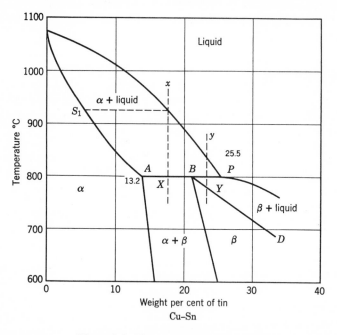

Figure 3.6   Binary peritectic phase diagram.

composition x. At first solid crystals of composition S_1 form. As deposition of solid proceeds the solid changes its composition to A while the liquid moves to composition P. This, of course, assumes equilibrium of the solid maintained throughout the cooling. Usually the cooling is too rapid for this to be achieved. At this stage the ratio of liquid to solid is equal to AX/PX. The method of obtaining these ratios is given in Section 3.5. The remaining liquid reacts at this stage with the solid of composition A to form a new intermediate phase β of composition B. It should be noted that since X lies between A and B the liquid will be exhausted before the solid crystals of composition A. The alloy will then consist of solid α and solid β crystals of composition A and B respectively.

Let us now examine the solidification of an alloy of composition y which lies between B and P. As before, α crystals are first deposited, the solid changing in composition to A as freezing proceeds. If equilibrium is maintained, the α crystals convert to composition B and phase β. The excess liquid of composition P solidifies by deposition of β crystals, which then change in composition along the solidus line BD until the point Y is reached.

The main features of binary equilibrium phase diagrams have now been demonstrated. More complex systems are, of course, produced by increasing the number of components to more than two but no new fundamental principles are involved.

3.5 The Lever Rule

The *lever rule* is a simple rule by which the relative proportions of two phases in a binary alloy can be quickly deduced from the composition of

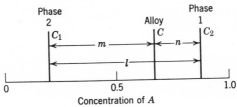

Figure 3.7   The lever rule.

the alloy and the compositions of the two phases. Suppose that we have an alloy of two components A and B, the weight concentrations (i.e., fractions by weight) being C and $1 - C$ respectively. The alloy is a mixture of two phases 1 and 2 in which the concentrations of A are respectively C_1 and C_2 (see Fig. 3.7). Let the proportion of phase 1 in the alloy be x so that the proportion of phase 2 is $1 - x$. The problem is to find x and $1 - x$ in terms of C, C_1, and C_2. If the total weight of alloy is W, the weight of A is CW. The weight of A in phase 1 is xC_1W, and the weight of A in phase 2 is $(1 - x)C_2W$. Hence $CW = xC_1W + (1 - x)C_2W$, so that

$$\left. \begin{array}{l} x = \dfrac{C - C_2}{C_1 - C_2} = \dfrac{m}{l} \\[3mm] 1 - x = \dfrac{C_1 - C}{C_1 - C_2} = \dfrac{n}{l} \\[3mm] \dfrac{x}{1 - x} = \dfrac{C - C_2}{C_1 - C} = \dfrac{m}{n} \end{array} \right\} \qquad (3.8)$$

and

Equation 3.8 expresses the lever rule. In Fig. 3.4, application of the rule shows that at temperature T an alloy of composition P would be in the form of a mixture of liquid and solid phases so that the ratio, weight of liquid of composition Y: weight of α solid of composition $X = PX/PY$.

3.6   The Preparation of Very Pure Materials

The presence of quite small numbers of foreign atoms in a solid element markedly affects many of the physical characteristics of the element. This is not surprising since it may be easily calculated that in a solid with, say, one foreign atom per thousand lattice atoms, few points in the solid, if it is homogeneous, are more distant from a foreign atom than about eight atomic spacings.

Zone refining is a powerful method for the purification of metals and some intermediate compounds. It has made possible the purification of germanium and silicon to the degree necessary for use in transistors and other solid state electronic devices. The principles of the method will be outlined in a manner following the original work of Pfann (1958).

In a binary alloy the presence of solute may lower or raise the freezing point temperature of the solvent. If the freezing point is lowered, the equilibrium phase diagram will take the form at low solute concentrations

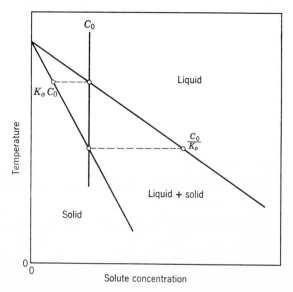

Figure 3.8   Equilibrium phase diagram at low concentration of solute that lowers the melting point of the solvent.

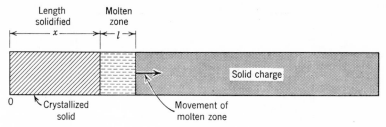

Figure 3.9   Molten zone passing along length of metal as in zone refining.

shown in Fig. 3.8.   Here K_0, which is the ratio of solute concentration in solid to solute concentration in liquid, is less than unity.   In the solidification of a dilute alloy of this nature, the solute will be concentrated in the last regions to freeze.

Let us consider a rod of constant cross section and uniform concentration C_0 of solute along its length.   This may be produced in a number of ways, for example by rapid freezing from the melt as in chill casting.   Now suppose that, as in Fig. 3.9, a molten zone of short length l is made to pass from left to right along the rod.   This may be done by moving the rod in a suitable refractory through a small furnace or alternatively and more commonly by moving the furnace.   At $x = 0$ the first solid to freeze is of concentration $K_0 C_0$.   If $K_0 < 1$, the liquid is enriched in solute by the solidification.   As the zone progresses, the liquid continues to be enriched until it attains the solute concentration C_0/K_0.   When this condition is reached, the concentrations of solute in the solid entering and leaving the molten zone are identical.

The concentration C of solute at a position x in the zone melted bar is given, except in the last zone, by the equation

$$\frac{C}{C_0} = 1 - (1 - K_0)e^{-K_0 x/l} \tag{3.9}$$

Equation 3.9 giving solute concentration as a function of x is plotted in Fig. 3.10a.   In Fig. 3.10b the zone-melting curves with C_0 equal to unity are drawn for various values of K_0 and for lengths solidified of up to nine times the zone length.   Both Fig. 3.10a and Fig. 3.10b give the concentrations after a single pass of the molten zone.   As can be seen for small values of K_0, considerable purification can be effected in the initial portion of the rod by even single-pass zone melting.

Much greater purification is attained by passing the zone repeatedly down the solid bar always in the same direction.   This is often done by returning the furnace quickly to the starting point after completion of a slow zone pass.   During each pass the molten zone picks up solute on its way and deposits it at the end of the rod.   After repeated passes in one

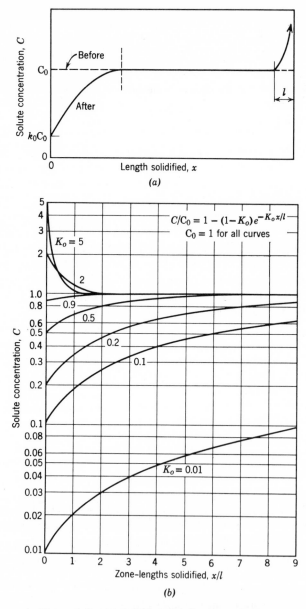

Figure 3.10 (a) Solute concentration at different distances along metal rod after a single pass of the molten zone. (b) Solute concentrations after a single pass for $C_0 - 1$ and various values of K_0. (After Pfann)

direction, a distribution of solute is reached that cannot be further changed. Figure 3.11 shows the ultimate distribution after multiple zone refining for various K_0 values. From the diagram with $K_0 = 0.1$ and the zone length one-tenth of the bar length, we see that the ultimate concentration at $x = 0$ is less than C_0 by a factor of 10^{14}. In addition, since the concentration at the starting end is decreased by a factor of the order of K_0 for each pass (see Fig. 3.10b), at least fourteen passes are required to reach the ultimate distribution.

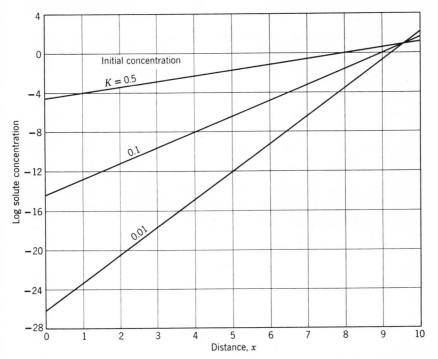

Figure 3.11 Ultimate distribution attainable by zone refining for several values of K, for an ingot 10 zones long. K is the *effective* value of the distribution coefficient K_0 appropriate to non-equilibrium conditions. (After Pfann)

While impurities with $K_0 < 1$ are transported with the liquid zone, impurities with $K_0 > 1$ move in the opposite direction. If both types of impurity are present, in order to obtain a highly refined rod it is necessary to crop both ends and use only the central portion.

For germanium it has been possible by the zone-refining process to reduce impurities to a level less than one impurity atom in 10^{10} germanium atoms. Since the ultimate purity is dependent on the relevant value of K_0, however, such a refinement is not always possible.

REFERENCES

W. Hume-Rothery and G. V. Raynor, *The Structure of Metals and Alloys*, 3rd ed., The Institute of Metals, London, 1954.

W. Hume-Rothery, J. W. Christian, and W. B. Pearson, *Metallurgical Equilibrium Diagrams*, The Institute of Physics, London, 1952.

J. S. Marsh, *Principles of Phase Diagrams*, McGraw-Hill Book Company, New York, 1956.

W. G. Pfann, *Zone Melting*, John Wiley and Sons, New York, 1958.

G. V. Raynor, *Progress in Metal Physics*, Vol. 1, Interscience Publishers, New York, 1949.

A.S.M. Handbook of Metals, American Society for Metals, Cleveland.

EXERCISES

1. The size factor favors solid solibility for each of the following alloys. Consider the relative valency effect and say whether or not solibility will be favored or restricted. Solute follows solvent

K	—	Rb	Mg	—	Cd	Ag	—	Sn
Rb	—	Cs	As	—	Sb	Sn	—	Ag
Ag	—	Au	Se	—	Te	Pd	—	Pt
Cu	—	Si	Cu	—	Ge	Ag	—	Mg
Si	—	Cu	Ge	—	Cu	Mg	—	Ag

2. In the compound CuZn there are two atoms and three valency electrons (one from the copper and two from the zinc). The electron-atom ratio is thus $3:2$. The following compounds are grouped according to their electron-atom ratios. Work out the effective valencies for each element.

Ratio	$3:2$	$21:13$	$7:4$
	CuBe	Cu_5Zn_8	$CuZn_3$
	AgMg	Cu_5Cd_8	$CuCd_3$
	AgZn	Cu_9Al_4	Cu_3Sn
	AgCd	Cu_9Ga_4	Ag_3Sn
	AuZn	Cu_9In_4	Ag_5Al_3
	CoAl	$Cu_{31}Si_8$	Au_5Al_3

   For a number of these compounds calculate the percentage by weight of the elements. Refer to a table of atomic weights.

3. Suppose that an activated process (such as grain growth) in a solid has an activation energy of 30 kcal per mole. If the process is completed in 1 hour at 500°C, how long would it take at 0°C?

4. Decide whether the carbon atoms are interstitial or substitutional in the iron-carbon alloy whose characteristics are given.

   Per cent weight of carbon $= 0.8$
   Structure: face-centered cubic
   Lattice parameter $a = 3.583$ Å.
   Density of alloy $= 8142$ kgm^{-3}

5. The copper–nickel equilibrium diagram of Fig. 3.2 shows complete solid solubility. Liquid copper–nickel alloys containing respectively 80 per cent, 50 per cent, and 10 per cent by weight of nickel are cooled from the melt. Give the compositions of the first solid to form in each case. If one kilogram of the 50 per cent nickel alloy is used, how much solid can be filtered out at 1300°C?

6. Consider the silver–copper equilibrium diagram of Fig. 3.4. Determine the percentage of α solid solution in the eutectic micro-constituent following solidification of the 28.5 per cent copper alloy. Using the 70 per cent by weight copper alloy, tell the phases and percentages of each at (a) 960.5°C; (b) 850°C; (c) 700°C.

7. Consider the copper–tin equilibrium diagram of Fig. 3.6. Using the 25.5 per cent tin alloy, tell the phases and percentages of each at (a) 1000°C; (b) 850°C; (c) 760°C.

8. Sketch roughly the form of the temperature time dependence for these alloys of Fig. 3.4 as they lose heat at a constant rate and transform from the liquid to the solid phase, (a) 0 per cent copper; (b) 20 per cent copper; (c) 28.5 per cent copper; (d) 60 per cent copper; (e) 100 per cent copper.

9. From Fig. 3.2 estimate roughly the value of K_0 (page 61) for a very dilute alloy of copper in nickel. Suppose that a rod of nickel containing 0.1 per cent by weight of copper is zone refined with the molten zone being about one-tenth of the length of the rod. Estimate the ultimate purity attainable and give the number of zone passes necessary.

4

Vacancies and Diffusion

In nature crystals are never perfect; they contain various forms of imperfection. Seitz (1952) suggests that six primary imperfections exist in nearly perfect crystals, the interactions between these imperfections markedly affecting the physical properties of the crystal. The six imperfections are: (a) foreign atoms, (b) vacant lattice sites and interstitial atoms, (c) dislocations, (d) phonons, (e) electrons and holes, and (f) excitons.

In Chapter 3 we discussed foreign atoms. In this chapter we deal with vacant lattice sites and interstitial atoms. Types c, d, e, and f will be treated in Chapters 5, 10, 11, and 13 respectively. Interactions exist between imperfections of the same group, some of these interactions in fact producing imperfections of a different type. The six types are therefore not independent of one another.

4.1 Vacant Lattice Sites and Interstitial Atoms

The two simplest types of lattice vacancy are illustrated in Fig. 4.1a and b. The *Schottky defect* in (a) is a simple lattice vacancy or missing atom in the lattice. The missing atom may have been transferred to the surface of the crystal or to a dislocation (see Chapter 5) or to some other sink associated with a disordered portion of the lattice. If, however, the missing atom is transferred to an interstitial site in the lattice, a *Frenkel defect*, shown in b results. Vacancies and interstitials often exist in pairs. In addition, interstitials may interact with one another to form stable clusters, rather like diatomic or triatomic molecules. Similarly, vacancies can cluster in groups which range in size from pair combinations to large voids in the lattice.

An important property of vacancies and interstitials is that under *thermal activation* they can migrate through a crystal relatively easily and so give rise to diffusion. Indeed these imperfections were introduced into theory to explain facts concerning diffusion and electrolytic conductivity, the latter phenomenon being closely related to the first in salts, where the

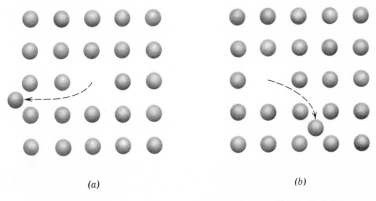

(a)   (b)

Figure 4.1   Lattice vacancies. (a) Schottky defect. (b) Frenkel defect.

migrating atoms are charged. In sodium chloride, for example, where vacant positive and negative ion sites are found in equal numbers, there is a complete correlation between the numbers of sodium atoms diffusing through the lattice, calculated from electrolytic conductivity measurements and the numbers determined by mass flow measurements.

4.2   The Equilibrium Number of Defects

Thermal energy in a solid exists as nearly elastic vibrations of the lattice atoms. The vibrations interact with one another, and in fact may combine at a localized region of the lattice to produce a large displacement of one or two atoms. This can cause atoms to jump from normal to interstitial positions, thereby producing both interstitial atoms and vacant lattice sites. If the lattice vibrations are in thermal equilibrium, which they will be if the solid remains at a constant temperature for sufficient time, the density of imperfections so produced can be determined by the laws of statistical mechanics. We will reproduce such a calculation for Schottky defects since it is illustrative of concepts of wide application in the physics of solids. We will see that the equilibrium number of defects is greater at higher temperatures. This number has been estimated to be as high as 0.01 per cent at the melting point of some of the silver salts. If a solid is held at a high temperature and then suddenly cooled, a number of defects higher than the equilibrium number may persist at the lower temperature.

Above absolute zero there will always be disorder in a crystal. The amount of disorder is related to the entropy S by the Boltzmann relation

$$S = k \log p \tag{4.1}$$

where k is Boltzmann's constant ($= 1.38 \times 10^{-23}$ joule $^\circ$K^{-1}) and p is the number of ways in which the thermal vibration energy is distributed or the number of ways in which atoms or defects may be arranged among the available number of sites.

The first choice for p leads to an expression for the *thermal entropy* whereas the second leads to an expression for the *configurational entropy*. In our calculation of the equilibrium number of Schottky defects at a particular temperature, we will first calculate the configurational entropy of such defects.

It is possible to take n atoms from N lattice sites in $N!/(N - n)!\, n!$ different ways. Thus the entropy increase S, because of the presence of the n Schottky defects, is given by

$$S = k \log \frac{N!}{(N - n)!\, n!}$$

$$= k[\log N! - \log (N - n)! - \log n!] \tag{4.2}$$

To deal with terms like $\log n!$, we use Stirling's formula which reads $\log n! = n \log n - n$. It is substantially true if $n > 10$. Thus

$$S = k[N \log N - (N - n) \log (N - n) - n \log n]$$

Now if W is the work done to move a single atom from a lattice site to the surface, that is to form a Schottky defect, the energy E of n such defects is given by

$$E = nW \tag{4.3}$$

We now have expressions for the configurational entropy S and for the energy E of formation of n defects. It remains to impose the condition characterizing equilibrium. This has already been discussed in Section 3.2 where it was shown that for a particular temperature T equilibrium is reached when the *free energy* F is a minimum.

In our calculation

$$F = E - TS = nW - kT[N \log N - (N - n) \log (N - n) - n \log n].$$

The condition for F to be a minimum by adjustment of the number is given by $\partial F/\partial n = 0$. This leads to

$$W = kT[\log (N - n) - \log n]$$

that is

$$W = kT \log \frac{N - n}{n}$$

Thus the equilibrium ratio of the number of vacancies to the number of atoms in lattice positions at temperature T is given by

$$\frac{n}{N - n} \simeq \frac{n}{N} \simeq e^{-W/kT} \tag{4.4}$$

If we insert $W \simeq 1$ eV and $T \simeq 1000°$K in the equation, the proportion of vacancies is of the order of 0.001 per cent.

It is often more favorable to form pairs of positive and negative vacancies. This is especially true in ionic crystals since the surface of the crystal will then be electrostatically neutral. The number of ways in which n separated pairs can form is $[N!/(N - n)! \, n!]^2$, and a calculation similar to the one earlier gives the fractional number of pairs as

$$\frac{n}{N} = e^{-W_r/2kT} \tag{4.5}$$

where W_r is the energy of formation of a pair.

The energy of formation of lattice defects gives an extra contribution to the heat capacity of a crystal. With silver bromide, for example, the heat capacity increases linearly but very little with temperature up to about 500°C. Between this temperature and the melting point at 700°C defects are formed thermally, and the heat capacity increases to about three times its value at 500°C.

It should be again emphasized that, as in the formation of alloys (Chapter 3), although the equilibrium state describes the condition toward which the system tends, in solids with low rates of diffusion it is seldom, if ever, attained.

4.3 Diffusion

In Chapter 3 we have seen that all phase changes in alloys involve a redistribution of the atoms present. This is true of many physical changes in solids, the kinetics of such changes being controlled by the migration of the participating atoms. This migration is called *diffusion*.

The hardening of steels is an industrial process based on the diffusion of carbon and other elements through iron. The production of age-hardened alloys depends on the dispersal of hardening compounds in a metallic matrix, the dispersal being brought about by diffusion. The basis of powder metallurgy, which is growing daily in importance, is the diffusion at elevated temperatures and pressures of atoms from one grain to another. Crystals in a polycrystalline aggregate can grow in size under suitable conditions by the diffusion of atoms.

Surface oxidation is a phenomenon dependent on the diffusion penetration of a solid by oxygen atoms. At elevated temperatures and in the presence of an electric field the ions of the alkali halides can diffuse through the solid carrying electrical charges and thus leading to ionic conductivity. These are only a few of the many examples of the diffusion phenomenon in solids which are of great scientific and industrial importance.

In a discussion of diffusion it is important at the outset to distinguish between macroscopic flow of atoms and the individual atomic movements which constitute it. In the ensuing treatment the term diffusion will mean the macroscopic flow.

Thermal agitation supplies an atom at occasional intervals with sufficient energy to enable it to climb the potential barrier between one atomic site and the next. The directions of the collisions between neighboring atoms are quite random, the resulting path of an individual migrating atom being therefore a haphazard zigzag. If, however, we consider a cross-sectional plane through a solid bar with a higher concentration of solute atoms or defects on one side of the plane than on the other, more solute atoms or defects will cross the plane from one side to the other than in the opposite direction, simply because more of them are available for such movement on the higher concentration side. There will be a statistical drift down the concentration gradient.

In 1885 Fick proposed a set of equations to describe this mass flow by diffusion. These equations are the analogues of Fourier's heat flow equations. We will develop these equations for two particular sets of circumstances.

Steady State Flow.   First let us discuss the Fick equations for the case in which the concentration gradients do not change with time over the region of flow. This is often the case for, say, flow of gases through metals where a constant pressure of gas is maintained on one side of a metal specimen, the gas being removed on the other. Hydrogen, nitrogen, and oxygen, for example, diffuse rapidly through many metals at elevated temperatures. In such instances, solubility is necessary for diffusion, an insoluble gas being able to pass only through pores and cracks and not through the solid metal.

Suppose in Fig. 4.2 that the two vertical lines represent adjacent atomic planes 1 and 2 distant a apart in a solid. Each plane is of unit area. The concentrations c_1 and c_2 of solute atoms are the fractions of the total numbers of atoms on the respective planes. Let us also suppose that a concentration gradient $\partial c / \partial x$ of solute atoms exists in the direction marked, that is, $c_1 > c_2$. The argument which follows will apply equally well to defects.

There are $c_1 N$ and $c_2 N$ *solute* atoms on the respective planes if N is the number of atoms on the planes. If the frequency of jumping, by thermal action, of solute atoms from each plane is n times per second, then in unit

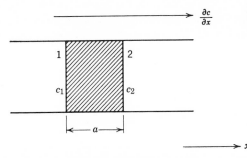

Figure 4.2   Derivation of Fick's Laws.

time $nc_1 N/2$ solute atoms will jump from plane 1 to plane 2. In the same time $nc_2 N/2$ will jump from plane 2 to plane 1. Thus the net number J of atoms transferred per second from plane 1 to plane 2 is $\frac{1}{2} n N(c_1 - c_2)$, that is,

$$J = \tfrac{1}{2} n N(c_1 - c_2)$$

$$= -\tfrac{1}{2} n N a \frac{\partial c}{\partial x} \text{ where } c_1 - c_2 = -a \frac{\partial c}{\partial x}$$

$$= -D_1 \frac{\partial c}{\partial x} \tag{4.6}$$

where D_1 is the *diffusion coefficient* or *diffusivity*. D_1 is measured in units of square meters per second. It is dependent on temperature and frequently varies with concentration. When this is so the concentration must be known at each point x in the solid in order to apply equation 4.6.

Nonsteady State Flow.   We shall now set up a much more general equation than 4.6 to describe nonsteady states of flow where the average concentration in a given region varies with time. This is the normal circumstance when solute atoms or defects migrate through a solid solvent.

Consider the two atomic planes of Fig. 4.2 to be in this case a distance l apart where l is greater than one atomic distance. If the concentration of solute atoms on plane 1 is c, the concentration on plane 2 is $c + (\partial c/\partial x)l$. The *rate of exit* of solute atoms from the shaded volume element across plane 1 is $-\frac{1}{2}nNa(\partial c/\partial x)$. In addition, the *rate of entry* across plane 2 is $\frac{1}{2}nNa(\partial/\partial x)[c + (\partial c/\partial x)l]$. Thus the rate of accumulation of solute atoms in the volume element is

$$\frac{1}{2}nNa\left[\frac{\partial}{\partial x}\left(c + \frac{\partial c}{\partial x}l\right) - \frac{\partial c}{\partial x}\right]$$

that is,

$$\frac{1}{2}nNal\frac{\partial^2 c}{\partial x^2}$$

Since there are l/a planes in the volume element, the rate of accumulation on any particular plane of the element is given by

$$\frac{\partial}{\partial t}(Nc) = \frac{1}{2}nNa^2\frac{\partial^2 c}{\partial x^2}$$

Thus

$$\frac{\partial c}{\partial t} = \frac{1}{2}na^2\frac{\partial^2 c}{\partial x^2}$$

(4.7)

or

$$\frac{\partial c}{\partial t} = D_2\frac{\partial^2 c}{\partial x^2}$$

where $D_2(=\frac{1}{2}a^2 n)$ is the diffusion coefficient. Equation 4.7 expresses Fick's Law in a more general form.

Where diffusion is not unidirectional but where the solid is isotropic with respect to diffusion, the following partial differential equation applies:

$$\frac{\partial c}{\partial t} = D_2\left(\frac{\partial^2 c}{\partial x^2} + \frac{\partial^2 c}{\partial y^2} + \frac{\partial^2 c}{\partial z^2}\right)$$

(4.8)

or

$$\frac{\partial c}{\partial t} = D_2\nabla^2 c$$

Cubic crystals fulfill the isotropic condition, whereas hexagonal, rhombohedral, and tetragonal crystals require two diffusion coefficients.

As in other theories in physics the differential equation must be solved for particular boundary conditions appropriate to the situation. As an example we will quote the solution of equation 4.8 for one set of boundary conditions. Consider diffusion across a plane interface between adjoining columns of solid solution and solid solvent. If the columns of solution and solvent are sufficiently long so that no appreciable change in composition occurs at their outer ends during the course of the observations, the columns can be regarded as of infinite length.

Under these conditions

$$c = \frac{c_0}{2}\left[1 - \frac{2}{\sqrt{\pi}} \int_0^{\frac{x}{2\pi\sqrt{D_2 t}}} e^{-y^2}\, dy\right] \tag{4.9}$$

where c is the concentration of solute in solvent after time t at a distance x from the interface, c_0 being the initial concentration, D_2 the coefficient of diffusion, and the second term in the bracket is the *probability integral*, values of which may be found in most books on statistics and probability.

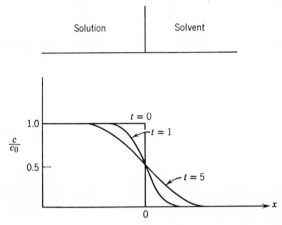

Figure 4.3   Boundary diffusion. The concentration of solute in the solution is c_0 at time $t = 0$.

Figure 4.3 shows the concentration c as a function of penetration x measured from the interface, for various times of diffusion. The solution of equation 4.8 which is quoted in 4.9 is only applicable if D_2 is a constant, independent of composition. Coefficient D_2 does usually vary with composition and the penetration curves are, as a consequence, distorted from those of Fig. 4.3.

4.4   Activation Energy for Diffusion

It has been shown experimentally that for nearly all diffusion phenomena the coefficient of diffusion varies with temperature according to an exponential law

$$D_2 = D_0 e^{-Q/RT} \tag{4.10}$$

where D_0 is a constant, Q is the *activation energy* (per mole) *for diffusion*, R is the Boltzmann constant per mole, and T is the absolute temperature.

It will be recalled that equation 3.7, dealing with rates of chemical reaction, is of the same form as 4.10. This is typical of processes in which an energy barrier of magnitude Q must be overcome by thermal fluctuations. Figure 4.4 shows that equation 4.10 is well obeyed in the diffusion of carbon in alpha iron.

Let us try to get a little more insight into the nature of the factor D_0. Equation 4.7 for unidirectional flow gave $D_2 = \frac{1}{2}a^2 n$ where a is the atomic

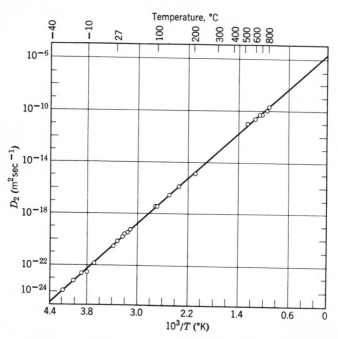

Figure 4.4   Diffusion coefficient of carbon in α-iron. (After Wert)

spacing and n the frequency of jumps in the x direction. But the frequency of jumps by any particular atom may also be regarded as the product of the number of atomic oscillations per unit time having the correct direction of oscillation, and the probability that the energy associated with this oscillation is large enough to surmount the potential energy barrier between one atomic site and the next.

This product, the jump frequency, will be given approximately by $\frac{1}{3}\nu e^{-Q/RT}$, where ν is the frequency of atomic oscillations and the fraction $\frac{1}{3}$ is introduced to take care of the fact that we are concerned in this unidirectional problem with oscillations along only one of the three coordinate axes. We have already discussed the probability factor $e^{-Q/RT}$ in Section 3.3.

If, therefore,
$$n = \tfrac{1}{3}ve^{-Q/RT}$$

then
$$D_2 = \tfrac{1}{6}a^2ve^{-Q/RT} \tag{4.11}$$

Comparison of equations 4.10 and 4.11 gives the approximate value for D_0 of
$$D_0 = \tfrac{1}{6}a^2v \tag{4.12}$$

For a metal where v might be approximately 10^{13} sec^{-1} and $a \simeq 3 \times 10^{-10}$ m, then $D_0 \simeq 10^{-7}$ m^2 sec^{-1}. In practice, D_0 varies widely about this value.

4.5　Experimental Methods for the Determination of D

The *steady state* method in which solute is supplied at a constant known rate to one face of the solvent layer and removed at another known rate from the opposite face is generally limited to systems in which the solute is volatile.

Carbon diffusivity in iron has been measured by the steady state method. A constant mixture of methane and hydrogen was passed across one face of a γ iron (austenite) disk. The carbon in the methane diffuses into the austenite. The amount of carbon passing through the disk (i.e., J in equation 4.6) was determined by analysis of a hydrogen and water vapor stream flowing across the other face of the disk. The disk was later sectioned and analyzed for carbon at different penetrations giving $(\partial c/\partial x)$ as a function of x. The variation of diffusivity D_1 with concentration can then be calculated. This determination is of considerable metallurgical interest since austenite is surface hardened by the diffusion penetration of carbon in the *carburizing* process.

Normally in solid diffusion the nonsteady state equation 4.8 applies and D_2 is determined. Two layers of solvent containing different concentrations of solute are brought into intimate contact. This diffusion couple is then heated for a recorded time at a controlled temperature. The concentration gradient is then determined across the couple. A number of methods exist for the determination of the solute concentration as a function of penetration depth. These methods fall into two classes.

Chemical Methods. Thin layers are removed from the diffusion couple by careful machining or lapping. These layers are then analyzed for solute concentration by chemical or spectrographic analysis.

Radioactive Methods. These methods depend on the availability of a radioactive isotope of the solute. In one method the solute is plated on to one surface of the solvent. The rate of penetration of the solute by diffusion into the solvent is then determined by observation of the rate of decay of surface radioactivity. The concentration gradient may also be determined by measurement of the radioactivity of thin slices removed from the diffusion couple.

The radioactive tracer methods are to be preferred. With the discovery of artificial radioactivity they are now of wide application. An obvious advantage over chemical methods is that coefficients of *self-diffusion* can be readily determined. By self-diffusion is meant the movement of atoms from one position to another in a solid specimen of pure element. A radioactive isotope of the pure element is used to trace the atomic transport.

4.6 Diffusion Mechanisms in Solids

So far we have dealt with the mathematical description of diffusion but have said little of the actual movements of the atoms or vacancies concerned in the migration of solute atoms through solvents or the interchange

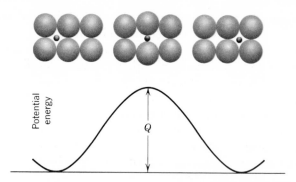

Figure 4.5   Migration of an interstitial atom with the potential energy of the atom shown for each position.

of lattice sites in self diffusion. This section will give the more plausible mechanisms which have been proposed.

We will differentiate between the diffusion of interstitial atoms through a lattice and the diffusion of substitutional atoms. Discussion of the latter should be regarded as including self diffusion.

Interstitial Atoms.   An interstitial atom must be supplied with energy in order to squeeze past solvent atoms on their lattice sites to reach a neighboring interstitial position. If the interstitial atom is considerably smaller than the solvent atom, as for instance it is for carbon in iron, thermal fluctuations can supply this energy and diffusion of the interstitial atom can take place. Figure 4.5 shows an interstitial atom in three positions with respect to neighboring solvent atoms and the energy associated with each position.

Substitutional Atoms. In substitutional alloys, on the other hand, where the atomic size of the solute atom is almost equal to that of the

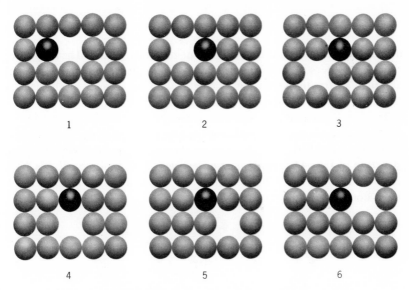

Figure 4.6   Migration of a solute atom associated with a vacancy.

solvent (see Section 3.1), the mechanism of Fig. 4.5 is energetically unfavorable and diffusion must take place in other ways. Three possible mechanisms are now described.

The first of these involves the *migration of vacancies*. An atom adjacent to a vacancy may jump into the vacancy position, a series of such jumps leading to diffusion; Fig. 4.6 shows the mechanism. In a close-packed metal like copper, self-diffusion is estimated to be by the vacancy mechanism. The calculated activation energy here is about 44 kcal mole^{-1}.

The second diffusion mechanism is by the *migration of atoms through interstitial sites*. This is shown in Fig. 4.7. Although the creation of such defects by thermal means is considered to be unlikely because of the high energy involved, nevertheless, if such defects are produced by other means such as neutron irradiation, the activation energy for diffusion is sufficiently low to allow for mass transport by such defects. Clusters of such

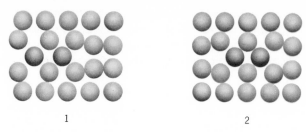

1   2

Figure 4.7   Migration of solute atoms through interstitial sites.

defects migrate much more easily than an individual defect. The activation energy for interstitial diffusion in copper is about 60 kcal mole^{-1} which, although greater than the value associated with the vacancy mechanism, is still low enough to contribute to the overall self diffusion.

The third mechanism is considered less likely than the other two. It involves an exchange of position by groups or rings of atoms. Possible two-, three-, and four-ring groups are shown for the face-centered cubic structure in Fig. 4.8. An activation energy of 90 kcal mole^{-1} has been calculated for the four-ring mechanism in copper, a value which, although high, does not entirely exclude the possibility.

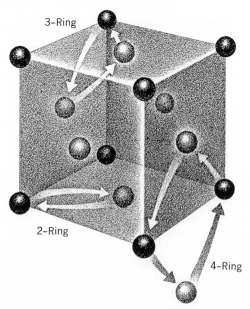

Figure 4.8   Two-, three-, and four-ring groups in a face-centered cubic solid. Interchange of atoms around the ring can cause diffusion.

To sum up, it would appear that energetically the vacancy mechanism for diffusion in substitutional alloys and in self-diffusion seems the most likely, with less possibility of interstitial and still less of ring rotation. It is possible, however, that in certain solids all three mechanisms exist.

4.7 Factors Affecting Diffusion

So far only the temperature variation of D_2 in equation 4.8 has been discussed. In practice the value of D_2 obtained by experimentation

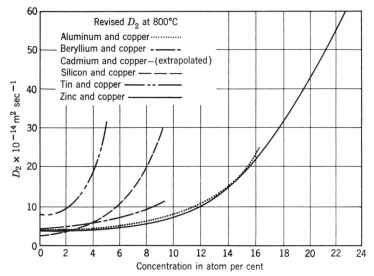

Figure 4.9   Variation of diffusivity D_2 with composition in alloys of copper. (After Rhines and Mehl)

represents an average over the conditions of the experiment. We will briefly discuss a number of factors which also affect the diffusion coefficient.

Concentration. The variation of D_2 with concentration naturally does not apply to the case of self-diffusion. If, however, in a solid solution the concentration varies appreciably, the coefficient of diffusion also invariably varies. It follows from equation 4.10 that D_2 must be very sensitive to changes in Q, the activation energy. The type of variation of D_2 with composition that is found in a number of copper alloys is shown in Fig. 4.9. It is seen that the presence of foreign atoms in the copper increases the diffusion of these atoms through the copper. The activation energy for diffusion is decreased.

It is difficult to predict concentration dependence of Q or D_2. In general it might be said that solute elements which decrease the freezing point of the solvent have diffusion coefficients larger than these for self-diffusion of the solvent, whereas solute elements which raise the freezing point have diffusion coefficients smaller than these for self-diffusion of the solvent. In a qualitative way it can be said that foreign atoms which bind the lattice more tightly together and raise the freezing point have more difficulty in diffusing through the lattice than the lattice atoms themselves, and vice versa.

Strain. Many fabricating processes result in permanent distortion of the crystal lattice. Various types of defect remain, and we would expect that the coefficient of diffusion would consequently increase. This is true in metals, although quantitative results are difficult to obtain. This is because raising the temperature of the specimen, to obtain measurable diffusion in short times, tends to anneal out the defects.

Grain Boundary and Surface Diffusion. So far the remarks on diffusion have dealt almost exclusively with volume diffusion in single crystals. In polycrystalline material diffusion along grain boundaries is also possible. In addition, atoms residing on a crystal surface will be less tightly bound than those within the volume of the crystal, or even within the disorganized region of a grain boundary, and as a consequence can diffuse more easily. Thus, as we would expect,

$$Q_{\text{volume}} > Q_{\text{grain boundary}} > Q_{\text{surface}}$$

As we will see in Section 5.16 on tilt boundaries, there is greater disorganization of the lattice in a high-angle boundary than in a low. It has been found, not surprisingly, that the activation energy for diffusion decreases with increase of boundary angle. Also in Section 5.16 we shall discover that low angle tilt boundaries consist of line imperfections called dislocations fairly regularly spaced along the boundary and running at specific angles to it. Diffusion in such low-angle boundaries is greatest down the dislocation lines and is consequently orientation dependent. Often in grain boundary diffusion the activation energy is as low as only half that for volume diffusion.

REFERENCES

C. E. Birchenall, *Physical Metallurgy*, McGraw-Hill Book Company, New York, 1959.

B. Chalmers, (editor), *Progress in Metal Physics*, vol. 1, Butterworth's Scientific Publications, London, 1949.

A. H. Cottrell, *Theoretical Structural Metallurgy*, Edward Arnold and Co., London, 1948.

F. Seitz, Paper 1 in *Imperfections in Nearly Perfect Crystals*, John Wiley and Sons, New York, 1952.

EXERCISES

1. Write an expression for (a) the number of ways that n atoms may be removed from N lattice sites and (b) the number of ways these n atoms may be put in N' interstitial positions to form n Frenkel defects. Show, by a calculation similar to that given in Section 4.3, that the number n of Frenkel defects in equilibrium at temperature T is given by

$$n \simeq (NN')^{1/2} e^{-W/2kT}$$

where $n \ll N$, N' and W is the energy to remove an atom from a lattice site to an interstitial position.
If the energy of formation of a Frenkel defect in a silver halide is 1.5 eV, calculate the ratio of the number of defects to that at 100°K produced by quenching the halide specimen to that temperature after prolonged annealing at 600°K.

2. Suppose that the energy of motion of a Frenkel defect in AgBr is 0.5 eV and the energy of formation is 1.5 eV. The structure of AgBr is cubic (NaCl) with a lattice constant of about 6 Å. The atomic vibration frequency may be taken as 10^{13} sec^{-1}. Estimate the magnitude of D_0 from equation 4.12 and the magnitude of D_2 at 500°K.

3. A piece of iron is held for 10 hours at 1700°K in an atmosphere of carburizing gases so that the concentration of carbon in the surface layers of the iron is 1.3 weight per cent. Plot the concentration of the carbon as a function of penetration depth at the conclusion of the carburizing process. The average diffusion coefficient of carbon in iron at 1700°K is 1.5×10^{-11} m^2 sec^{-1} (*Hint:* Use equation 4.9.)

4. The three mechanisms for self-diffusion in copper with the estimated activation energies are as follows:

(a) Vacancy mechanism   44 kcal mole^{-1}
(b) Migration through interstitial sites   60 kcal mole^{-1}
(c) Four-ring mechanism   90 kcal mole^{-1}

Calculate the ratios of the self-diffusion coefficients at 100°C and also at 500°C.

5. Calculate the appropriate coefficients of diffusion D_2 at 300°K for the following cases:

Diffusing metal	Matrix	D_0 m^2 sec^{-1}	Q kcal mole^{-1}
Copper	aluminum	2×10^{-4}	33.9
Silver	silver	0.72×10^{-4}	45.0
	(Volume diffusion)		
Silver	silver	0.14×10^{-4}	21.5
	(grain boundary)		

6. In a number of examples of high temperature oxidation of metals, the rapidity of diffusion of metal ions through the oxide scale is so much greater than oxide through the scale that the latter may be neglected. A constant difference exists throughout the process between the metal concentration at the oxide surface, and the metal concentration at the metal surface. Show that these observations suggest a parabolic relationship between thickness of oxide layer and time.

5

Elastic and Plastic Properties of Solids

For most engineers the mechanical properties of a solid are of the greatest importance. Such properties describe the behavior of the solid when subjected to a deforming force and include measures of strength, hardness, ductility, and so on. If the deformation caused by the force is small, it is proportional to the force. This is *Hooke's Law*. The theory of elasticity relates deformation to force and assumes the truth of the law. Above a certain limit of deformation, the *elastic limit*, the deformation is no longer a linear function of the deforming force. For most work of a technological nature, however, the deductions from elasticity theory are sufficiently good approximations and in addition the laws of elasticity still serve, and will probably always serve, as mathematical models against which the actual behavior of materials can be judged.

In this chapter we first discuss *elastic deformation* in isotropic and anisotropic solids. Later we discuss the behavior of materials subjected to forces which exceed the elastic limits, thus causing *plastic deformation*, and will describe the influence of other factors such as temperature, purity, etc. The successful *dislocation model* of plastic deformation will then be presented.

5.1 Stress and Strain

In a test of the tensile or compressive strength of a solid material, a force is applied normal to a cross-section of the specimen and a measurement made in the same direction as the force of the extension or reduction respectively in specimen length. The normal stress σ is equal to the magnitude of the force divided by the area normal to the force over which the force is applied. The strain ϵ, produced by this stress, is then the fractional change in length of the specimen.

For small strains the strain is proportional to the stress and

$$\epsilon = \frac{\sigma}{E} \tag{5.1}$$

where the constant of proportionality E is called *Young's Modulus* and is a property of the material under test.

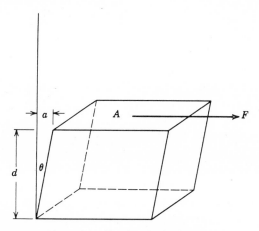

Figure 5.1   Simple cube in shear.

On the other hand, if the stress is applied tangentially to an imaginary plane in the material, a lateral displacement of the plane relative to another parallel plane constitutes a *shearing strain*. The magnitude γ of shear strain is given by the tangent of the angle through which one is displaced relative to the other. In Fig. 5.1 we have

$$\gamma = \frac{a}{d} = \tan \theta \tag{5.2}$$

In the elastic region the shear stress τ is related to γ, the shear strain, by the equation

$$\gamma = \frac{\tau}{G} \tag{5.3}$$

where G is the *shear modulus*.

5.2   Elastic Deformation in Isotropic Materials

The elastic properties of a single crystal are usually dependent on the crystallographic direction in the crystal, that is, they are *anisotropic*. Solids are usually encountered in the polycrystalline form, however, and if there is no preferred orientation of the individual crystals, the solid material may still follow closely the elasticity laws for an isotropic material. The laws are of course applicable to noncrystalline or amorphous materials. These laws will be very briefly discussed.

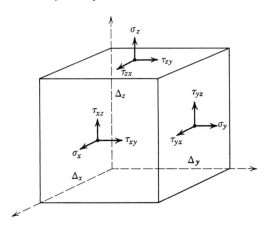

Figure 5.2   Tensile and shear stresses acting on a cube of isotropic material.

Suppose a stress σ_x is applied to a bar of isotropic material in the x direction. There will be an elongation or strain ϵ_x in the x direction and a consequent contraction in directions at right angles to the x direction. If ϵ_y and ϵ_z are the strains parallel to the y and z directions, then

$$-\epsilon_y = -\epsilon_z = \nu\epsilon_x = \frac{\nu\sigma_x}{E} \tag{5.4}$$

where ν is called Poisson's ratio and is a constant for the material under investigation. Many metals have values of ν of about 0.3.

Let us now examine the relationships in a cube of isotropic material. Rectangular axes Δ_x, Δ_y, and Δ_z are chosen as in Fig. 5.2, and the tensile, compressive, and shearing stresses applied to the cube are also shown in the figure. The method of designating a particular stress is as follows. A compressive or tensile stress acting perpendicular to a plane whose normal is in the Δ_x direction is designated σ_x. A shear stress applied tangentially to a plane whose normal is in the Δ_x direction, the stress being in the Δ_y direction, is designated τ_{xy}. The choice of suffix for the designation of strain follows similar rules.

In all there are three stresses normal to the cube faces and six shear stresses acting across the cube faces. If the small cube is in equilibrium under the applied forces, the normal stress in the Δ_x direction must be balanced by a normal stress in the opposite direction. In addition, the shear stresses must balance at the edges of the cube. These two conditions mean that all relations such as the following exist.

$$\sigma_x = \sigma_{-x} \tag{5.5}$$

$$\tau_{xy} = \tau_{yx} \tag{5.6}$$

The six components of stress necessary and independent are σ_x, σ_y, σ_z, τ_{xy}, τ_{yz}, τ_{zx}, and the components of strain are ϵ_x, ϵ_y, ϵ_z, γ_{xy}, γ_{yz}, γ_{zx}.

If the coordinate axes are chosen so that the shear stresses on all faces of the cube are zero, a choice which is always possible, the stresses normal to the cube faces are called the *principal stresses* and are designated σ_1, σ_2, and σ_3. The relationships between principal stresses and principal strains in an isotropic material are particularly simple. They are as follows:

$$\epsilon_1 = \frac{1}{E}[\sigma_1 - \nu(\sigma_2 + \sigma_3)]$$

$$\epsilon_2 = \frac{1}{E}[\sigma_2 - \nu(\sigma_1 + \sigma_3)] \tag{5.7}$$

$$\epsilon_3 = \frac{1}{E}[\sigma_3 - \nu(\sigma_1 + \sigma_2)]$$

5.3   Elastic Deformation in Single Crystals

So far we have dealt with isotropic materials. With single crystals the moduli relating stress and strain are dependent on crystallographic direction. Referring again to Fig. 5.2, the generalized Hooke's Law relationships between stress and strain then take the form:

$$\begin{aligned}
\epsilon_x &= S_{11}\sigma_x + S_{12}\sigma_y + S_{13}\sigma_z + S_{14}\tau_{yz} + S_{15}\tau_{zx} + S_{16}\tau_{xy} \\
\epsilon_y &= S_{21}\sigma_x + S_{22}\sigma_y + S_{23}\sigma_z + S_{24}\tau_{yz} + S_{25}\tau_{zx} + S_{26}\tau_{xy} \\
\epsilon_z &= S_{31}\sigma_x + S_{32}\sigma_y + S_{33}\sigma_z + S_{34}\tau_{yz} + S_{35}\tau_{zx} + S_{36}\tau_{xy} \\
\gamma_{yz} &= S_{41}\sigma_x + S_{42}\sigma_y + S_{43}\sigma_z + S_{44}\tau_{yz} + S_{45}\tau_{zx} + S_{46}\tau_{xy} \\
\gamma_{zx} &= S_{51}\sigma_x + S_{52}\sigma_y + S_{53}\sigma_z + S_{54}\tau_{yz} + S_{55}\tau_{zx} + S_{56}\tau_{xy} \\
\gamma_{xy} &= S_{61}\sigma_x + S_{62}\sigma_y + S_{63}\sigma_z + S_{64}\tau_{yz} + S_{65}\tau_{zx} + S_{66}\tau_{xy}
\end{aligned} \tag{5.8}$$

The stress components are written as linear functions of strain as follows:

$$\begin{aligned}
\sigma_x &= C_{11}\epsilon_x + C_{12}\epsilon_y + C_{13}\epsilon_z + C_{14}\gamma_{yz} + C_{15}\gamma_{zx} + C_{16}\gamma_{xy} \\
\sigma_y &= C_{21}\epsilon_x + C_{22}\epsilon_y + C_{23}\epsilon_z + C_{24}\gamma_{yz} + C_{25}\gamma_{zx} + C_{26}\gamma_{xy} \\
\sigma_z &= C_{31}\epsilon_x + C_{32}\epsilon_y + C_{33}\epsilon_z + C_{34}\gamma_{yz} + C_{35}\gamma_{zx} + C_{36}\gamma_{xy} \\
\tau_{yz} &= C_{41}\epsilon_x + C_{42}\epsilon_y + C_{43}\epsilon_z + C_{44}\gamma_{yz} + C_{45}\gamma_{zx} + C_{46}\gamma_{xy} \\
\tau_{zx} &= C_{51}\epsilon_x + C_{52}\epsilon_y + C_{53}\epsilon_z + C_{54}\gamma_{yz} + C_{55}\gamma_{zx} + C_{56}\gamma_{xy} \\
\tau_{xy} &= C_{61}\epsilon_x + C_{62}\epsilon_y + C_{63}\epsilon_z + C_{64}\gamma_{yz} + C_{65}\gamma_{zx} + C_{66}\gamma_{xy}
\end{aligned} \tag{5.9}$$

The coefficients S_{ij} are called the *elastic compliance constants* and C_{ij} the *moduli of elasticity*. They differ for each material. The number of independent coefficients decreases as the symmetry of the crystal increases. It may be shown that $S_{ij} = S_{ji}$ so that even in triclinic crystals the number of independent coefficients is twenty-one. In hexagonal crystals the number is five and in cubic crystals three. The coefficients on the right hand side of equation 5.9 become for hexagonal crystals:

$$\text{Hexagonal} \begin{Vmatrix}
C_{11} & C_{12} & C_{13} & 0 & 0 & 0 \\
C_{12} & C_{11} & C_{13} & 0 & 0 & 0 \\
C_{13} & C_{13} & C_{33} & 0 & 0 & 0 \\
0 & 0 & 0 & C_{44} & 0 & 0 \\
0 & 0 & 0 & 0 & C_{44} & 0 \\
0 & 0 & 0 & 0 & 0 & \dfrac{C_{11} - C_{12}}{2}
\end{Vmatrix} \tag{5.10}$$

and for cubic crystals:

$$\text{Cubic} \begin{Vmatrix}
C_{11} & C_{12} & C_{12} & 0 & 0 & 0 \\
C_{12} & C_{11} & C_{12} & 0 & 0 & 0 \\
C_{12} & C_{12} & C_{11} & 0 & 0 & 0 \\
0 & 0 & 0 & C_{44} & 0 & 0 \\
0 & 0 & 0 & 0 & C_{44} & 0 \\
0 & 0 & 0 & 0 & 0 & C_{44}
\end{Vmatrix} \tag{5.11}$$

Table 5.1 gives values of the elastic moduli of a number of cubic crystals.
In practice, single crystals are often prepared in cylindrical or bar form. The orientation of the longitudinal axis with respect to the major axes of the structure may be determined by X-ray diffraction techniques. Let us

suppose that the longitudinal axis of a single crystal of the *cubic* system makes angles α, β, and γ with the cubic axes. It may be shown that if the bar is pulled in a tensile test machine, the effective values of Young's and shear moduli are given by

$$\frac{1}{E} = S_{11} - 2[(S_{11} - S_{12}) - \tfrac{1}{2}S_{44}][\cos^2\alpha\cos^2\beta + \cos^2\beta\cos^2\gamma + \cos^2\alpha\cos^2\gamma]$$

$$(5.12)$$

and

$$\frac{1}{G} = S_{44} + 4[(S_{11} - S_{12}) - \tfrac{1}{2}S_{44}][\cos^2\alpha\cos^2\beta + \cos^2\beta\cos^2\gamma + \cos^2\alpha\cos^2\gamma]$$

Table 5.1   Elastic Moduli of Cubic Crystals at Room Temperature

Moduli in 10^{11} newtons m^{-2} (or in 10^{12} dynes cm^{-2})

CRYSTAL	C_{11}	C_{12}	C_{44}
Fe	2.37	1.41	1.16
W	5.01	1.98	1.15
Cu	1.684	1.214	0.75
Diamond	9.2	3.9	4.3
Si	1.66	0.64	0.79
Ge	1.29	0.48	0.67
Al	1.08	0.62	0.28
Pb	0.48	0.41	0.14
NaCl	0.486	0.127	0.128

For a *hexagonal* crystal with the specimen axis making an angle α with the c hexagonal axis, then:

$$\frac{1}{E} = S_{11}(1 - \cos^2\alpha)^2 + S_{33}\cos^4\alpha + (2S_{13} + S_{44})\cos^2\alpha(1 - \cos^2\alpha)$$

$$\frac{1}{G} = S_{44} + [(S_{11} - S_{12}) - \tfrac{1}{2}S_{44}][1 - \cos^2\alpha]$$
$$+ 2(S_{11} + S_{33} - 2S_{13} - S_{44})\cos^2\alpha(1 - \cos^2\alpha) \quad (5.13)$$

The foregoing formulae enable us to calculate changes in dimensions of isotropic or crystalline solids when subject to stress, provided the changes are within the elastic range. Engineering materials do not in general behave as perfectly elastic solids because of structural imperfections. For large deformations the linear relationship between stress and strain no longer exists.

The classical methods of measuring the elastic constants of solids involve direct measurement of strain under applied stress. More recently, an ultrasonic pulse method has replaced the older methods. In this method the velocity of an acoustic pulse is measured electronically along specific directions in the crystal. The velocity in each direction is simply related to the appropriate modulus of elasticity.

5.4 Plastic Deformation

A solid is deformed plastically when a permanent strain remains after the deforming stress has been removed. Many processes in the fabrication of metal objects involve plastic deformation, such processes for example as forging, pressing, rolling, extruding, etc. A number of aspects of plastic deformation in metals will be briefly reviewed before we proceed to a discussion of the physical nature of the phenomenon. Two mechanisms encountered in plastic deformation are *slip* and *twinning*.

5.5 Slip

In slip, one portion of the crystal is displaced with respect to another by a shearing stress, the displacement taking place on a crystallographic plane called the *slip plane* in a crystallographic direction called the *slip direction*.

The slip plane is always a plane of dense packing of atoms and the slip direction is a plane of maximum density of line packing. The selection of operative plane on which slip takes place is quite often influenced by temperature; the slip direction, however, nearly always remains constant.

Let us suppose that in a certain solid the slip planes are of the type {111}. When slip occurs we might suppose that each (111) plane carries its share of the total slip deformation. This does not happen. Only certain active slip planes, quite often separated from one another in metals by distances of about 1 μ, carry the displacement. Each unit displacement constitutes a motion of one plane laterally over its neighbor by one atomic distance, the active slip planes, however, carrying many such unit displacements. The edges of the slip planes at the polished surface of a deformed crystal become visible once the displacement has reached a large number of units, and the trace seen on the surface is called a *slip band*.

The applied stress necessary to produce plastic deformation in shear is called a *critical shear stress*. The critical shear stress is dependent on temperature, purity, previous mechanical history, and rate of deformation. The effects of these factors on the plastic behavior of metals will be discussed in succeeding sections.

5.6 Twinning

In a number of crystals (usually either hexagonal close-packed or body-centered cubic), and particularly at low temperatures, an important

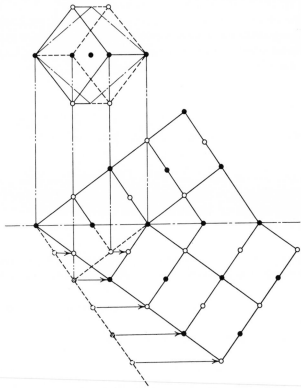

Figure 5.3   Shear movements of atoms (shown by arrows)
for twinning in a body-centered cubic crystal. (After Barrett)

mechanism of deformation is *twinning*. This is a shearing motion of atomic planes over one another, the magnitude of translation of each plane being proportional to its distance from a particular plane in the lattice called the *twinning plane*. Figure 5.3, taken from Barrett, shows the shear movements for twinning in a body-centered cubic crystal. In the unit cube drawn in the upper part of the figure, the twinning plane which is the (211) is indicated by dot-dash lines. This plane stands perpendicular to the paper in the lower part of the figure, and the atom movements to form a twin are indicated by arrows. In slip we saw that considerable movement occurs on a few widely separated slip planes. In twinning a small displacement occurs on many neighboring planes. During deformation, twins may be produced very suddenly. They are also sometimes produced by annealing, probably as the result of growth from minute twinned regions produced by previous strain.

Measurements of a critical shear stress for twinning are complicated by the fact that slip in most metals at room temperature occurs at a lower critical stress than that necessary for twinning. The critical shear stress for slip rises with decreasing temperature, however, and twinning becomes relatively more likely. Thus deformation in α-iron at temperatures around 80°K has been shown to be by twinning.

5.7   Temperature Dependence of Plastic Deformation

The critical shear stress for a metal decreases with increasing temperature, dropping almost to zero at the melting point or solidus temperature

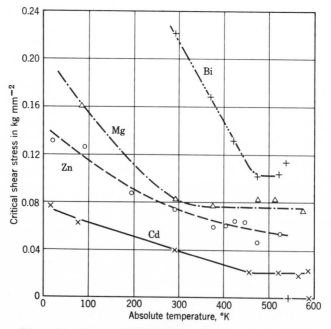

Figure 5.4   Temperature dependence of critical shear stress for a number of metals. (After Schmid and Boas)

in alloys. Figure 5.4 shows the temperature dependence of critical shear stress for a number of metals. The change in shear strength with temperature is not uniform on all planes of a lattice and hence in several metals at certain temperatures the type of plane carrying the slip deformation may change. The overall change in critical shear stress with temperature is not great in many metals, and thus even at very low temperatures ductility still remains.

5.8   Effect of Purity on Plastic Deformation

As we have seen, foreign atoms in a solid may be soluble or insoluble. An *insoluble* impurity has no atomic bonding with the matrix lattice but may produce stress gradients within the matrix because of volume differences. These stress gradients may tend to increase the critical shear stress. The magnitude of the increase is strongly dependent on the degree of dispersion of the insoluble impurity or precipitate. An alloy quenched from an elevated temperature so that it consists of a supersaturated solid solution is often quite soft. If this alloy is aged at a lower temperature than that of the prequenching temperature, more and more of the impurity precipitates out of solution. The size of the precipitated particles gradually increases, and the yield strength increases. As more small particles of precipitate are replaced by a few large ones, the alloy again becomes softer or *overaged*. This process of hardening, which is called *precipitation* or *age hardening*, is of considerable technological importance.

In general, *soluble* impurities have a more marked effect on the critical shear stress than do insoluble impurities. The effect is shown in Fig. 5.5 where the shear stress of zinc-tin and zinc-cadmium alloys are shown as a function of weight per cent of tin or cadmium. Cadmium is soluble in zinc whereas tin is not in the concentrations shown, and it is seen that the dependence of strength on amount of soluble impurity is much greater than on amount of insoluble impurity.

The soluble impurities of an interstitial nature such as carbon in iron or nitrogen in molybdenum give rise to a stress-strain diagram of the type shown in Fig. 5.6 which is that of mild steel. Between the origin and the point *P* there is essentially a linear relationship between stress and strain. The value of stress corresponding to *P* is called the *proportional limit*. Just above *P*, and in ductile materials essentially at the same point, is *E*, the *elastic limit*, which is the greatest stress the material can withstand without permanent distortion. Both points are difficult to obtain with accuracy in practical tests. The point *Y* is the *upper yield point* and *L* the *lower yield point*. It is this little kink around *Y* and *L* that characterizes

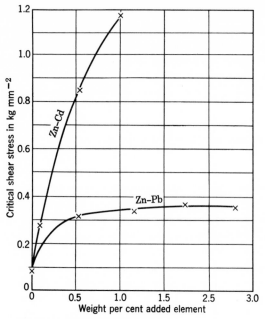

Figure 5.5   Critical shear stress of zinc-cadmium and zinc-tin plotted against weight per cent of added cadmium or tin.   (After Rosbaud and Schmid)

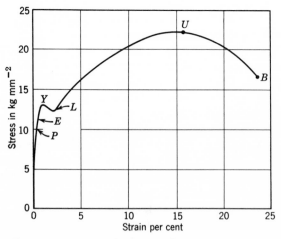

Figure 5.6   Stress-strain diagram for mild steel in tension.

the diagram. Beyond the lower yield point deformation increases rapidly with stress. The point *U* is the *ultimate tensile strength* of the mild steel. Beyond this point the mild steel specimen appreciably narrows in diameter as deformation proceeds and finally breaks at the point *B* which corresponds to the *fracture stress*.

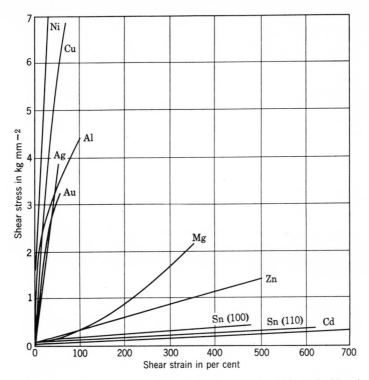

Figure 5.7   Stress-strain diagrams for various metals. (After Schmid and Boas)

Many substances such as rolled steel, hardened steel, cast iron, aluminum, and copper do not show the yield points. Shear stress-strain diagrams for various metals are shown in Fig. 5.7.

5.9   Effect of Prior Deformation on Plastic Deformation

If the temperature of a plastically deformed metal is raised, new crystals or grains grow at the expense of the old ones. This is called *recrystallization*. If, however, the temperature is too low for recrystallization, plastic deformation, often called *cold work*, will increase the critical stress necessary for further plastic strain. This process is known as *strain hardening*.

Strain hardening for a single crystal of zinc is shown in Fig. 5.8. The stressing load is removed for half a minute after a strain corresponding to point *B* is reached. When the load is reapplied the stress-strain curve *DCE* is traced. The slope of *CD* is nearly equal to the slope of *OA* showing that the elasticity modulus has been little affected by the previous

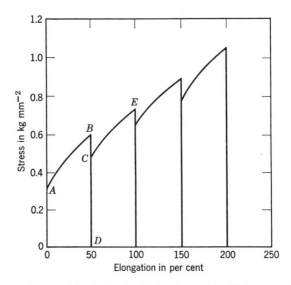

Figure 5.8   Strain hardening in a zinc single crystal showing the effect of repeated loading. (After Haase and Schmid)

strain. Yielding, however, now occurs at point *C* which is at a higher stress than point *A*. The critical shear stress has been increased by the previous strain, a process that may be repeated over strains of several hundred per cent.

5.10   Effect of Rate of Strain on Plastic Deformation

We have already mentioned that on raising the temperature of a plastically deformed metal specimen new grains or crystals grow at the expense of the old ones. The temperature at which this will take place in readily measurable times is called the *recrystallization temperature*. The greater the previous degree of strain hardening, the lower is the temperature of recrystallization. After recrystallization the strength and hardness of the metal is reduced and the ductility increased. There is complete release of internal stress in the material. At temperatures below the recrystallization temperature a process of stress relief known as *recovery* takes place. The

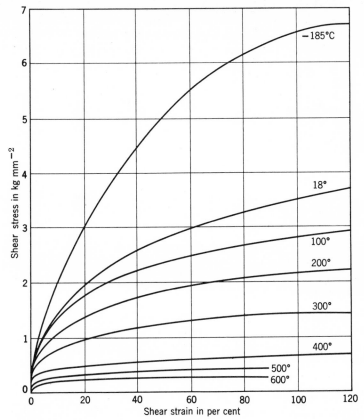

Figure 5.9   Strain hardening in aluminum at different temperatures. (After Boas and Schmid)

mechanical properties of metals are much less affected by recovery than by recrystallization.

It is therefore not surprising that the amount of strain hardening that can be produced in a metal is dependent on temperature. Stress-strain curves taken at temperatures where recovery or recrystallization occurs can be considered to be the result of a balance between the opposing thermal recovery and strain hardening. At low temperatures, hardening is always more important, whereas at high temperatures thermal recovery can proceed at a rate comparable to the rate of strain hardening and the stress-strain curve will be horizontal. In the recovery process a short time at a high temperature is always equivalent to a longer time at a lower temperature. Figure 5.9 shows strain hardening in aluminum at different temperatures.

Thus consideration of the effect of rate of deformation on the critical shear stress is partially a consideration of the balance between the opposing mechanisms—strain hardening and thermal recovery. Many solids when subject to a constant stress show a slow and progressive deformation

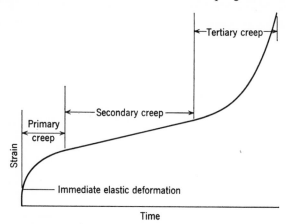

Figure 5.10   Creep behavior at constant low level of stress.

as a function of time. This property is called *creep* and is of considerable technological importance. Creep behavior is shown in Fig. 5.10. When the load is first applied there is an immediate elastic deformation. This is followed by a *primary stage* in which the creep rate slows to a minimum, followed by a *secondary stage* in which the strain slowly increases at this minimum rate. If the stress is sufficiently high, the creep condition reaches a *tertiary stage* in which the rate increases until fracture occurs. Creep is observed in metals, ionic crystals, and amorphous solids. In general the temperatures at which metals creep are higher than those for plastics and rubbers. Since it is found that the metals with high melting points have high recrystallization temperatures, creep is low in these cases. Lead with a low melting point exhibits creep at room temperature. Alloying to raise the recrystallization temperature will increase the creep resistance.

5.11   Estimation of the Magnitude of the Critical Shear Stress

In the previous sections we have seen that a strain occurs when a stress is applied to a solid, and that the magnitude of the strain per unit stress increment is much greater in the *plastic* deformation region than in the initial or *elastic* region. We have also seen that the critical shear stress which defines the onset of the plastic region is affected by temperature, by the presence of foreign atoms, and by the state of dispersion of these atoms. Finally we have seen that the amount of plastic strain for a given stress is dependent on the mechanical history of the solid and the rate at which the deformation is performed.

Let us now give some consideration to an estimate of the expected magnitude of the critical shear stress or critical shear strain. We will reproduce a calculation by Frenkel (1926). Later refinements to this

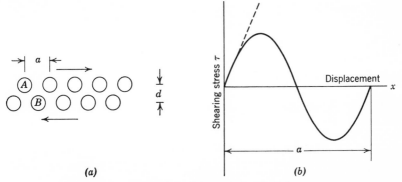

(a)   (b)

Figure 5.11   Calculation of theoretical critical shear stress.

calculation have not changed Frenkel's estimate by a factor of more than about five.

Suppose in Fig. 5.11a that A and B represent atoms of two adjacent planes. The spacing between the planes is d. A shear stress τ is applied so that the planes are translated with respect to one another, the relative displacement being designated x. We make the assumption *that the A plane of atoms moves over the B plane as a whole just as one card moves over the next in a deformed deck.*

The first task is to obtain a realistic relationship between the shearing stress τ and the shear displacement x. The stress is, of course, zero at the equilibrium positions of the atoms shown by A and B in Fig. 5.11a. When the displacement is such that atom A is directly over atom B, the planes are in unstable equilibrium and the stress is also zero. Let us suppose that the shear stress is a sinusoidal function of x with period a where a is the interatomic spacing in the direction of shear.

Then

$$\tau = K \sin \frac{2\pi x}{a} \qquad (5.14)$$

which is shown in Fig. 5.11b. The constant K can be determined from the condition that the initial slope (in Fig. 5.11b), that is, in the elastic region of very small strain, must agree with the shear modulus of the crystal. From (5.14) for small x we have

$$\tau = K \frac{2\pi x}{a}$$

Also from the Hooke's Law definition of G the shear modulus we have

$$\tau = \frac{Gx}{d}$$

Thus

$$\tau = \frac{aG}{2\pi d} \sin \frac{2\pi x}{a} \qquad (5.15)$$

The stress τ may be increased to its maximum or critical shear stress value τ_M, at which point the lattice becomes mechanically unstable and

Table 5.2   Comparison of Shear Modulus and Elastic Limit

	SHEAR MODULUS (nm^{-2})	ELASTIC LIMIT (nm^{-2})
Sn, single crystal	1.9×10^{10}	1.3×10^{8}
Ag, single crystal	2.8×10^{10}	6×10^{5}
Al, single crystal	2.5×10^{10}	4×10^{5}
Al, pure polycrystal	2.5×10^{10}	2.6×10^{7}
Al, commercial drawn	$\sim 2.5 \times 10^{10}$	9.9×10^{7}
Duralumin	$\sim 2.5 \times 10^{10}$	3.6×10^{8}
Fe, soft polycrystal	7.7×10^{10}	1.5×10^{8}
Heat treated carbon steel	$\sim 8 \times 10^{10}$	6.5×10^{8}
Nickel-chrome steel	$\sim 8 \times 10^{10}$	1.2×10^{9}

shear occurs. After shear the A plane of atoms will be displaced relative to the B plane by one atomic spacing, that is, by a.

Thus in magnitude,

$$\tau_M = \frac{aG}{2\pi d} \qquad (5.16)$$

Since $a \simeq d$, the theoretical critical shear stress should be about $G/2\pi$. Even with refinements to the theory, which take the possible deformation of the atoms into account, τ_M cannot be much less than about $G/30$.

This value for τ_M is several orders of magnitude too high when compared with experimental measurements. Table 5.2 gives the comparison of shear modulus G with critical shear stress (or elastic limit) for a number of materials in different forms. We are driven to the conclusion that *shear or slip does not occur in soft crystals by the simple mechanism pictured above of one layer of atoms being displaced together in one sheet over an adjacent layer of atoms.* Some source of mechanical weakness must exist in real crystals of such a kind that slip can start from the source at very low applied stress. In agreement with previous remarks, it is also obvious from the table that the presence of grain boundaries, cold work, and alloying components also increases the elastic limits.

X-ray experimental evidence has long shown that imperfections do occur in crystal lattices, and the idea that crystal weakness is associated with flaws is not a new one. The particular kinds of imperfections that occur in crystals and account for the low critical shear stress and a number of other mechanical properties are called *dislocations*.

Before we study the detailed nature of dislocations, let us speculate on the general form that this imperfection may take in a solid. Suppose a carpet lies on a floor and it is necessary to displace it by a short distance. In this analogy the carpet and the floor represent two adjacent planes of atoms and the requirement is to find with how small a force one may produce slip. There are, of course, two ways of proceeding. First, we can apply a force to one end sufficient in magnitude to cause the whole carpet to slip to the required position. The magnitude of the force depends on the force of attraction, gravitational in the analogy, and if the carpet is heavy the magnitude may be quite large. The second method of displacing the carpet over the floor is to make a small ruck or fold extending across the carpet. This corresponds to a fault in the atomic planes, which is a line imperfection or dislocation. It requires quite a small force to move the fold across the carpet. The displacement of the whole carpet caused by moving the fold right across the carpet is, on completion, indistinguishable from that produced by the first method.

In real crystals plastic deformation is caused by the movement of dislocations across slip planes in much the same manner as that suggested by the carpet analogy. Dislocations exist in the crystal and the critical shear stress is that force necessary to induce them to move.

5.12 Geometry of Dislocations

The actual form of the simplest types of dislocation, namely, the *edge dislocation* and the *screw dislocation* will now be discussed. Dislocation theory will then be used to account for the mechanical properties of crystals that we have already described.

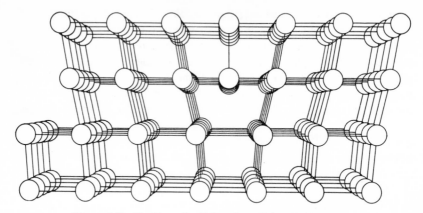

Figure 5.12   Positive edge dislocation. (After Goldman)

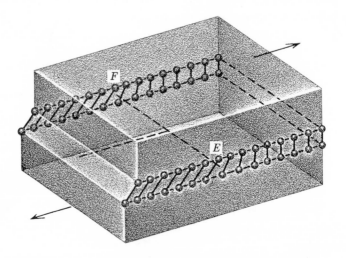

Figure 5.13   Edge dislocation *EF* marking the boundary between a slipped region on the left and a region of no slip on the right. (After Cottrell)

Edge Dislocation.   Figure 5.12 shows a *positive edge dislocation*. In the diagram it is seen that an extra vertical half-plane of atoms exists in the upper half of the crystal. The termination of the extra plane is a dislocation, extending out from the paper in Fig. 5.12, and able to move on the horizontal plane containing it. This horizontal plane is the *slip plane*. If the extra half-plane is below the slip plane, the edge dislocation is said to be *negative*. The edge-type dislocation is always perpendicular to the direction of slip. Figure 5.13 shows a cubic crystal in which slip of one atom distance has occurred over the left portion of the slip plane but not over the portion of the slip plane to the right of the dislocation EF.

Figure 5.14 shows how a positive dislocation, if present, may move under a shearing stress across a slip plane. In the sequence a, b, c, and d, a positive dislocation moves to the right whereas in e, f, g, and h, a negative dislocation moves to the left. It is to be noted that the resulting deformations are identical.

In a positive edge dislocation, as in Fig. 5.12, the atoms above the slip plane and just to the left of the dislocation will be attracted by the atoms below the slip plane, and on balance this attraction will be to the right.

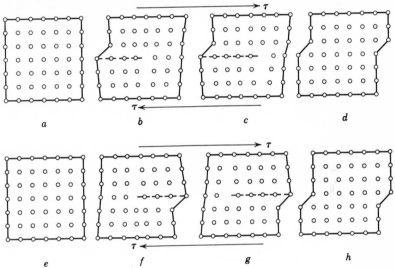

Figure 5.14   Movement of edge dislocation under a shearing stress; a, b, c, d, positive edge dislocation moving to right; e, f, g, h, negative dislocation moving to left. (After Taylor)

On the other hand, the atoms above the slip plane and just to the right of the dislocation will be attracted to the left. To a first approximation these two forces of attraction balance, and thus the external force required to move the dislocation will be quite small.

Screw Dislocation.   The second type of simple dislocation is the *screw dislocation* shown in Fig. 5.15. In Fig. 5.15a, slip has occurred over the area $ABEF$ in a direction parallel to the dislocation EF. Figure 5.15b shows the arrangement of atoms around a screw dislocation in a simple cubic structure. Here the two planes of atoms which meet on $ABCD$ are viewed from above $ABCD$. Full circles denote atoms above plane $ABCD$ and open circles atoms below $ABCD$. Going around the dislocation, we climb from one plane to another in a spiral manner which accounts for the name of the dislocation.

Dislocation rings are formed in solids and may be envisaged as formed from edge and screw dislocation components. The edge components are perpendicular to the slip direction and the screw parallel to the slip.

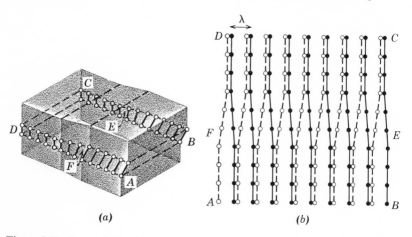

(a)   (b)

Figure 5.15   Screw dislocation EF lying parallel to the direction of slip in a crystal. In (a) slip has occurred over the region $ABEF$. In (b) the atoms (in a cubic structure) above and below $ABCD$ are viewed from above. Full circles denote atoms above the plane $ABCD$ and open circles denote atoms below that plane. (After Cottrell)

5.13   Force on a Dislocation

When sufficient force is applied to a crystal a dislocation will move, and the crystal is plastically deformed. The force acting on the dislocation will now be calculated.

Suppose that when a shear stress of magnitude τ acts on a slip plane of area A that an element dl of dislocation moves a distance dS; the area swept by the dislocation segment is $dS \cdot dl$. Now if the dislocation had swept over the entire slip plane A, the two half-crystals that meet on this plane would be displaced relative to one another by an amount b which is called the *Burgers vector* and is a unique characteristic of the dislocation. In our present example the mean relative displacement of the half-crystals is taken to be $(dS \cdot dl/A)b$, a result which is intuitively plausible.

The applied force is $A\tau$ so that the work done when the slip takes place is given by

$$A\tau(dS \cdot dl/A)b = \tau b \, dS \cdot dl \qquad (5.17)$$

If F_S is the force in the direction of displacement dS which acts on the dislocation then we can also write

$$\text{Work done by } F_S \text{ during slip} = F_S \cdot dS \qquad (5.18)$$

Thus from (5.17) and (5.18) the force acting on a length of dislocation dl is given by

$$F_S = \tau b \, dl \qquad (5.19)$$

The force F_S *per unit length of dislocation* is thus given by

$$F_S = \tau b \qquad (5.20)$$

Force F_S lies in the slip plane, is perpendicular to the dislocation line all along its length, and is directed toward the unslipped portion of the crystal.

5.14 Stress Fields of Dislocations

It is important to know the magnitudes and directions of the stresses introduced into a perfect lattice by the presence of a dislocation. We can then estimate the forces acting on a dislocation because of the presence of a second dislocation or an impurity atom. The method of calculation will be demonstrated for a screw dislocation, and the result will be merely quoted for the edge dislocation case.

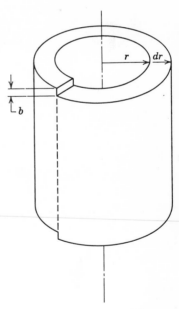

Screw Dislocation. Figure 5.16 shows a shell of deformed crystal surrounding a screw dislocation of Burgers vector b. The shell has been sheared a displacement b in a peripheral length $2\pi r$ thus giving a shear strain $\gamma = b/2\pi r$.

The shear stress is thus given by

$$\tau = G\gamma = \frac{Gb}{2\pi r}$$

The elastic energy dE_S of the shell due to the presence of the dislocation is given by

$$dE_S = \tfrac{1}{2}G(\gamma)^2 \, dV$$

Figure 5.16 Shell of deformed material surrounding a screw dislocation marked by dot-dash line.

where dV is the shell volume. Thus

$$dE_S = \frac{1}{2} G \left(\frac{b}{2\pi r}\right)^2 2\pi rl \cdot dr$$

$$= \left(\frac{Gb^2}{4\pi}\right)\frac{dr}{r} \cdot l$$

The elastic energy E_S per unit length of dislocation, because of the presence of a *screw* dislocation is

$$E_S = \int_{r_1}^{r_2} \left(\frac{Gb^2}{4\pi}\right)\frac{dr}{r} = \left(\frac{Gb^2}{4\pi}\right) \log\left(\frac{r_2}{r_1}\right) \tag{5.21}$$

where r_1 and r_2 are lower and upper limits for the radius of the material strained by the presence of the dislocation.

Although r_1 may be considered to have a magnitude of about the Burgers vector, r_2 usually may be regarded as about the dislocation spacing, that is about 10^{-6} m in well-annealed material.

Edge Dislocation.   The strain energy E_E per unit length of an *edge* dislocation is obtained by a calculation similar to the previous calculation, but rather more complicated. It is

$$E_E = \left[\frac{Gb^2}{4\pi(1-\nu)}\right] \log\left(\frac{r_2}{r_1}\right) \tag{5.22}$$

where ν is Poisson's ratio. Thus E_E is slightly greater than E_S.

5.15   Forces Between Dislocations

Let us now consider the magnitude of the forces that exist between dislocations. The result of the calculation will be quoted without proof for two *edge* dislocations with parallel Burgers vectors.

Following Cottrell, suppose that in Fig. 5.17 a positive edge dislocation lies along the z axis with a Burgers vector b along the x axis. A second positive edge dislocation situated at (x, y) lies parallel to the z axis with its Burgers vector also parallel to the x axis.

Then the components F_x and F_y of the force per unit length on the dislocation at (x, y) because of the presence of the dislocation at the origin are given by:

$$F_x = \frac{Gb^2}{2\pi(1-\nu)} \cdot \frac{x^2(x^2 - y^2)}{(x^2 + y^2)^2} \tag{5.23}$$

and

$$F_y = \frac{Gb^2}{2\pi(1-\nu)} \cdot \frac{y(3x^2 + y^2)}{(x^2 + y^2)^2} \tag{5.24}$$

In polar coordinates the components F_r and F_θ are given by

$$F_r = \frac{Gb^2}{2\pi(1-\nu)} \cdot \frac{1}{r} \tag{5.25}$$

$$F_\theta = \frac{Gb^2}{2\pi(1-\nu)} \cdot \frac{\sin 2\theta}{r} \tag{5.26}$$

If the dislocations have opposite signs, the signs of these forces are reversed.

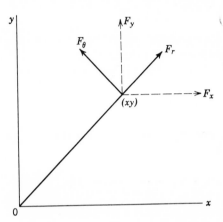

Figure 5.17   Calculation of forces between edge dislocations.

Equation 5.25, giving the force component on the line joining dislocations, shows that edge dislocations of the same sign repel each other along this line.

The variation of F_x with x from equation 5.23 is shown in Fig. 5.18. F_x is the component of force in the direction of slip and in Fig. 5.18 the unit of force is $Gb^2/2\pi(1-\nu)y$; x is measured along the slip plane using y as the unit of length. When F_x is positive, it acts in the direction of increasing x.

When $x > y$, that is, $x > 1$ in Fig. 5.18, F_x is positive for dislocations of the same sign which thus repel each other. When $x < y$, dislocations of the same sign attract each other.

The force between dislocations is zero at $x = y$, which is an unstable position, and also zero at $x = 0$. Thus an array of edge dislocations of the same sign will tend to align themselves on their respective slip planes so that they lie above one another along a line normal to the slip plane. The figure also shows that dislocations of opposite sign attract each other along the slip planes when $x > y$ and repel when $x < y$. The equilibrium is stable at $x = y$ and unstable at $x = 0$.

Pairs of screw dislocations have no stable positions since a screw dislocation may glide on any plane that contains it. Screw dislocations of the same sign thus repel each other to infinity whereas those of opposite sign attract each other until they annihilate.

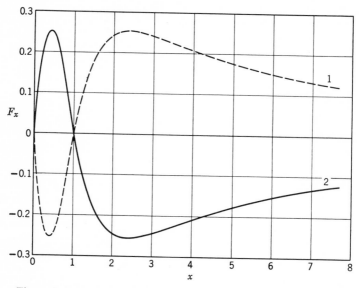

Figure 5.18   Variation of force between dislocations with distance apart. Curve 1 is for dislocations of the same sign and curve 2 for those of opposite sign. (After Cottrell)

5.16 Low-Angle Tilt Boundaries

The Burgers (1940) model of a small-angle boundary which has been produced by tilt of one section of a crystal relative to another is shown in Fig. 5.19 where positive edge dislocations denoted $\perp$ are aligned above one another. This configuration is a stable one as has been demonstrated in the previous section. In the diagram a cubic crystal with the tilt boundary on a (010) plane and the tilt axis [001] is shown.

The boundary is shown as an array of dislocations spaced d apart where the angle of the boundary θ is given by

$$\theta = \frac{b}{d} \tag{5.27}$$

Abundant experimental evidence has substantiated the Burgers model of low-angle boundaries.

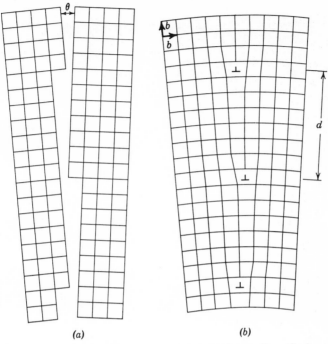

(a)   (b)

Figure 5.19   Low-angle tilt boundary envisaged as a line of edge dislocations. (After Burgers)

5.17   Estimates of the Density of Dislocations

Dislocation densities are quoted as the number which cross a unit area inside the crystal. The density may be from 10^9 to 10^{12} per square meter in well-annealed polycrystalline metals, whereas the best germanium and silicon single crystals give density values below 10^6 per square meter. In heavily deformed metals the densities increase to as high as 10^{15} or 10^{16} dislocations per square meter.

If a metal after severe deformation is heated in a calorimeter, it is possible to measure the release of energy associated with annealing. If the deformation is attributed to the introduction of dislocations, the dislocation density may be estimated from the calorimetric results.

Let us assume the measured maximum energy stored in the plastically deformed metal to be about 1 kilocalorie per kilogram. Most metals give stored energy values of about this magnitude. With a metal density of say 10^4 kg per cubic meter the stored energy is then about 4×10^7 joules per cubic meter. To estimate the number of dislocations per square meter we

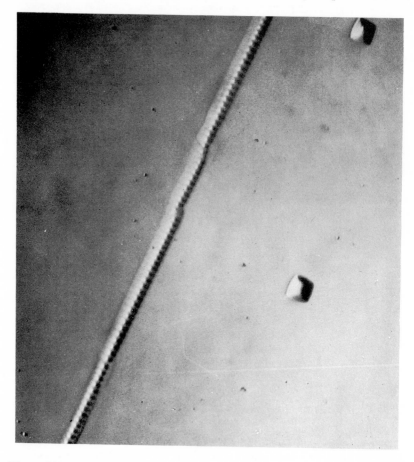

Figure 5.20   Dislocation ends at low-angle tilt boundary made visible by etching. (After Vogel)

must know the lattice energy per meter of dislocation. This can be calculated from equation 5.21 which gives the energy of a screw dislocation per meter as

$$E_S = \frac{Gb^2}{4\pi} \log \left(\frac{r_2}{r_1} \right)$$

Let us take $r_2 \simeq 10^{-6}$ m and $r_1 \simeq 10^{-10}$ m. Then E_S is approximately 7×10^{-9} joules m^{-1}. The total length of dislocation per cubic meter is then $4 \times 10^7/7 \times 10^{-9}$, that is, 6×10^{15} m. Thus the number of dislocations cutting the average square meter is about 2×10^{15}.

Other methods of estimating the density of dislocations in severely cold-worked crystals have been employed by Averbach and Warren (1950) from measurements of X-ray line broadening, by Dexter (1952) from resistivity changes and by Brown (1941) from magnetic saturation measurements.

If a dislocation loop meets a metal surface, the point of intersection can be preferentially etched and will appear as a small pit in the surface. A good estimate of the dislocation density can be obtained in well-annealed specimens by simply counting the number of etch pits. A low-angle tilt boundary is due, as we have seen, to a number of aligned edge dislocations. The trace of the boundary in the metal surface will thus contain the dislocation ends and should appear after etching as a line of small pits. Vogel (1955) has confirmed the truth of equation 5.27 by direct electron microscope measurement of the spacing between the dislocations and X-ray determination of the tilt boundary angle. Figure 5.20 shows one of his photographs of a boundary in germanium.

5.18 Dislocation Multiplication

Let us now make a rough estimate of the number of dislocations necessary to produce values of strain that are readily attainable in practice. We will use a greatly oversimplified model. Suppose in Fig. 5.21 that a

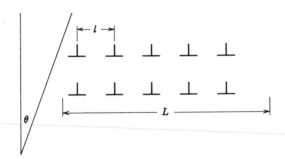

Figure 5.21   Calculation of possible strain by dislocation movement.

solid after solidification contains dislocations which are on the average spaced a distance l apart. Suppose now that this solid specimen is sheared and that each dislocation moves right across its slip plane from one boundary of the crystal to the other, a distance L. A dislocation generally will not move this far, and our model should give an overestimate of the strain produced. As each dislocation moves across the slip plane, the atomic planes above and below are translated relative to one another by the Burgers vector b. The total translation will be given by $(L/l)b$. The shear strain is thus Lb/l^2. Suppose the dislocation moves across a complete grain of average dimension say 10^{-3} m, then with $b \simeq 10^{-10}$ m and $l \simeq 10^{-6}$, the strain would be $\simeq 10^{-1}$. Thus *if the same number of dislocations are present throughout the process of deformation*, the maximum strain we could expect in the foregoing case would be $\simeq 10^{-1}$. In practice, strains of many times this value can be produced. It is clear that the number of dislocations must increase during the deformation process. The multiplication factor can be one thousandfold. A plausible model of dislocation multiplication has been proposed by Frank and Read (1950).

5.19   Frank-Read Dislocation Generator

Dislocations generally do not lie in a single slip plane. Instead they extend onto other neighboring slip planes by short segments called *jogs*. The dislocation is pinned at the points where it leaves the slip planes, and under the influence of an applied stress bows out from the pinning point. The elastic energy of a dislocation loop of radius r is $2\pi r$ times its energy per unit length and from equations 5.21 and 5.22 must be approximately

$$2\pi r \left(\frac{Gb^2}{4\pi}\right) \log \left(\frac{r_2}{r_1}\right)$$

The energy of the crystal is at the same time decreased by the product (stress per unit length) (area of loop πr^2). The change in energy ΔE on introducing the loop is therefore given by

$$\Delta E = \frac{Gb^2 r}{2} \log \left(\frac{r_2}{r_1}\right) - \pi r^2 \tau b$$

E passes through a maximum when $\partial(\Delta E)/\partial r = 0$, which condition reduces to

$$\frac{2r}{b} = \frac{G \log (r_2/r_1)}{2\tau\pi}$$

Since $\log (r_2/r_1) \simeq 2\pi$, the condition for the critical magnitude of loop radius is more simply written

$$\frac{2r}{b} = \frac{G}{\tau} \tag{5.28}$$

If l is the dislocation length between pinning points and if $2r > l$, further expansion of the loop decreases the radius and from (5.28) would require a greater stress. The dislocation loop under such circumstances is stable and will remain bowed out at the particular radius appropriate to the stress level. When, however, the stress level is increased to a point beyond which $l/b = G/\tau$, the dislocation loop expands into a larger loop which completes itself, generates a new dislocation, and repeats the whole

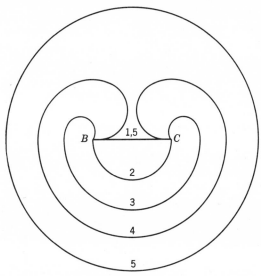

Figure 5.22   Dislocation multiplication by Frank-Read generator. The numbers indicate successive stages in position of dislocation loop.

process. The stages of dislocation multiplication are shown in Fig. 5.22. This mode of multiplication, which has been confirmed by experiment, is called a *Frank-Read generator*.

5.20   Microscopic Evidence for the Presence of Dislocations

Three different experimental techniques have been devised which render dislocations "visible," and show them to have many of the properties already attributed. These techniques are:

1. Etching to show the point at which dislocation loops intersect a polished surface.

2. Decoration of dislocations within a transparent crystal by deposits of metallic atoms.

3. Electron microscope detection of the density variation across a dislocation line in thin metallic foils.

Method 1 has already been discussed in Section 5.18. The other two methods will be illustrated by specific examples.

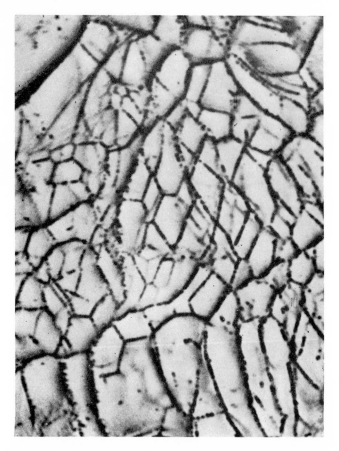

Figure 5.23 Dislocation network decorated by deposit of silver. (After Hedges and Mitchell)

Dislocation Decoration. Mitchell and Hedges (1953) first photographed dislocation patterns within large transparent crystals of AgBr after producing print-out of the silver. The regular patterns of particles of photolytic silver clearly correspond to dislocation networks within the crystal. Figure 5.23 shows such a "chicken wire" three-dimensional crossing network of dislocations.

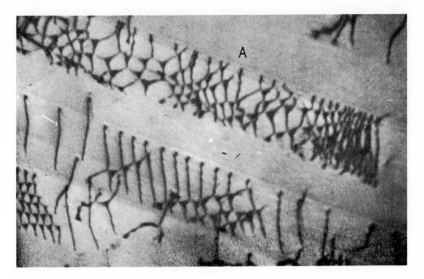

Figure 5.24   Electron microscope evidence of dislocation network in steel. (After Hirsch, Partridge, and Segall)

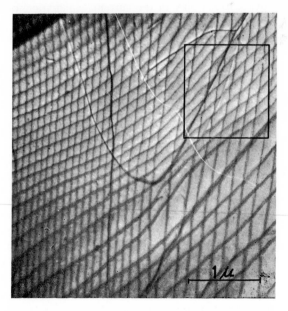

Figure 5.25   Crossing dislocation lines in bismuth telluride shown by electron microscope. (After Delavignette and Amelinckx)

Electron Microscope Dislocation Studies in Metals. In 1956 Hirsch and others showed that transmission electron microscopy through metallic foils thinned by beating or electropolishing can reveal the presence of dislocations. The specimen foils must be thinned to a few thousandths of an inch and the electron microscope operated at about 100 kv. A number of studies of dislocations including the taking of movie pictures to reveal rearrangement have already been made. Figure 5.24 shows dislocation networks at the surface of annealed stainless steel after fatigue bending. Figure 5.25 shows crossing dislocation lines in the basal plane of bismuth telluride.

It is clear that these techniques give beautifully detailed information on dislocation behavior, and they should prove powerful tools in the elucidation of the remaining problems of plastic deformation in solids.

5.21   The Role of Dislocations

Sections 5.4 to 5.10 of this chapter gave a discussion of a number of properties of the phenomenon of plastic deformation. From Section 5.12 on we have described the nature of dislocations. We now briefly discuss the role that dislocations play in the current explanation of the plastic properties.

It has been shown that the low yield stress in pure crystals is because of the ease with which the dislocations present can be made to glide across a slip plane with the resulting plastic deformation. If solid material can be made without dislocations, we would expect it to be 1000 times stronger than normal. In fact whiskers of tin and iron have been made of diameters about 1 μ in which no easily moved dislocations are present. These whiskers can be bent elastically into sharp radii which indicate yield stresses in excess of one thousand times the values in normal sized crystals.

Any method of impeding dislocation motion will increase the strength of a solid. For instance, the presence of foreign atoms can block dislocation motion especially if the impurity is in the form of dispersed particles.

If the precipitated particles are closely dispersed in the crystal, quite high stresses are necessary to force the dislocation loop between them. If, however, the particles coagulate into more widely dispersed groups, the dislocation loop may bow out between the stressed areas and rejoin to give easier plastic flow. It is not surprising, therefore, to find that a critical dispersion of particles such as Al_2Cu in aluminum should give an age-hardened alloy of greatest strength, as was discussed in Section 5.8.

Dilute solid solutions are stronger than the pure solvent because of pinning of the dislocations by the solute atoms. The solute atom will tend to "condense" on the dislocation in the expanded or compressed region of the dislocation according to the relative size of solute and matrix atom. The most stable position for interstitial carbon in iron, for example, is just above the slip plane at a positive edge dislocation (see Fig. 5.12). For small displacement of the dislocation the carbon atoms pin the dislocation. As soon as the distance of the dislocation from the carbon "atmosphere" exceeds a critical value, slip can occur at a lower stress level. This gives rise to the upper and lower yield points in mild steel (see Fig. 5.6).

The process of work hardening, described in Section 5.10, is the result of the difficulty of causing a dislocation to move through the forest of dislocations already produced by the previous plastic deformation. Such a passage may produce lattice vacancies with a consequent expenditure of the energy of formation of such vacancies.

Both recovery and recrystallization involve rearrangement, under the influence of thermal energy, of the dislocation pattern into one of lower energy. In recrystallization the rearrangement probably leaves portions of the crystal in an unstrained condition, these portions growing at the expense of the strained regions. Any process of rearrangement in which the dislocations have to climb out of their original slip planes must be a slow one. The laws of diffusion govern such a process (see Chapter 4), which is highly temperature dependent. Deformation during recovery and recrystallization, as in creep, will therefore also be highly temperature dependent.

The foregoing processes are all temperature dependent, an increase in temperature in all cases decreasing the yield strength. The search for superalloys for use at very high temperatures is therefore a search for alloys with reduced diffusion rates, where the strengthening mechanisms will survive to higher temperatures.

REFERENCES

B. L. Averbach and B. E. Warren, *J. Appl. Phys.* **21**, 595 (1950).

C. S. Barrett, *Structure of Metals*, McGraw-Hill Book Company, New York, 1952.

W. F. Brown, Jr., *Phys. Rev.* **60**, 139 (1941).

J. M. Burgers, *Proc. Phys. Soc.* (*London*) **52**, 23 (1940).

A. H. Cottrell, *Dislocations and Plastic Flow in Crystals*, Clarendon Press, Oxford, 1953.

D. L. Dexter, *Phys. Rev.* **86**, 770 (1952).

F. C. Frank and W. T. Read, *Phys. Rev.* **79**, 722 (1950).

J. Frenkel, *Z. Physik* **37**, 572 (1926).

J. M. Hedges and J. W. Mitchell, *Phil. Mag.* **44**, 223 (1953).

P. B. Hirsch, R. W. Horne, and M. J. Whelan, *Phil. Mag.* **1**, 677 (1956).

W. T. Read, Dislocations in Crystals, McGraw-Hill Book Company, New York, 1953.

F. L. Vogel, Jr., *Acta Met.* **3**, 245 (1955).

EXERCISES

1. A plate-like specimen of fine grained metal with no preferred orientation is subject to the principal stresses σ_1 and σ_2 lying in the plane of the free surface. Obtain an expression for the sum of the principal stresses in terms of the change in spacing of atomic planes lying parallel to the surface. Using Copper $K\alpha$ X-radiation ($\lambda = 1.54$ Å) with an aluminum specimen ($a = 4.08$ Å) which diffraction ring would we use for the measurement of stress?

2. A cylindrical single crystal has a tensile stress σ applied to each end. If the normal to a slip plane in the crystal makes an angle ϕ with the cylindrical axis and the direction of slip on the slip plane makes an angle λ with the axis, show that the shear stress across the slip plane in the direction of slip is given by $\sigma \cos \phi \cos \lambda$. If the critical shear stress for copper is 10^6n m^{-2} what is the minimum tensile applied stress to produce shear deformation?

3. Confirm that the stresses $\sigma_x{}^n$, $\sigma_y{}^n$, $\sigma_z{}^n$ acting on a plane whose normal makes direction cosines α, β, γ with the coordinate axes are given by

$$\sigma_x{}^n = \alpha\sigma_x + \beta\tau_{yx} + \gamma\tau_{zx}$$
$$\sigma_y{}^n = \alpha\tau_{xy} + \beta\sigma_y + \gamma\tau_{zy}$$
$$\sigma_z{}^n = \alpha\tau_{xz} + \beta\tau_{yz} + \gamma\sigma_z$$

4. Calculate the elongation of a 10^{-1} m rod of cross section 10^{-4} m^2 when subjected to a tensile force of 0.1n. For aluminum $S_{11} = 15.9 \times 10^{-12}$ m^{2}n^{-1}

$$S_{12} = -5.8 \times 10^{-12} \text{ m}^2\text{n}^{-1}$$
$$S_{44} = 35.2 \times 10^{-12} \text{ m}^2\text{n}^{-1}$$

6. How much heat in calories would be evolved by the complete annihilation of dislocations when 20 c.c. of cold-worked copper is annealed if the original dislocation density was 6×10^{11} cm^{-2}. Assume a dislocation energy of 1 eV per Å.

7. A single crystal of copper contains a low angle tilt boundary with the boundary on a (010) plane and the tilt axis parallel to the [001] direction. Calculate the tilt angle if the spacing of dislocations in the boundary is 1.5×10^{-6} m.

6

Introductory Wave Mechanics

The physical properties of solids that we have discussed in the previous chapters derive from the geometrical characteristics of the atomic packing. Before this treatment can be extended to cover the electrical properties of matter, an understanding must be reached of the nature of the charges that give rise to these properties. This will involve, in turn, a study of the nature of electrons, the electronic properties of atoms, and, finally, the behavior of electrons in the periodic lattice of the solids.

This preparatory material may seem at times to take us rather far from our real aim, the properties of solids. The electrical properties of solids cannot be adequately understood, however without a knowledge of wave mechanics methods and the application of these to various problems including, specifically, the physics of atoms.

6.1 The Particle Nature of Electrons

The electron was first clearly identified as an elementary particle by J. J. Thomson in 1897. His work on the deflection of a cathode ray beam in electric and magnetic fields showed that the constituents of the beam had a unique ratio of charge to mass, regardless of their source. This suggested the interpretation of the cathode ray beam in terms of a stream of elementary particles each of charge e and mass m. The currently accepted values are $e = 1.6021 \times 10^{-19}$ coulomb and $m = 9.1085 \times 10^{-31}$ kg (at rest). Many properties of electrons can be described using nothing more than the assumption of a particle with a fixed charge and mass which obeys the laws of electrodynamics. The properties that can be so described are mostly those involving the interaction between electrons and electrostatic and electromagnetic fields, that is, the properties of electrons in free space. The treatment breaks down when the problem of electrons in matter is considered and the necessary revisions to the theory are taken up later in this chapter.

The classical electrodynamics of charged particles is treated in the books on electricity but, because of the frequent use which must be made of it in the remaining part of this book, we wish to give a summary of the relations governing motion of a charge in electric and magnetic fields.

The force $\mathbf{F}$ on a charge e situated in a field $\mathscr{E}$ is, by definition

$$\mathbf{F} = e\mathscr{E} \tag{6.1}$$

The work W done in moving a charge from point A to point B in an electrostatic field is

$$W_{AB} = e \int_A^B \mathscr{E} \cdot \mathbf{ds} \tag{6.2}$$

and this is written in terms of the electrostatic potential V as

$$W_{AB} = e(V_B - V_A) \tag{6.3}$$

Equation 6.3 enables us to define commonly used units of work. If one *coulomb* of charge is moved through a potential difference of one *volt*, the amount of work done is one *joule*. The work done in moving an *electron* through a potential difference of one *volt* is one *electron-volt* (eV). From the value of the charge on the electron we thus have

$$1 \text{ eV} = 1.6021 \times 10^{-19} \text{ joule}$$

Following the definition of a scalar potential in equation 6.3, we write the relation between field $\mathscr{E}$ and potential V as

$$\mathscr{E} = -\left(\frac{\partial V}{\partial x}\mathbf{i} + \frac{\partial V}{\partial y}\mathbf{j} + \frac{\partial V}{\partial z}\mathbf{k}\right) \tag{6.4}$$

where $\mathbf{i}$, $\mathbf{j}$, and $\mathbf{k}$ are unit vectors in the x, y, and z directions respectively.

Equation 6.4 is often written

$$\mathscr{E} = -\text{grad } V$$

The forces between moving charges are more complex than those already discussed. They are usually described in terms of a magnetic field of induction $\mathbf{B}$. Consider a charge e moving with velocity $\mathbf{v}$ through a field $\mathbf{B}$. The force $\mathbf{F}$ on the charge is then given in magnitude by

$$F = evB \sin \theta \tag{6.5}$$

where θ is the angle between the directions of **v** and **B**. The force **F** may be written in terms of a vector product

$$\mathbf{F} = e(\mathbf{v} \times \mathbf{B}) \qquad (6.6)$$

In the special case where the particle e is moving in a plane normal to the direction of **B**, θ is 90° and **F** is in a direction normal to **v**. The charge e will thus move in a circular path whose radius r is determined by the equation expressing the balance between electromagnetic and inertial forces. This equation is

$$Bev = \frac{mv^2}{r}$$

that is, $r = \dfrac{mv}{Be} \qquad (6.7)$

We might note in passing that the time required for a complete circuit of the circular path is

$$t = \frac{2\pi r}{v} = \frac{2\pi m}{Be} \qquad (6.8)$$

The time is thus independent of the velocity of the particle. This feature is fundamental to the design of many particle-accelerating machines and will also be encountered later in the electronic properties of metals and semiconductors.

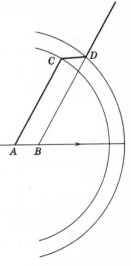

Figure 6.1   The distortion of the lines of force which constitutes the pulse of electromagnetic energy emitted from an accelerated charge.

Equations 6.1 to 6.6 refer to charges at rest relative to each other or in uniform relative motion. The case of accelerated motion requires further treatment. The circumstances can be imagined most clearly for a sudden deceleration. Consider that at a certain time t_0 a moving charge is abruptly decelerated to rest within a very short time Δt. Prior to stopping, the charge was surrounded by a spherically uniform electrostatic field which moved with the charge. The information regarding the changed velocity of the charge will be propagated along the lines of force at the speed of electromagnetic interactions, that is, the speed of light. Now consider the circumstances at a time t_1 after the charge was stopped, as they are illustrated in Fig. 6.1. The point at which the particle was stopped is A. At a great distance (i.e., greater than ct_1) from the charge, the field lines have not yet received the information that the charge has stopped and so remain as a spherical distribution around the point B that the particle would have reached at time t_1 had it not stopped. For distances smaller than ct_1 the field lines will be stationary and centered on A. Thus there must be a region of distortion CD on each field line spreading out with velocity c and this corresponds to a spherical pulse of electromagnetic energy of thickness $c \, \Delta t$. The conclusion is, therefore, that the effect of acceleration (positive or negative) on a charge is to cause it to radiate energy. Probably the most common example of this phenomenon is in X-ray tubes. Here the deceleration arises as a fast-moving electron strikes a target. Since the slowing down process is arbitrary, no distinct wavelengths are emitted, and the radiation spectrum is continuous. If sufficiently fast electrons (i.e., those that have been accelerated through some thousands of volts) are used, the resulting radiation is sufficiently energetic to lie in the X-ray region, and this is the origin of the "white" X-ray spectrum mentioned on p. 26.

The foregoing recapitulation of elementary electrostatic and electromagnetic theory illustrates the *particle* properties of electrons. This model is completely adequate for most practical work on electron beams in tubes, gaseous discharges, etc. It is, however, inadequate for the discussion of many aspects of the behavior of electrons in atoms and solids. For this purpose we must give a description of the electron in terms of wave mechanics.

6.2   The Wave Nature of Electrons

The previous section discusses the aspects of electron behavior that could be interpreted on the "charged billiard ball" model. Because other properties of electrons can be observed that cannot be treated by this model the wave mechanics treatment that we are about to discuss was developed. Actually, the suggestion that we can picture electrons in terms of a wave came from a converse proposal made in 1901–1905 by Planck and Einstein that electromagnetic radiation could be regarded (and in many cases had to be regarded) not as a smooth continuous wave but as a shower of discrete packets of energy, and to each of which was given the name *quantum* or *photon*. The essential feature of this hypothesis is that the radiation can exchange energy with a system only in units of a definite size. Energy changes smaller than that corresponding to one quantum are not permitted. Planck proposed that the energy E of a single quantum should be related linearly to the frequency ν of the radiation by the equation

$$E = h\nu \qquad (6.9)$$

where h is Planck's constant, of which the currently accepted value is 6.62517×10^{-34} joule sec.

The proposal found almost immediate application and support in the photoelectric effect. This effect is discussed more fully in Chapter 9, and it is sufficient to say here that the evidence was, as Einstein pointed out, that an electron in a solid could gain energy from a monochromatic light beam only in definite amounts, and that this quantity of energy depended linearly on the frequency of the light.

The use of the alternative particle or wave models for the description of electromagnetic radiation is dictated by circumstance. Phenomena like reflection, refraction, interference, or diffraction can be treated in terms of a continuous wave. On the other hand, in many problems such as those involving absorption and emission of radiation by atoms, the quantum picture may be required.

It is instructive to calculate the number of photons concerned in ordinary processes. Suppose a sodium vapor lamp emits one watt of radiation in the familiar yellow light of wavelength 5.9×10^{-7} m. The energy of each quantum is given by equation 6.9 and is 4×10^{-19} joule. The number of photons emitted per second is consequently 2.5×10^{18}. In processes, such as reflection, that involve the behavior of a beam composed of such a large number of photons, it is not surprising that the radiation can be considered as continuous.

By 1924 the concept of quanta of energy had become sufficiently well established to prompt de Broglie to speculate that if electromagnetic radiation could be regarded as displaying either wave or particle characteristics, depending on the type of experiment, so might matter display a similar duality. Shortly after de Broglie made this proposal, experimental observation was made by Davisson and Germer and by G. P. Thomson of diffraction of an electron beam by a crystal. The concept was then placed on a firmer mathematical basis by Schroedinger in 1926, and it is the Schroedinger formulation that will be used in the following treatment.

de Broglie proposed that the properties of a particle can be described by a wave that is defined to have a wavelength, λ, given by

$$p = \frac{h}{\lambda} \tag{6.10}$$

where p is the momentum of the particle. This proposal is obviously of immediate significance in cases where wave-like properties of electrons can be observed directly, as in electron diffraction. We now proceed, however, to make the assumption that the description of a particle in terms of a wave can be applied generally to all circumstances. The case of electron diffraction in which the diffraction angles can be calculated using the de Broglie wavelength alone has already been discussed in Section 2.5. We shall therefore proceed directly to the treatment of other problems in which the amplitude of the de Broglie wave is involved.

It is intended that the properties of the particle should be represented by those of the de Broglie wave, which we can assume to be represented generally by the equation

$$\Psi = A \cos 2\pi \left(\frac{x}{\lambda} - vt \right) + B \sin 2\pi \left(\frac{x}{\lambda} - vt \right) \qquad (6.11)$$

or, as it is more commonly written

$$\Psi = A \cos (\kappa x - \omega t) + B \sin (\kappa x - \omega t)$$

where $\kappa = 2\pi/\lambda$ and $\omega = 2\pi v$. The quantity Ψ does not necessarily correspond to anything observable in the behavior of the particle. It is an invented concept and the way in which it is interpreted to give observable behavior will be given below. A and B are constants, for the moment undetermined. κ will be called the wave number of the wave (care must be taken to distinguish between $1/\lambda$, which is frequently termed the wave number, and the quantity $2\pi/\lambda$ which is, for convenience, being termed the wave number here). The frequency of the wave is v and ω is the angular frequency. We here assume that the de Broglie wave constitutes a quantum so that v and ω are given in terms of the particle energy E by

$$E = hv = \frac{h\omega}{2\pi}$$

Now the wave number κ and the angular frequency ω of the de Broglie wave must be related, because the momentum and energy of the particle are related. This is equivalent to a stipulation on the value of the velocity of the de Broglie wave. It actually emerges that the wave velocity of the de Broglie wave is not a particularly useful quantity but, on the other hand, it is instructive to calculate the group velocity. For any wave, the group velocity, that is the velocity at which amplitude modulation of the wave (and hence information) moves, is given by

$$v_g = \frac{dv}{d(1/\lambda)} = \frac{d\omega}{d\kappa} \qquad (6.12)$$

Since, (neglecting potential energy), the energy and momentum of a nonrelativistic particle are related by

$$E = \frac{p^2}{2m}$$

we can write

$$\omega = \frac{2\pi E}{h} = \frac{\pi p^2}{mh}$$

Thus

$$\omega = \frac{h\kappa^2}{4\pi m}$$

and the group velocity is given by

$$v_g = \frac{h}{4\pi m} \cdot 2\kappa$$

$$= \frac{h\kappa}{2\pi m} = \frac{mv}{m} = v \tag{6.13}$$

Thus we have the fortunate result that the group velocity of the de Broglie waves, the velocity with which they transmit information, is the same as the velocity of the particle.

Only two problems remain. The first is the interpretation of the wave function Ψ and the second is the application of the de Broglie wave principle to actual problems. The first problem is solved by a postulate formulated by Born that the square of the wave function Ψ gives the probability density of observing electron properties. By this we mean that if we consider a small volume $dx\,dy\,dz$ in a region occupied by an electron,

$$|\Psi|^2\,dx\,dy\,dz = \text{probability of finding an electron}$$
$$\text{in the volume } dx\,dy\,dz \tag{6.14}$$

It remains only to find a way of evaluating the distribution of this function Ψ within a region occupied by an electron so as to solve the problem of what the electron does in this particular environment. In other words, we should be able to find out what the electron does when it is placed, say, in the field of a proton to form a hydrogen atom or in the field of an array of atoms in a solid. The quantity which specifies the environment of the electron is the potential V which the electron experiences. Thus, since we want a solution for Ψ that refers to a particular environment, we want a Ψ which is specific to a certain value of V. In other words, we must construct an equation relating Ψ and V. (Note that V may be quite a complicated function of both space and time, e.g., the electron might be in an atom, subject to the static field of a nucleus and subject simultaneously to the time-dependent field of an approaching ion).

Now we have an equation involving V and the properties of the particle. It is

$$\text{Kinetic energy} + V = \text{total energy}$$

which we can write in terms of the momentum, p,

$$\frac{p^2}{2m} + V = E \qquad (6.15)$$

or, in terms of the wave constants

$$\frac{h^2 \kappa^2}{8\pi^2 m} + V = \frac{h\omega}{2\pi} \qquad (6.16)$$

If we can express κ and ω in terms of Ψ for substitution in equation 6.16, we shall obtain the required relation between Ψ and V. We can obtain values for κ and ω in terms of Ψ by differentiation of equation 6.11

$$\frac{\partial \Psi}{\partial t} = \omega[A \sin (\kappa x - \omega t) - B \cos (\kappa x - \omega t)]$$

giving

$$\omega = \frac{1}{A \sin (\kappa x - \omega t) - B \cos (\kappa x - \omega t)} \cdot \frac{\partial \Psi}{\partial t}$$

Also

$$\frac{\partial \Psi}{\partial x} = \kappa[-A \sin (\kappa x - \omega t) + B \cos (\kappa x - \omega t)]$$

but we need κ^2, so try

$$\frac{\partial^2 \Psi}{\partial x^2} = \kappa^2[-A \cos (\kappa x - \omega t) - B \sin (\kappa x - \omega t)]$$

$$= -\kappa^2 \Psi$$

and

$$\kappa^2 = -\frac{1}{\Psi} \frac{\partial^2 \Psi}{\partial x^2}$$

We can now substitute for κ^2 and ω in equation 6.16 to obtain

$$\frac{h^2}{8\pi^2 m}\left(-\frac{1}{\Psi} \frac{\partial^2 \Psi}{\partial x^2}\right) + V = \frac{h}{2\pi} \frac{1}{(A \sin (\kappa x - \omega t) - B \cos (\kappa x - \omega t)]} \frac{\partial \Psi}{\partial t}$$

This would be an equation wholly in Ψ if we could express the function

$$A \sin (\kappa x - \omega t) - B \cos (\kappa x - \omega t)$$

in terms of Ψ. That is, can we write

$$A \sin (\kappa x - \omega t) - B \cos (\kappa x - \omega t)$$

$$= C[A \cos (\kappa x - \omega t) + B \sin (\kappa x - \omega t)]$$

where C is some constant?

Clearly we can, if we have values for A, B, and C as follows:

$$A = 1$$
$$B = i$$
$$C = -i$$

When we make these substitutions, the equation becomes

$$-\frac{h^2}{8\pi^2 m}\frac{\partial^2 \Psi}{\partial x^2} + V\Psi = \frac{ih}{2\pi}\frac{\partial \Psi}{\partial t} \tag{6.17}$$

This is the celebrated *time-dependent Schroedinger equation*. It has a solution which, in accordance with the foregoing values of A and B must be complex in form.

$$\Psi = \cos(\kappa x - \omega t) + i\sin(\kappa x - \omega t) \tag{6.18}$$

(We ignore, for the moment, the possibility of a constant multiplying the whole function Ψ).

The principle of the wave mechanics method is therefore to specify the problem in terms of V, solve the Schroedinger equation using that particular value of V, obtain a solution for Ψ as a function of space and time, and interpret that solution using equation 6.14. Note that the type of solution given by this method differs from that found in classical mechanics. In classical mechanics the solution tells us that a particular particle will be at a particular point at a definite time and this deterministic solution has now been replaced by probabilities only. This is a characteristic feature of wave mechanics solutions and will be illustrated by specific examples later in this chapter.

If the environment of the electron happens to be static so that V is a function of space only, a simplification can be carried out. It will appear that the solution for Ψ can be written in separable form, in terms of a function ψ of x only and a function φ of t only.

$$\Psi(x, t) = \psi(x)\varphi(t) \tag{6.19}$$

To show that this is so, substitute this form for Ψ into equation 6.17. We obtain

$$-\frac{h^2}{8\pi^2 m}\frac{\partial^2 \psi}{\partial x^2}\varphi + V\psi\varphi = \frac{ih}{2\pi}\psi\frac{\partial \varphi}{\partial t}$$

Divide by $\psi\,\varphi$

$$-\frac{1}{\psi}\left(\frac{h^2}{8\pi^2 m}\right)\frac{\partial^2 \psi}{\partial x^2} + V = \frac{ih}{2\pi}\frac{1}{\varphi}\frac{\partial \varphi}{\partial t} \tag{6.20}$$

Now the left hand side is a function of x only because of our assumption about V, and the right hand side is a function of t only. This situation is possible only if each side is equal to a constant D. Thus we can write

$$\frac{ih}{2\pi} \frac{1}{\varphi} \frac{\partial \varphi}{\partial t} = D$$

giving

$$\varphi = e^{-(2\pi i/h)Dt}$$

This is a simple oscillation in time, with frequency.

$$\nu = \frac{D}{h}$$

But, because of the assumption represented by equation 6.9, we have

$$\nu = \frac{E}{h}$$

whence

$$D = E$$

Thus we can write

$$\varphi(t) = e^{-(2\pi i/h)Et}$$

The left hand side of equation 6.20 which gives the space-dependent part of the wave function must also be equal to E, so we have

$$-\frac{1}{\psi}\left(\frac{h^2}{8\pi^2 m}\right)\frac{\partial^2 \psi}{\partial x^2} + V = E$$

or

$$\frac{\partial^2 \psi}{\partial x^2} + \frac{8\pi^2 m}{h^2}(E - V)\psi = 0 \qquad (6.21)$$

This is the *time-independent Schroedinger equation.* It is an equation which, for a potential that does not vary with time, gives the space-dependent part of the wave function Ψ. The complete solution for such a static problem is then a space variation for the wave function ψ multiplied by an oscillation in time at the frequency E/h, subject always to the interpretation that ψ^2 (or $|\Psi\Psi^*|$ where Ψ^* is the complex conjugate of Ψ) at a point is a measure of the probability of observing a particle at that point. The whole solution can thus be regarded as a shimmering distribution of charge density of a certain shape. This nebulous solution is in contrast to the sharp solutions of classical mechanics, the definite predictions of the latter being replaced by probabilities.

As in classical oscillation theory, the type of solution will depend on the number of constraints enforced by the boundary conditions. Recall the case of a vibrating string where two constants (e.g., the coordinates of each fixed end) specify exactly the possible wavelengths of vibration. Similarly in the Schroedinger equation, it will be found that we can divide the solutions into two classes, *free* and *bound*. In the former the energy is unspecified and in the latter the energy (like the wavelengths of the vibrating violin string) is determined by the constants of the problem. Let us consider two simple problems illustrating, in turn, first a free solution and then a bound solution.

6.3   An Electron Meeting a Potential Discontinuity

Consider an electron free to move along the x axis. Consider that in the regions on either side of $x = 0$ the electron would have a constant potential

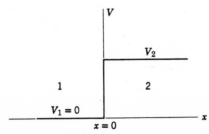

Figure 6.2   A potential discontinuity.

energy of $V_1 = 0$ for $x < 0$ (region 1) and $V = V_2$ for $x > 0$ (region 2). Let there be a discontinuous change of potential energy at $x = 0$. The diagram of potential with distance is given in Fig. 6.2. Let the total energy of the electron be E. This state of affairs is an idealization of circumstances encountered, for example, at the surface of a metal electrode, at the junction of two different metals, and in a number of other practical systems. The classical solution to this problem is simple. If E is larger than V_2, the particle can surmount the barrier to reach region 2. If E is smaller than V_2, the particle must be reflected. As might be expected, the wave mechanics solution will show some other features.

The time-independent Schroedinger equation appropriate to region 1 can be written

$$\frac{\partial^2 \psi}{\partial x^2} + \frac{8\pi^2 m}{h^2} E\psi = 0$$

Let us refer to the constant $8\pi^2 mE/h^2$ by the symbol α^2 to give

$$\frac{\partial^2 \psi}{\partial x^2} + \alpha^2 \psi = 0$$

This equation is a simple one to solve because it represents a simple harmonic variation of ψ with x. Since the differential equation is insensitive to the direction of propagation of such a wave, we must write the solution in the form

$$\psi = e^{i\alpha x} + Ae^{-i\alpha x}$$

where the constant A will have to be determined by the boundary conditions. The complete wave function is then

$$\Psi = (e^{i\alpha x} + Ae^{-i\alpha x})e^{-(2\pi iE/h)t}$$

Since each term is of the form

$$e^{i(\kappa x - \omega t)}$$

the whole solution is in traveling wave form.

In region 2 the Schroedinger equation can be written

$$\frac{\partial^2 \psi}{\partial x^2} + \frac{8\pi^2 m}{h^2}(E - V_2)\psi = 0$$

and, if we write $8\pi^2 m/h^2(E - V_2) = \beta^2$, we can write the solution

$$\Psi = Be^{i\beta x}e^{-(2\pi iE/h)t}$$

This solution is, again, a traveling wave and the constant B will be determined, as for A, by the boundary conditions. (There is no point in considering a term in $e^{-i\beta x}$ because there is no chance of encountering an electron approaching the barrier from the *opposite* side.) The boundary conditions from which A and B must be calculated can be shown to be:

$$\psi \text{ must be continuous at } x = 0$$
$$\partial\psi/\partial x \text{ must be continuous at } x = 0$$

Interesting features are apparent in the nature of the transmitted wave, that is in the form of the solution in region 2. This form clearly depends on β and so, in turn, on the relative values of E and V_2. Let us consider two cases.

1. When $E > V_2$. In this case $\beta^2 > 0$, and the wave in region 2 is real. We thus have a wave in region 1 incident upon the boundary, a reflected wave in region 1 and a transmitted wave in region 2 as illustrated in Fig. 6.3. Each wave has an amplitude determined by the boundary conditions, leading to calculable probabilities for transmission and reflection. Note once again that this is in conflict with Newtonian mechanics which, if $E > V_2$, would predict uniform transmission across the potential step.

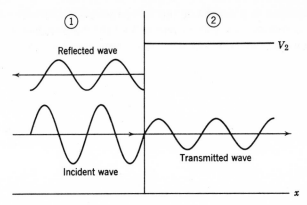

Figure 6.3 Electron waves incident on, reflected from, and transmitted through a potential discontinuity when $E > V_2$.

2. When $E < V_2$. This time $\beta^2 < 0$ and the solution has the form

$$\Psi = Be^{-\gamma x}e^{-(2\pi iE/h)t}$$

where $$\gamma^2 = -\beta^2$$

Since the quantity i in the exponent of the x term has disappeared, this equation does *not* represent a traveling wave. It is an oscillation in *time* with an amplitude that depends on distance through the $e^{-\gamma x}$ term. It is, in fact, the so-called standing wave with an amplitude that decays exponentially from $x = 0$. The rate at which the amplitude decays depends on γ. The decay is steep if $E \ll V_2$ and less steep as E is closer in value to V_2. This situation is illustrated in Fig. 6.4.

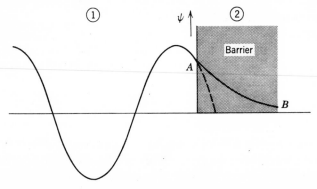

Figure 6.4 The stationary oscillation AB behind a potential discontinuity when $E < V_2$.

Let us extend this analysis to the interesting and important case where region 2 is followed by a third region 3 where the potential V_3 is again zero. As we see in Fig. 6.5 we are dealing now with a potential barrier of width d.

In region 3 the solution is

$$\Psi = Ce^{i\alpha x}e^{-(2\pi iE/h)t}$$

which is once again as in region 1 a traveling wave of amplitude C which represents the probability of finding electron properties in the region.

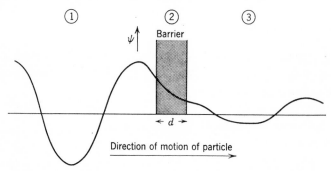

Figure 6.5   Tunneling: the penetration of a particle wave through a barrier.

Continuity conditions across the second potential step determine C, and so C depends on the value to which $Be^{-\gamma x}$ has decayed over the distance d.

Thus there exists a certain probability of transmission of the electron through the barrier, even though the energy of the electron E is less than the potential step V_2. This is impossible in Newtonian mechanics. We can deduce the probability of transmission T, after taking all the continuity conditions into account, to be

$$T = \frac{\text{No. of electrons penetrating the barrier}}{\text{No. of electrons arriving at the barrier}}$$

$$= \frac{4}{4\cosh^2 \gamma d + \left(\frac{\gamma}{\alpha} - \frac{\alpha}{\gamma}\right)^2 \sinh^2 \gamma d}$$

This phenomenon by which an electron has a chance of appearing on the far side of a barrier with the same energy as when incident on the barrier is called the *tunnel effect*. As will be seen later, it is fundamental to a discussion of electron behavior at intermetal contacts and of electron emission from metal surfaces.

Let us obtain an idea of the magnitude of the tunnel effect by considering an electron of energy 5 eV incident on an insulating barrier of thickness 5×10^{-10} m between two metals when the barrier height is 6 eV. We find γ to be 5×10^9 and T about 1.5 per cent.

Thus each electron stands a 1.5 per cent chance of penetrating the barrier, and so if N electrons meet the barrier per second the number transmitted is 0.015N. The probability of transmission falls off very rapidly with barrier width d and in general can be neglected for barriers thicker than about 10^{-9} m.

6.4 Electron in a Box

Let us now solve a bound electron problem. Consider an electron, free to move along the x axis as in Fig. 6.6, and confined between potential discontinuities of infinite height at positions $x = 0$ and $x = a$.

The Schroedinger equation in the region $0 < x < a$ is

$$\frac{\partial^2 \psi}{\partial x^2} + \frac{8\pi^2 m}{h^2} E\psi = 0$$

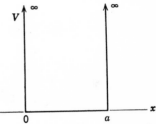

The equation has to be solved subject to the conditions $\psi = 0$ at $x = 0$ and at $x = a$ because the probability of observing an electron outside $0 < x < a$ is zero.

Figure 6.6 A box defined by potential discontinuities.

The space-dependent part of the solution is, once again, harmonic in form, and may be written

$$\psi = A \cos \alpha x + B \sin \alpha x$$

where, as before,

$$\alpha^2 = \frac{8\pi^2 m}{h^2} E$$

Inserting the boundary conditions into this trial solution we obtain

$$\text{at } x = 0, \qquad \psi = 0 = A$$
$$\text{and at } x = a, \qquad \psi = 0 = B \sin \alpha a$$

These conditions are met only if $\alpha a = n\pi$ where n is integral, that is,

$$a\sqrt{8\pi^2 mE/h^2} = n\pi, \qquad n = 1, 2, 3, \ldots$$

Thus solutions of the Schroedinger equation exist only if E is confined to the magnitudes

$$E_n = \frac{n^2 h^2}{8ma^2}, \qquad n = 1, 2, 3, \ldots.$$

We have thus demonstrated that the bound electron may only have certain energies or *energy levels*. The levels for this particular problem are shown in Fig. 6.7. This concept of energy levels in general plays a dominating role in the study of the electron properties of matter, the essential

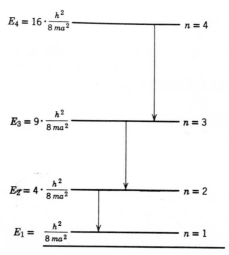

Figure 6.7   The energy levels of a particle in a box.

feature being that the solution for Ψ will exist only if the energy of the electron has one or other of a number of definite values. Note in passing that the mathematical formulation is exactly analogous to the classical mechanics solution of the violin string problem where only certain wavelengths are permitted.

Since the electron can exist only in certain energy levels, the energy that is emitted from, or absorbed by, the system can have only certain discrete values. This uniqueness of transition energy is one of the most striking features of atomic physics. It is also conveniently consistent with Planck's quantum postulate concerning radiation since we can imagine the quanta to correspond to the energy changes between levels.

The solution for ψ is now completed by calculating the value of B. This is done by making the obvious assumption that the electron must be somewhere between $x = 0$ and $x = a$ so that

$$\int_0^a B^2 \sin^2 \alpha x \, dx = 1$$

which yields

$$B = \sqrt{2/a}$$

The final solution for ψ is therefore

$$\psi = \sqrt{2/a} \sin \alpha x$$

Figure 6.8 illustrates the wave function ψ and the probability ψ^2 as functions of x for $n = 1$, 2, and 3.

Remember that these graphs are to be interpreted as the spatial dependence of an oscillating function whose amplitude squared gives the probability of finding an electron at any point.

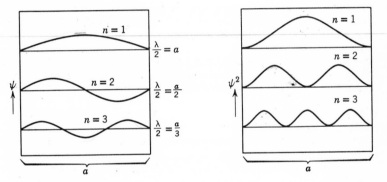

Figure 6.8   The wave functions and probability distributions for an electron in a box.

The solution illustrated in Fig. 6.8 is in marked contrast to the classical picture of a particle trapped between perfectly reflecting walls, for instance a billiard ball bouncing back and forth between the cushions. Here the probability of finding the ball is uniform along the path of the ball, since the velocity is constant between collisions with the cushion. The wave mechanical solution corresponding to the lowest energy state, that is, $n = 1$, departs most noticeably from the classical solution, being peaked midway between the reflecting walls. The wave functions corresponding to higher energy states tend to approximate more and more closely to the uniform classical solution. This is a common relation between wave mechanical and classical solutions.

REFERENCES

C. S. Cook, *Modern Atomic and Nuclear Physics*, Van Nostrand, Princeton, N.J., 1961.

R. M. Eisberg, *Fundamentals of Modern Physics*, John Wiley and Sons, New York, 1961.

R. B. Leighton, *Principles of Modern Physics*, McGraw-Hill Book Company, New York, 1959.

E. Merzbacher, *Quantum Mechanics*, John Wiley and Sons, New York, 1961.

N. F. Mott and I. N. Sneddon, *Wave Mechanics and its Applications*, Clarendon Press, Oxford, 1948.

R. L. Sproull, *Modern Physics*, John Wiley and Sons, New York, 1956.

EXERCISES

1. An electron is accelerated through 500 volts. It enters a field of 0.5 webers m^{-2} with an angle of 45° between its velocity vector and the field vector. What is the pitch and radius of the resulting helical path and what is the frequency of the rotational motion?

2. A sodium vapor lamp is sending out 1 watt of monochromatic radiation at a wavelength of 5893 Å. Assuming radial symmetry calculate the number of photons falling on a surface of 1 square meter, set perpendicularly to the radiation at a distance of 1 m.

3. An X-ray photon has a wavelength of 1 Å. Through what potential difference must an electron be accelerated in order that it can, on colliding with a target, generate such a photon. Assume that all the electron's energy is transferred to the photon.

4. Consider the electron discussed in exercise 3. What would be its de Broglie wavelength after acceleration?

5. What is the wavelength associated with an α particle (He^4 nucleus) of kinetic energy 8 MeV?

6. An electron in a metal has an energy of 5 eV. What is its de Broglie wavelength?

7. An electron in a metal encounters a barrier layer of height 6 eV and thickness 5 Å. If the electron's energy is 5 eV, what is the probability of tunneling through the barrier?

8. Consider the one-dimensional case only and calculate the energy interval between the ground state and the first excited state for an electron contained within infinite potential barriers, (a) 5 Å apart and (b) 1 cm apart. What would be the wavelength of the radiation produced by a transition between the first excited state and the ground state in each case?

7

Electronic Energy Levels

in Atoms, Molecules, and Solids

The principal aim of this chapter is to discuss the nature of the energy levels of a single electron in solids, but we must first make a preliminary study of the nature of the levels in a single atom. This study of the single isolated atom, here and in Chapter 8, serves first as a preliminary to the study of electron levels in a periodic lattice and second as a key to the many properties of solids which depend on the detailed atomic properties of the lattice. It is perhaps possible to give a superficial description of some solid-state properties without reference to the atomic structure of the lattice, but many other phenomena cannot be treated at all without an understanding of atomic properties. We shall start with the simplest of all atomic configurations, that of the hydrogen, or hydrogen-like, atom.

7.1 The Wave Mechanics of the Hydrogen Atom

We suppose the existence of an infinitely massive, positively charged nucleus of charge Ze where Z is the atomic number and e the charge on the electron. The single electron of hydrogen (when at a distance r from the nucleus) moves with a potential energy $V(r)$ given by

$$V(r) = -\frac{Ze^2}{4\pi\epsilon_0 r} \text{ (mks units)} \tag{7.1}$$

These are the circumstances appropriate to a neutral hydrogen atom, a singly ionized helium atom, a doubly ionized lithium atom, and so on.

The time-independent Schroedinger equation can be written in three dimensions:

$$\left(\frac{\partial^2\psi}{\partial x^2} + \frac{\partial^2\psi}{\partial y^2} + \frac{\partial^2\psi}{\partial z^2}\right) + \frac{8\pi^2 m}{h^2}(E - V)\psi = 0$$

or more briefly

$$\nabla^2\psi + \frac{8\pi^2 m}{h^2}(E - V)\psi = 0 \qquad (7.2)$$

Substituting for the value of V appropriate to the problem from (7.1) gives

$$\nabla^2\psi + \frac{8\pi^2 m}{h^2}\left(E + \frac{Ze^2}{4\pi\epsilon_0 r}\right)\psi = 0 \qquad (7.3)$$

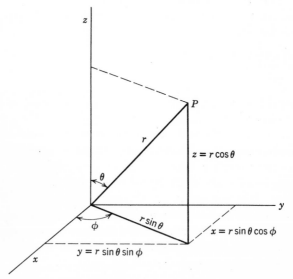

Figure 7.1   The relation between rectangular Cartesian and spherical polar coordinates.

Equation 7.3 is not simple to solve, and we shall not attempt a complete solution. We shall discuss the circumstances under which a solution exists, for these will give us as much as we need at the moment about the physical properties of the system.

Since V is a simple function of r, equation 7.3 is first expressed in polar coordinates, which are illustrated in Fig. 7.1, using the value for the operator ∇^2 in spherical polar coordinates, namely,

$$\nabla^2 \equiv \frac{1}{r^2}\frac{\partial}{\partial r}\left(r^2\frac{\partial}{\partial r}\right) + \frac{1}{r^2\sin\theta}\frac{\partial}{\partial\theta}\left(\sin\theta\frac{\partial}{\partial\theta}\right) + \frac{1}{r^2\sin^2\theta}\frac{\partial^2}{\partial\phi^2}$$

This gives

$$\frac{1}{r^2}\frac{\partial}{\partial r}\left(r^2\frac{\partial\psi}{\partial r}\right) + \frac{1}{r^2\sin\theta}\frac{\partial}{\partial\theta}\left(\sin\theta\frac{\partial\psi}{\partial\theta}\right)$$

$$+ \frac{1}{r^2\sin^2\theta}\frac{\partial^2\psi}{\partial\phi^2} + \frac{8\pi^2 m}{h^2}\left(E + \frac{Ze^2}{4\pi\epsilon_0 r}\right)\psi = 0 \qquad (7.4)$$

We now make the assumption that the parts of the solution corresponding to the three coordinates r, θ, and ϕ are independent so that the solution of the equation can be written in the form

$$\psi = R(r)\Theta(\theta)\Phi(\phi) \qquad (7.5)$$

where R is a function of r alone, Θ of θ alone, and Φ of ϕ alone.

If we insert this form for ψ in equation 7.4 and divide through by $R\Theta\Phi$, the equation becomes

$$\left[\frac{1}{R}\frac{1}{r^2}\frac{\partial}{\partial r}\left(r^2\frac{dR}{dr}\right) + \frac{8\pi^2 m}{h^2}\left(E + \frac{Ze^2}{4\pi\epsilon_0 r}\right)\right]$$

$$+ \frac{1}{r^2}\left[\frac{1}{\Theta}\frac{1}{\sin\theta}\frac{\partial}{\partial\theta}\left(\sin\theta\frac{d\Theta}{d\theta}\right)\right] + \frac{1}{r^2\sin^2\theta}\left(\frac{1}{\Phi}\frac{d^2\Phi}{d\phi^2}\right) = 0 \qquad (7.6)$$

The procedure has effected a convenient separation of the variables R, Θ, and Φ and we can obtain a solution of (7.6) term by term. Consider the last term

$$\frac{1}{\Phi}\frac{d^2\Phi}{d\phi^2}$$

It is, by definition, a function of ϕ only, and yet the equation shows that it is equal to a function of r and θ only. To avoid this contradiction it must therefore be a function of none of r, θ, or ϕ, and so must be a constant. Let us call this constant $-m_l^2$.

Thus we can write

$$\frac{1}{\Phi}\frac{d^2\Phi}{d\phi^2} = -m_l^2$$

or

$$\frac{d^2\Phi}{d\phi^2} + m_l^2\Phi = 0$$

which has the solution

$$\Phi = \cos m_l\phi$$

This means that the spatial dependence of the wave function must have a wavelike form as it goes around the ϕ direction. For Φ to be unique, it should repeat for values of ϕ increasing by 2π. Thus m_l must be integral or

$$m_l = 0, \pm 1, \pm 2, \pm 3, \ldots \qquad (7.7)$$

Equation 7.6 can now be rewritten

$$\left[\frac{1}{R}\frac{1}{r^2}\frac{\partial}{\partial r}\left(r^2\frac{dR}{dr}\right) + \frac{8\pi^2 m}{h^2}\left(E + \frac{2e^2}{4\pi\epsilon_0 r}\right)\right]$$

$$+ \frac{1}{r^2}\left[\frac{1}{\Theta}\frac{1}{\sin\theta}\frac{\partial}{\partial\theta}\left(\sin\theta\frac{d\theta}{d\theta}\right) - \frac{m_l^2}{\sin^2\theta}\right] = 0 \quad (7.8)$$

and we have reduced the equation to one of two variables.

By the argument just used, the last term, being simultaneously a function of r only and of θ only, must be a constant. Let us write this constant $-l(l + 1)$. This constant gives a differential equation for Θ called the associated Legendre equation, whose solutions are functions called associated Legendre polynomials; these functions give the shape of the Θ function in much the same way as Bessel functions give the shape of the solution for a vibrating membrane such as a drum. The associated Legendre polynomials exist only if l is integral and satisfies the condition

$$|m_l| \leqslant l$$

It is now possible to obtain the final part of the solution for R. It is convenient to change the variables, thus reducing the algebraic complexity of the R function. Remembering that we wrote $-l(l + 1)$ for the Θ function, if we also write

$$\frac{8\pi^2 mE}{h^2} = -a^2 \qquad b = \frac{\pi mZe^2}{\epsilon_0 h^2 a}$$

$$x = ar \qquad X = rR,$$

then it is easy to verify that equation 7.7 reduces to

$$\frac{d^2X^2}{dx^2} + \left[-1 - \frac{l(l + 1)}{x^2} + \frac{2b}{x}\right]X = 0 \qquad (7.9)$$

Without obtaining the complete solution to this equation we can, by making some plausible assumptions about the nature of the solution, obtain several conditions with which the constants must comply. For instance for very small values of x, equation 7.9 implies a simple power law for X, that is,

$$X \propto x^n$$

Also, for very large x, $\qquad X \propto e^{-x}$

Let us therefore assume that the solution of (7.9) for X can be written in the form

$$X = Ax^n e^{-x}$$

To see what conditions must be satisfied to permit this to be a solution, substitute it back into equation 7.9. We obtain

$$\left\{\frac{1}{x^2}[n(n-1)-l(l+1)]+\frac{2}{x}(b-n)\right\}Ax^n e^{-x}=0 \qquad (7.10)$$

Now if $A \neq 0$, equation 7.10 will be satisfied for all values of x only if the coefficients of $\frac{1}{x^2}$ and $\frac{1}{x}$ are separately zero. This gives

$$n = l + 1$$

and
$$b = n$$

It actually turns out that other solutions are permitted, giving a final relationship between n and l of

$$l \leqslant n-1 \qquad \text{where} \qquad n = 1, 2, 3, \ldots \qquad (7.11)$$

The second condition, that is, $b = n$, can be rewritten

$$n = \frac{\pi Z e^2}{\epsilon_0 h^2 a}$$

or
$$E = -\frac{me^4 Z^2}{8\epsilon_0^2 h^2}\frac{1}{n^2} \qquad (7.12)$$

The solution for X in equation 7.9 will exist only if this condition is met, and thus the energy of the atom is restricted to those values resulting from integral values of n.

The atom will normally reside in the state with $n = 1$. The states of higher n will be occupied only after the atom has been excited by the addition of energy from the outside. This excited state will decay after a very short time ($\sim 10^{-8}$ sec) with the emission of a quantum or series of quanta of electromagnetic energy until the ground state, $n = 1$, is reached.

The energy levels for the hydrogen atom are illustrated in Fig. 7.2. The actual energy values for the different levels are obtained from equation 7.12. Level E_1 has the value 13.6 eV, which is thus the energy that would have to be supplied to remove the electron from a hydrogen atom. Such an atom minus its valence electron is called an *ion*, and the necessary energy the *ionization potential*. It is obvious that E_2 (for $n = 2$) has a value one-fourth of the value of E_1. In a transition between E_2 and E_1, 10.2 eV of energy are emitted as a photon. The frequency of the photon is given by equation 6.10, the value of ν being 9.7×10^{14} sec^{-1}. This value corresponds to a wavelength of 3.1×10^{-7} m, which places the spectrum line well into the ultraviolet. The reader may readily verify that the only transitions giving wavelengths in the visible region are those between the levels $n = 3$ and $n = 2$, $n = 4$ and $n = 2$, $n = 5$ and $n = 2$.

We must bear in mind at this point that we have not obtained a complete solution for the R function, but only the conditions under which such a complete solution may exist. It is clear, however, that the R function is the one specifying the size of the electron distribution just as the Θ function specifies its shape. The form of the R functions are illustrated in Fig. 7.3 for $n = 1$ and $n = 2$.

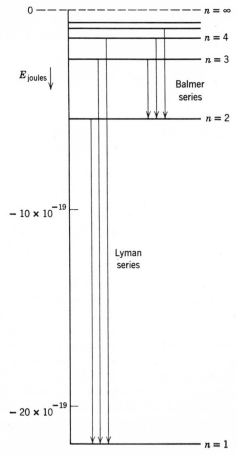

Figure 7.2   The energy levels of atomic hydrogen.

It will be recalled that the probability of finding an electron at a particular position is proportional to $|\psi|^2$. To find the probability of an electron at distance r from the nucleus, the appropriate volume element is a spherical shell of radius r and thickness dr that is of volume $4\pi r^2 \, dr$, and so the charge distribution follows the function $|\psi|^2 r^2$. This function is plotted as a function of r in Fig. 7.4. The atom is thus seen to possess a kind of shell

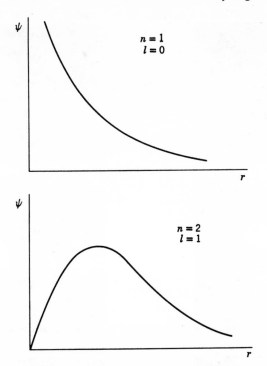

Figure 7.3   The radial part of the wave function for the ground state and one excited state of atomic hydrogen.

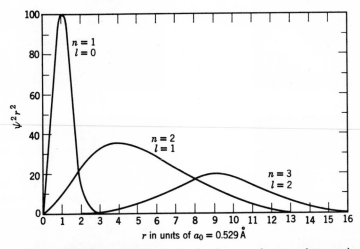

Figure 7.4   The probability density for the ground state and two excited states of atomic hydrogen showing the shell structure.

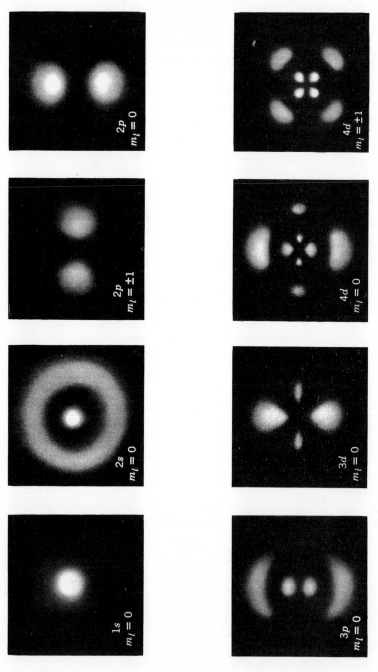

Figure 7.5   Diagrams of one plane of the electron probability density for various excited states of the hydrogen atom.

structure of a size that increases with the degree of excitation. The shape of the atom is spherically uniform only when $l = 0$. When $l \neq 0$ the Θ function multiplies the foregoing R variations to give shape to the atom. The form of the $|\psi|^2$ function for various values of n, l, and m_l is shown in Fig. 7.5.

The actual value for the size of the charge distribution cannot easily be obtained from the preceding treatment. The calculation shows that the maximum charge distribution is at a distance of 0.53×10^{-10} m from the nucleus for the ground state $n = 1$, $l = 0$, and at a distance of 2.1×10^{-10} m for the excited state $n = 2$, $l = 1$. These are actually the same values given by an elementary treatment of the hydrogen problem first proposed by Bohr. The Bohr model, however, implies that the distribution is sharp, which is in contrast to the wave mechanical picture and to the implications of actual experimental findings.

7.2 The Significance of the Quantum Numbers n, l, and m_l

The Quantum Number n. As we have just seen, the role of n is simply to determine the overall energy of the state and, in general terms, the radius of the electron distribution. As stated earlier, the hydrogen atom will normally exist in the ground state with $n = 1$ and the upper states will be occupied only after energy has been absorbed by the atom, and then only temporarily.

The Quantum Number l. The significance of l is found in the second term in equation 7.9. Obviously the quantity $l(l + 1)/x^2$ must be dimensionless. This implies that we can write

$$l(l + 1) = cx^2$$

where c is a dimensionless constant.

That is,

$$l(l + 1) = cx^2$$

If we draw a crude analogy with the classical model of a point mass m circulating around the nucleus with velocity v, the energy can be written

$$E = \tfrac{1}{2} mv^2$$

so that

$$l(l + 1) = c\,\frac{8\pi^2 mr^2}{h^2}\frac{1}{2}mv^2$$

or

$$l(l + 1)\,\frac{h^2}{4\pi^2} = c(mvr)^2 = cL^2$$

The quantity in parenthesis on the right-hand side is the angular momentum of the electron charge distribution. Although we have only indicated that there is a connection, through a simple number, between the angular momentum L and the quantity $\sqrt{l(l+1)}(h/2\pi)$, a more rigorous treatment shows them to be actually equal.

This equality, then, is the significance of the quantum number l. Associated as it is with the shape of the electron charge distribution, l is a measure of the angular momentum of the atom. It emerges that the angular momentum of the atomic state can often be a more important factor in the atom's behavior than the overall energy state governed by n. Therefore it is common to specify the atomic state by a conventional symbol which is related to the l value. States with $l = 0$ are designated *s-states*,

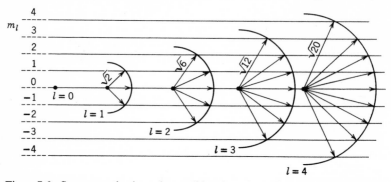

Figure 7.6   Space quantization; the possible orientations of the angular momentum vector with respect to an external field direction.

with $l = 1$ *p-states*, with $l = 2$ *d-states*, with $l = 3$ *f-states*. A 3p state, for example, is one in which $n = 3$ and $l = 1$.

The Quantum Number m_l. It can be shown, although not by elementary means, that the quantity $m_l(h/2\pi)$ gives the value of the component of the orbital angular momentum, along the z axis. This means that L may only be aligned at certain angles to the z axis so that the components be an integral number times $h/2\pi$. There are in fact $2l + 1$ possible orientations of L with respect to the z axis. Figure 7.6 illustrates such L orientations for m_l values of up to ± 4. The number of possible orientations is termed the *multiplicity* of the state.

It will be recalled that the solution in which m_l appeared was associated with the ϕ coordinate, which describes the distribution around the z axis. As long as the z axis remains undefined, the states of differing m_l are indistinguishable. If, however, such a direction is imposed on the atom from the outside in a manner that modifies the atomic behavior, the quantum number m_l becomes significant. The normal method of doing this is to apply a magnetic field. For this reason m_l is often called the *magnetic quantum number* and gives the possible orientations of the atomic angular momentum vector with respect to an external magnetic field. As we have seen only certain orientations are allowed, so that there is, in fact, a "space quantization."

7.3 Intrinsic Spin

We must now consider a further quantum property of the atom which cannot be predicted by elementary wave mechanical theory. There are many instances where the theory we have considered so far predicts a single energy level whereas actual observation shows that the level must be double. The familiar yellow double line in the spectrum of sodium is the consequence of transitions from such a double level. It was therefore found necessary to postulate the existence of another quantum number. This quantum number was attributed by Uhlenbeck and Goudsmit in 1925 to *spin* of the electron about its own axis. If we suppose the spin to be quantized with a quantum number s, the value of s may be obtained from the number of possible orientations of the spin angular momentum vector with respect to some fixed direction in the atom. This multiplicity must have value $2|s| + 1$ analogously to the $2l + 1$ of the orbital angular momentum states. The multiplicity is observed to be 2 which gives

$$2 |s| + 1 = 2$$

or
$$|s| = \tfrac{1}{2}$$

We therefore say that the electron has an intrinsic spin angular momentum of a value L_s where

$$L_s = \sqrt{|s| (|s| + 1)} \, \frac{h}{2\pi}$$

with $s = \pm\tfrac{1}{2}$, the two signs representing the two possible orientations with respect to some axis in the atom.

Subsequent to the suggestion of Uhlenbeck and Goudsmit, it was shown by Dirac in his theory of relativistic wave mechanics that the existence of electron spin could be predicted as a fundamental intrinsic property of the electron.

7.4 Summary of the Quantum Number Characteristics

We can summarize the predictions of the wave mechanical treatment of the hydrogen atom as a set of energy levels governed by the quantum numbers n, l, m_l and s with the following properties:

1. n determines the state of excitation of the atom and can have any integral value. The ground state of the hydrogen atom has $n = 1$, and

$n = \infty$ corresponds to $E = 0$ and complete removal of the electron from the atom, that is, ionization.

2. l determines the value of the orbital angular momentum in accordance with

$$L = \sqrt{l(l + 1)} \, \frac{h}{2\pi}$$

where l can take any integral value between 0 and $n - 1$.

3. m_l determines the possible orientations of the angular momentum with respect to an external magnetic field. Only orientations that make the component of the angular momentum along the field direction equal to $m_l(h/2\pi)$, where m_l takes all integral values between l and $-l$, are permitted.

4. s gives the spin state of the electron. The value of s is $\frac{1}{2}$, and the orientation of the spin angular momentum may be in one or other of two directions with respect to any significant reference directions such as an external magnetic field or the orbital angular momentum vector **L**.

Note that the energy of the atomic state on our simple wave mechanical model of the atom is determined only by n. This is a consequence of our assuming a strict coulomb potential between the nucleus and the electron. When this assumption breaks down either through the existence of electron spin, because of the presence of more than one electron in the atom, or because of the presence of an external magnetic or electric field, the energy levels are split according to the particular l, m_l, and s values.

At this stage we have completed the description of the behavior of a single electron in an isolated atom. We must eventually extend the treatment to cover multielectron atoms but that will be left until Chapter 8. In the meantime we shall continue the discussion of the properties of a single electron in situations which lead toward the solid state.

7.5   The Two Square Well Problem

Although we could start immediately with a discussion of the general solid, it is preferable to start with the simplest structure which shows the beginning of solid properties. This should enable the reader to have a clearer physical picture of the situation when we progress to the general case. The simplest structure to serve as an introduction to solids is the hydrogen ion molecule, which consists of one electron moving in the field of two adjacent protons.

Before considering the hydrogen ion molecule, however, it is instructive to investigate the solution of the Schroedinger equation for the simpler conditions in which an electron can occupy two one-dimensional square well potentials as shown in Fig. 7.7a. Since these are wells of finite depth, we do not have the strict harmonic functions found in Section 6.8 and we can represent the wave functions as shown in Fig. 7.7a. The only difference between the solutions for the infinitely deep well and for the well of finite depth which are significant for our purpose is that for the finite well the solutions do not go to zero at the boundaries of the well but extend for a distance on either side. There will be one part of the solution in each well, and, if the two wells are far enough apart, there is effectively no interaction

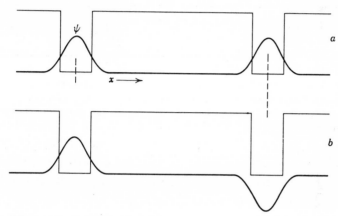

Figure 7.7   Symmetric and antisymmetric wave functions for the two square well problem. (After Sproull)

between the two parts of the wave function. This is because each part of the solution has become sufficiently close to zero in the region between the wells that there is no problem of matching the two parts of the solution.

The significant feature of the two-well problem is that another solution of the Schroedinger equation is possible. This solution is shown in Fig. 7.7b where the ψ in one well is 180° out of phase with respect to the ψ in the other well. Figure 7.7a shows the *symmetric* wave function and Fig. 7.7b the *antisymmetric*. There exists practically no difference in energy between the two ψ configurations whe.: the wells are far apart.

Suppose now that the distance between the wells decreases. Interaction between the two parts of the wave function becomes important, and differences in energy between the symmetric and antisymmetric states appear. The complete calculation of the energies for the symmetric and antisymmetric cases as a function of the distance between the wells is difficult, but it is possible to get some insight into the nature of the answer by considering the limiting case when the two wells come into contact.

This condition is illustrated in Fig. 7.8a in which it is seen that we are now dealing with one well twice as wide as the earlier ones. Figure 7.8a shows the symmetric wave function for the limiting case and Fig. 7.8b the anti-symmetric wave function. It is now recognized that Fig. 7.8a illustrates a

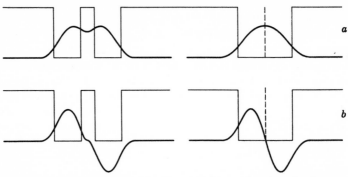

Figure 7.8   The symmetric and antisymmetric wave functions for the case in which the two wells are close, and also for the limiting case. (After Sproull)

ground state wave function ($n = 1$) and Fig. 7.8b a *first excited* state wave function ($n = 2$) for the new well. In Section 6.4 we showed that for an infinitely deep well the energy was proportional to $n^2/(\text{width})^2$, and thus

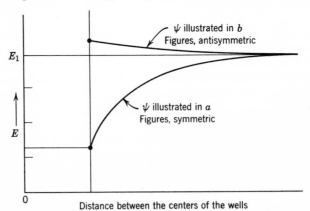

Figure 7.9   The variation of energy with distance apart of the wells, for the symmetric and antisymmetric wave functions. (After Sproull)

the ground state for a well of width $2a$ has an energy of only one quarter that for the ground state of width a. On the other hand, the first excited state for a well of width $2a$ has an energy equal to that of the ground state for a well of width a.

Although these figures are not exactly correct for a well of finite depth, it is now clear that two possibilities exist for the energy, depending on whether the wave function is symmetric or antisymmetric. The energy versus distance plot is shown in Fig. 7.9 for the two cases.

7.6 The Hydrogen Ion Molecule

The foregoing argument can be repeated for an inverse square law of force in order to describe the conditions experienced by the electron in a hydrogen ion molecule. Here we can consider the wave functions appropriate to s states and, as before, a distinction between symmetric and

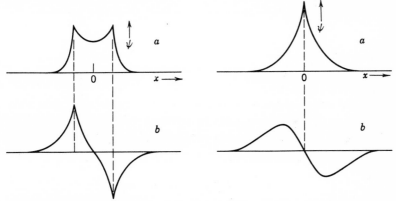

Figure 7.10 Symmetric and antisymmetric wave functions for the hydrogen molecule ion. (After Sproull)

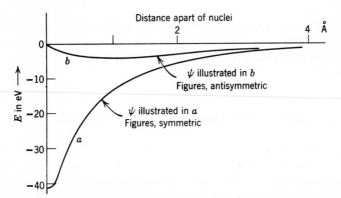

Figure 7.11 The variation of energy with distance between nuclei for the symmetric and antisymmetric wave functions for the hydrogen molecule ion. (After Sproull)

antisymmetric wave functions is possible as shown in Fig. 7.10. The variation of state energy with distance apart of the two nuclei of the molecule is quite similar to the plot of Fig. 7.9 and is given in Fig. 7.11. In this case, however, we must add the energy of repulsion of the two protons in order to obtain the total energy of the system. This repulsion is proportional to the inverse square of the distance apart. Figure 7.12 is a graph showing the total energy with distance. Since an energy minimum

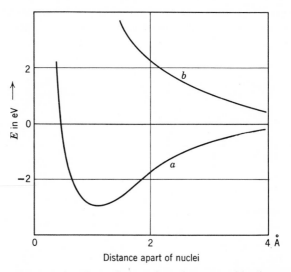

Figure 7.12 The variation of total energy with distance between the two nuclei for the hydrogen molecule ion. (After Sproull)

gives stable equilibrium, the hydrogen molecule is stable only when the wave function for the electron is symmetric. The position of the minimum should give the equilibrium distance between the two protons and approximately does so.

7.7   The Case of More Than Two Nuclei

We can construct a picture of electron behavior in the solid state by extending the preceding argument to three or more nuclei. We find that the effect is to increase the number of wave functions available. The ground state wave function possibilities are illustrated in Fig. 7.13 for three nuclei, and Fig. 7.14 shows the corresponding energy versus distance plots.

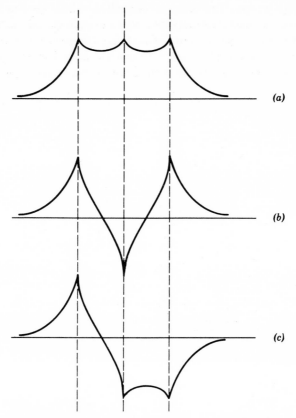

Figure 7.13 Symmetric and antisymmetric wave functions for three nuclei.

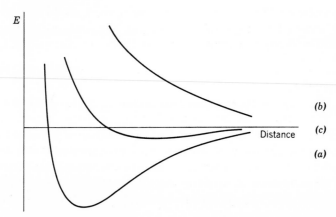

Figure 7.14 The variation of total energy with distance apart of the nuclei for three nuclei.

It can thus be seen that if we have N nuclei in whose field the electron is moving, we shall have a subdivision of the ground state into N separate levels. In pieces of solid matter of everyday experience, N is very large; for instance even a milligram of copper contains approximately 10^{19} atoms. Under these circumstances the subdivision of the energy range into 10^{19}

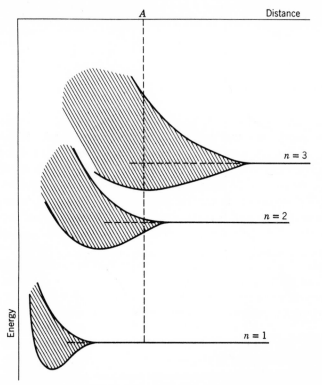

Figure 7.15   The energy level diagram for solid hydrogen as a function of distance between the nuclei.

separate levels becomes meaningless, and we talk instead of a *band* of allowed energies.

It is clear that the wave functions that correspond to excited states with $n = 2, 3$, etc., and which have a wider distribution in space than the ground state will be affected first by decreasing the distance between nuclei. The energy associated with the states of $n = 1, 2$, and 3 is plotted as a function of distance apart of the nuclei in Fig. 7.15. At any particular distance apart of the nuclei (e.g., at A) the inner levels are virtually unaffected by the presence of other nuclei, and the upper levels become bands, the width of which increases with energy.

In molecules or solids of multielectron atoms the number of filled levels depends on the number of electrons in a way that is discussed later. Thus there are electrons in both sharp levels and in bands. Transitions between lower levels give rise to line spectra (as in X-ray spectra), whereas transitions between higher levels give band spectra (as in thermal radiation). The equilibrium spacing of the atoms in the molecule or solid is again determined by the minimizing of the whole energy of the nuclei and electron shells.

7.8   The Motion of an Electron in a Periodic Lattice

As we saw in Chapter 1, atoms are usually arranged in solids in a periodic array. We will now study in greater detail the motion of an electron in the field arising from an array of nuclei. By an extension of the H atom treatment to a single electron in the field of an array of nuclei, we have shown that the sharp energy levels peculiar to isolated atoms are spread out into bands of available energy. The discussion given in Section 7.7 was qualitative only. Therefore, in view of the very great importance of this topic, we shall now consider in greater detail the motion of an electron in the field of an array of nuclei. The actual potential energy of an electron in a linear array of positive nuclei must be as shown in Fig. 7.16. This array is a very complicated potential distribution, and for the sake of simplicity we must revert to the simple case in which we treat the nucleus as a rectangular potential well of finite depth. Initially we will discuss the one-dimensional case illustrated in Fig. 7.17. In this model, constructed by Kronig and Penny, the spacing is $a + b$, and the depth of the wells is greater than the energy of the electron.

The time-independent Schroedinger equation takes the form for the different regions

$$0 < x < a \qquad \frac{\partial^2 \psi}{\partial x^2} + \frac{8\pi^2 m}{h^2} E\psi = 0 \qquad (7.13)$$

$$-b < x < 0 \qquad \frac{\partial^2 \psi}{\partial x^2} + \frac{8\pi^2 m}{h^2} (E - V_0)\psi = 0 \qquad (7.14)$$

Let us write

$$\alpha^2 = \frac{8\pi^2 m}{h^2} E, \quad \text{and} \quad \beta^2 = \frac{8\pi^2 m}{h^2} (V_0 - E)$$

We have to find a solution that will be appropriate for both of these regions and that will satisfy boundary conditions at the potential barriers. The form chosen for the solution follows from a theorem by Bloch dealing with wave functions of particles moving in a periodic potential. Bloch showed that the solution must be periodic with the period of the lattice.

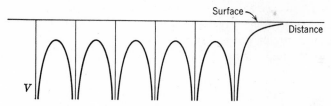

Figure 7.16   The potential energy of an electron in a periodic lattice.

The electron is therefore described by a wave with a certain wave number κ traveling through the crystal with an amplitude that is not constant but whose modulation is periodic.

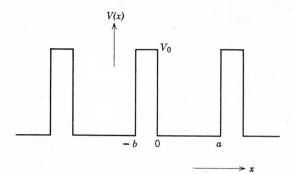

Figure 7.17   The potential distribution in a one-dimensional square well lattice.

We can write this type of solution

$$\psi = e^{i\kappa x}u(x) \tag{7.15}$$

where the first part represents the oscillating part of the wave and $u(x)$ represents the amplitude modulation. We now substitute the solution (7.15) in both (7.13) and (7.14). Hence, for

$$0 < x < a; \quad \frac{d^2u}{dx^2} + 2i\kappa\frac{du}{dx} - (\kappa^2 - \alpha^2)u = 0 \tag{7.16}$$

and

$$-b < x < 0; \quad \frac{d^2u}{dx^2} + 2i\kappa\frac{du}{dx} - (\kappa^2 + \beta^2)u = 0 \tag{7.17}$$

As may be readily verified by substitution, solutions for the equations 7.16 and 7.17 may be written

$$0 < x < a; \qquad u = Ae^{(-i\kappa + i\alpha)x} + Be^{(-i\kappa - i\alpha)x} \qquad (7.18)$$

$$-b < x < 0; \qquad u = Ce^{(-i\kappa + \beta)x} + De^{(-i\kappa - \beta)x} \qquad (7.19)$$

Equations 7.18 and 7.19 both represent two waves, one traveling in the x-direction and the other in the negative x-direction. All four waves are subject to the boundary conditions that both ψ and $d\psi/dx$, that is, u and $\partial u/\partial x$ must be continuous at $x = 0$ and $x = a$ and also that u must be periodic in distance $a + b$.

From the boundary conditions we can now obtain four equations that constitute the restrictions on the values of A, B, C, and D so that equations 7.13 and 7.14 will be solutions of the Schroedinger equation.

These four restriction equations, which will be more our concern than the actual solutions, are written accompanying the associated condition as follows:

For continuity of u at $x = 0$, $\quad A + B = C + D$.

For continuity of $\partial u/\partial x$ at $x = 0$,

$$A(-i\kappa + i\alpha) + B(-i\kappa - i\alpha) = C(-i\kappa + \beta) + D(-i\kappa - \beta).$$

For periodicity of u,

$$Ae^{(-i\kappa + i\alpha)a} + Be^{(-i\kappa - i\alpha)a} = Ce^{(-i\kappa + \beta)(-b)} + De^{(-i\kappa - \beta)(-b)}.$$

For periodicity of $\partial u/\partial x$,

$$A(-i\kappa + i\alpha)e^{(-i\kappa + i\alpha)a} + B(-i\kappa - i\alpha)e^{(-i\kappa - i\alpha)a}$$
$$= C(-i\kappa + \beta)e^{(-i\kappa + \beta)(-b)} + D(-i\kappa - \beta)e^{(-i\kappa - \beta)(-b)}$$

If these four condition equations are to be consistent, the determinant of the coefficients of A, B, C, and D must be zero. This can be verified to give

$$\frac{\beta^2 - \alpha^2}{2\alpha\beta} \sinh \beta b \sin \alpha a + \cosh \beta b \cos \alpha a = \cos \kappa(a + b) \qquad (7.20)$$

Equation 7.20 is quite complicated, but a simplification is possible. Let us consider the possibility that b should diminish while at the same time V_0 increases in such a way that the product $V_0 b$ remains finite. The model is thereby modified to one of a series of wells separated by infinitely thin potential barriers of which the Limit $\underset{\substack{V_0 \to \infty \\ b \to 0}}{(V_0 b)}$ represents the barrier strength.

With this limit, equation 7.20 becomes

$$\frac{1}{2\alpha} \frac{8\pi^2 m(V_0 b)}{h^2} \sin \alpha a + \cos \alpha a = \cos \kappa a \qquad (7.21)$$

and if we define P by the equation

$$P = \frac{4\pi^2 m a(V_0 b)}{h^2}$$

then 7.21 reduces to

$$P\frac{\sin \alpha a}{\alpha a} + \cos \alpha a = \cos \kappa a \tag{7.22}$$

The reader should remember that this equation is a condition of the existence of a solution for the electron wave function. It gives the values

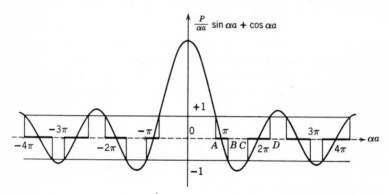

Figure 7.18   The function $P\dfrac{\sin \alpha a}{\alpha a} + \cos \alpha a$ plotted to show the regions in which its value falls between ± 1.

of α (the only variable in (7.22)) that permit a solution of the Schroedinger equation to exist. Now α is a function of the electron energy E, and thus once again the wave mechanical solution restricts the energy to certain permitted values. The nature of the energy restriction depends on the value of P.

In equation 7.22 the left-hand side (following the right-hand side) can only have values between ± 1. Figure 7.18 shows $P(\sin \alpha a/\alpha a) + \cos \alpha a$ plotted against αa with P given the value $3\pi/2$. The allowed ranges of αa which permit a wave-mechanical solution to exist are marked by heavy lines, for example, between A and B, C and D. Thus, as has been suggested before, the motion of electrons in a periodic lattice is characterized by bands of allowed energy, with the band width increasing with the energy.

Let us discuss for a moment the effect of varying P. It will be remembered that P is a measure of the potential barrier strength. If P is large, the barriers are strong, and the electron, in the limit of P infinitely large, can be considered to be confined to a single well. If, on the other hand, P is small, the barrier strength is small, and the electron can, in the limit of P

equal to zero, range freely through the lattice. Between these two limits
the energy band structure varies with the value of P, the variation being
shown in Fig. 7.19. This graph shows the position of the points A, B, C,
and D on a vertical axis for any particular P value.

At one extreme when P is at the right-hand side of the diagram, the
situation corresponds to an electron in an infinitely deep well, and we see

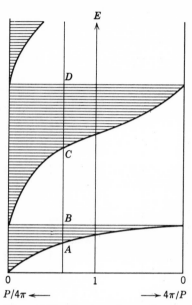

Figure 7.19   The dependence of energy
band width on the value of P.

that the levels are sharp. These levels are easily calculated since if $P \rightarrow \infty$
then $\sin \alpha a \rightarrow 0$. This is true when

$$\alpha a = n\pi$$

with n an integer, or

$$E = \frac{n^2 h^2}{8ma^2}.$$

which is the result previously obtained in Section 6.4.

On the other hand, when $P \rightarrow 0$ the situation corresponds to no barrier,
and the electron can be considered to be free. Substitution of $P = 0$ in
equation 7.22 lead to

$$\cos \alpha a = \cos \kappa a$$

or

$$\alpha = \kappa$$

Thus

$$\frac{8\pi^2 m E}{h^2} = \kappa^2$$

If we replace the wave number κ by the de Broglie value $2\pi/h$ where p is the momentum, then

$$E = \frac{p^2}{2m}$$

which is, as expected, appropriate to a completely free particle (see Section 6.2). Here no energy level structure exists, and all energies are

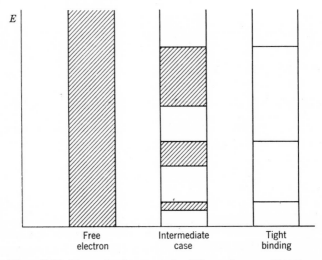

Figure 7.20   Energy level structure for different degrees of binding.

possible for the electron. The energy level diagrams for the cases of the tightly bound electron, the completely free electron and the intermediate case are shown in Fig. 7.20.

The behavior of electrons in a solid will thus depend on the tightness of the binding, and in the next chapter we will consider various possibilities. We must in the meantime, however continue the discussion of the possible energy values.

7.9   Brillouin Zones

In One Dimension.   We have considered the motion of an electron along a one-dimensional periodic lattice. We have assumed the electron to travel with a momentum p thus defining the de Broglie wave number κ. We have seen that, although the electron has been assumed to have arbitrary values of κ, its energy is nevertheless restricted to certain bands. It must be remembered that our intuitive notions about the relationship between energy and momentum hold for a free particle only. The electron we are considering is *not* free, and we must abandon preconceived ideas about its behavior. In fact the whole set of properties of the electron in a periodic lattice will be derived from the energy-momentum relation which is the result of the present treatment.

Let us now consider the values of κ at which the discontinuities in E

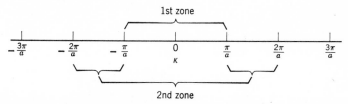

Figure 7.21   The first two Brillouin zones for a one-dimensional lattice.

occur. They occur whenever $\cos \kappa a$ reaches its maximum value, that is when $\cos \kappa a = \pm 1$ or, when

$$\kappa = \frac{n\pi}{a} \qquad \text{where} \qquad n = 1, 2, 3, \ldots . \qquad (7.23)$$

At these values of κ a small increase in electron momentum, that is, in κ, will make the energy of the electron jump discontinuously from the top of one allowed band to the bottom of the next. This situation is illustrated in Fig. 7.21. The region between the values of κ at which the first energy discontinuity occurs is called the *first Brillouin zone*. The region between the first and second values of κ for which discontinuities occur is called the *second Brillouin zone* and so on.

Within each zone the relationship between the energy E and κ is given by equation 7.22, since it will be remembered that α is related to E. The solutions for E as a function of κ are quite complicated and the analysis will not be attempted. However, Fig. 7.22 shows graphically the energy-wave number relationship in which it will be seen that E varies smoothly with κ between the discontinuities which occur at κ values of $\pm\pi/\alpha$, $\pm 2\pi/a$, etc. The dotted curve in Fig. 7.22 is the parabola

$$E = \frac{h^2}{8\pi^2 m} \kappa^2$$

which is the relation for a completely free electron. Note that this serves as an approximation of the behavior of the semibound electron whereas the role of the periodic lattice is principally to introduce the perturbations that result in the energy discontinuities.

In Two Dimensions.   We will now extend the foregoing discussion of the energy of an electron in a one-dimensional lattice to two and three-dimensional periodic arrays.   The treatment will be qualitative.

Let us first consider the motion of an electron in the field of a two-dimensional square lattice of characteristics similar to the previously

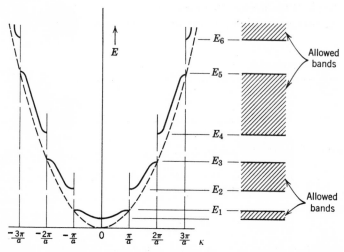

Figure 7.22   The relation between energy and wave number for a one-dimensional lattice.

considered linear lattice.   The motion of the electron in two dimensions can now be described using a wave number κ which is, as before, measured in the direction of propagation of the wave.   This wave number κ can be analyzed into components along the x and y axes which are respectively κ_x and κ_y.

To identify the first Brillouin zone, we note that along the κ_x axis in Fig. 7.23 the values of $\pm\pi/a$ represent the limits of the zone.   Similarly along the κ_y axis the values $\pm\pi/a$ also represent the limits of the zone. The first zone in two dimensions is therefore bounded along the axes by the points A, B, C, and D.   The remainder of the boundary is less easy to evaluate but it can be shown that, in general, just as the condition for an energy discontinuity in one dimension was

$$\kappa = \pm \frac{n\pi}{a} \qquad (7.24)$$

so in two dimensions the condition reads

$$\kappa_x n_1 + \kappa_y n_2 = \frac{\pi}{a}(n_1{}^2 + n_2{}^2) \tag{7.25}$$

where n_1 and n_2 are integers corresponding to the single integer n and referring to each one of the axes. To delineate the first zone, n_1 and n_2 are

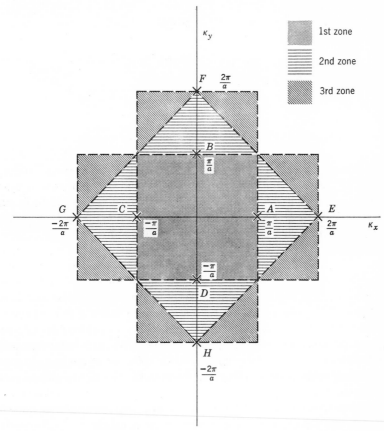

Figure 7.23   The first three Brillouin zones for a two-dimensional square lattice.

made equal in turn to ± 1 or 0. The equations of the lines bordering the first zone are therefore

$$n_1 = \pm 1, \qquad n_2 = 0, \qquad \text{giving} \quad \kappa_x = \pm \frac{\pi}{a}$$

and

$$n_1 = 0, \qquad n_2 = \pm 1, \qquad \text{giving} \quad \kappa_y = \pm \frac{\pi}{a}$$

The first Brillouin zone is thus a square passing through the points A, B, C, and D as shown in Fig. 7.23.

The second Brillouin zone must obviously pass through the points E, F, G, and H. The complete figure is obtained by taking n_1 and n_2 as the next integers in the series above those used for the first zone. These are $n_1 = \pm 1$ and $n_2 = \pm 1$. The equations of the second zone boundaries are therefore:

$$n_1 = +1, \qquad n_2 = +1, \quad \text{giving} \quad \kappa_x + \kappa_y = \frac{2\pi}{a}$$

$$n_1 = -1, \qquad n_2 = +1, \quad \text{giving} \quad -\kappa_x + \kappa_y = \frac{2\pi}{a}$$

$$n_1 = +1, \qquad n_2 = -1, \quad \text{giving} \quad \kappa_x - \kappa_y = \frac{2\pi}{a}$$

$$n_1 = -1, \qquad n_2 = -1, \quad \text{giving} \quad -\kappa_x - \kappa_y = \frac{2\pi}{a}$$

These four equations describe a set of four lines at 45° to the κ_x and κ_y axes passing through E, F, G, and H. The second Brillouin zone is thus the region between the squares $ABCD$ and $EFGH$. The third Brillouin zone is defined by giving n_1 and n_2 values of 0, ± 1, and ± 2. The reader can easily verify that its boundaries lie as shown in Fig. 7.23.

We must emphasize here that since the zone boundaries are measured in terms of $1/a$, they are a feature of the *lattice*. Their significance lies in the fact that while the electron is free to adopt almost any κ value in direction and magnitude in two dimensions (subject to a restriction to be described in Section 7.11), the energy of the electron will make a discontinuous change as the κ value crosses a zone boundary. Also from Fig. 7.22 we see that the functional dependence of the energy on the κ value becomes most markedly different from the parabolic behavior of the free electron when the κ value approaches a zone boundary. The full significance of this becomes clear later, when the acceleration properties are considered.

In Three Dimensions.   The form of the Brillouin zones in three dimensions are easily evaluated, using the applicable equation

$$\kappa_x n_1 + \kappa_y n_2 + \kappa_z n_3 = \frac{\pi}{a}(n_1^2 + n_2^2 + n_3^2) \qquad (7.26)$$

The first zone for a simple cubic lattice is clearly a cube intersecting the κ_x, κ_y, and κ_z axes at the points π/a. Analogously to the triangular form of the second zone in two dimensions, the second zone in three dimensions is obtained by adding a pyramid to each face of the first zone cube as illustrated in Fig. 7.24a.

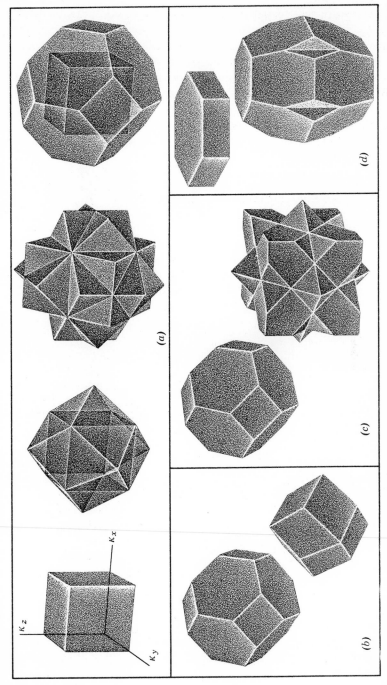

Figure 7.24   Three-dimensional Brillouin zones.   (a) The first four zones for a simple cubic lattice.   (b) The first two zones for a body-centered cubic lattice.   (c) The first two zones for a face-centered cubic lattice.   (d) The first two zones for a close-packed hexagonal lattice.

The zone structure for lattices other than simple cubic can be determined by simple extensions of equation 7.26, taking into account, for example, different lattice parameters in different directions. Figure 7.24 also illustrates some typical zone constructions.

We may notice in passing that the equations defining the boundaries of the Brillouin zones are identical with the interference conditions appropriate to Bragg reflection of a wave by the lattice. Such a condition obviously makes electron propagation through the lattice impossible and is consequently associated with the fact that the energy is undefined at the zone boundaries.

7.10   Constant Energy Curves and Surfaces

In one dimension the relation between energy and κ value (or momentum) is simply the curve given in Fig. 7.22. In two dimensions, however, we have an additional consideration. A line can be drawn in the κ plane as a locus of all points of equal energy. For the *completely free electron* the form of this line is simple. Since all points of equal κ value, that is, $\sqrt{\kappa_x{}^2 + \kappa_y{}^2}$ have the same energy, the curve is a *circle*. When, however, the electron is subject to a periodic potential and is therefore not completely free, we have seen that the E, κ relation is no longer simply parabolic, and for this case the loci of points with equal energy are shown in Fig. 7.25 for the first Brillouin zone of a square lattice. Since points close to the origin correspond to electrons with small momentum which suffer the least perturbation by the periodic lattice, the loci of equal energy will be circles near the center of the zone. For κ values that reach further out into the zone, the effect of the periodic perturbations becomes of greater importance and the curves of equal energy deviate markedly from circular form. The degree to which these curves deviate from circular depends, of course, on the strength of the electron binding (i.e., on the P value of equation 7.22); the stronger the binding the closer to the origin will departure from the circular form be found and vice versa.

The treatment giving the complete relation between E and κ for two- and three-dimensional lattices cannot be given here, but one result is that, in the neighborhood of the corners of the zone, the curves of equal energy approximate to circles centered on the corners.

This result gives rise to a very important new feature. Referring again to Fig. 7.25, consider first the change in energy along the direction AB. The energy must increase discontinuously as the zone boundary at B is crossed. Now consider the energy increase in the direction AC. A continuous increase in E with κ will be found, reaching at D the value corresponding to B. Now as the energy continues to increase from D, it may happen that the increase from D to C is greater than the discontinuous increase needed to cross the boundary at B. In other words the electron energy at C, just within the first zone, is greater than the energy just past B

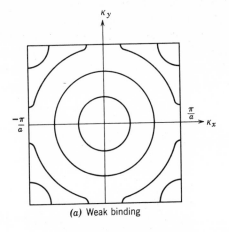

(a) Weak binding

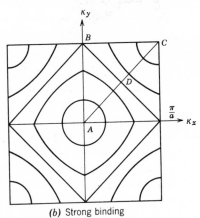

(b) Strong binding

Figure 7.25   Equal energy contours in the first Brillouin zone of a two-dimensional square lattice. (a) Weak binding. (b) Strong binding.

in the second zone. Here the *energy bands overlap*. This is often illustrated as in Fig. 7.26 where the energy is proportional to the vertical distance and different zones are shown by different hatching. Of course zone overlap can only occur in two or three dimensional lattices. It might appear at first that such overlap is more likely for strongly bound than for weakly bound electrons since, referring again to Fig. 7.25, the point D at which is found the same energy as at B is further from the corner C when the binding is stronger. We must not neglect the *size* of the energy discontinuity over the zone boundary at *B*, however. This discontinuity is greater for strong binding than for weak binding so that, overall, energy band overlap is more likely for weak binding than for strong binding.

If we extend the treatment to three dimensions, the constant energy contours that we have been discussing in two dimensions become surfaces. The significance of these surfaces is, as before in two dimensions, that if the κ vector of the electron terminates anywhere on the surface, the energy of the electron will be the same. For the free electron, the shape of the

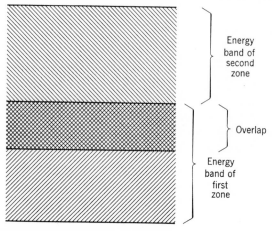

Figure 7.26   Overlapping energy bands.

surfaces is obvious—they are spheres, analogous to the circles seen at the center of the zones in Fig. 7.25. For the bound electron, however, the shapes are not simple and may become extremely complex. One of the simpler cases is illustrated in Fig. 8.17.

7.11   The Number of States in an Energy Band

In this chapter we have been concerned exclusively with the energies available to a single electron in various situations. We have said nothing about the total number of possibilities for an electron's κ value. To calculate the number of different wave functions which can be possessed by an electron in a lattice, that is, the number of different states it can occupy, consider a simple linear lattice. Let there be *N* atoms of spacing *a* so that the total length of the array is

$$d = Na$$

Now the wave function u, which must be periodic in distances of a or multiples of a, must be periodic in length d. This requires the wavelength of the wave function to satisfy such conditions as

$$\lambda = d,$$

$$\lambda = d/2,$$

$$\lambda = d/3, \text{ etc.}$$

or in general,

$$\lambda = \frac{d}{n}$$

The number of κ values is therefore obtained from the condition

$$\frac{1}{\lambda} = \frac{n}{d} = \frac{n}{Na} \quad \text{where} \quad n = \pm 1, \pm 2, \pm 3, \ldots$$

the different signs referring to opposite directions of propagation.

Now if we consider the first Brillouin zone only, the maximum value of κ is specified, and so the quantity we can calculate is the number of possible κ values in the first zone. The maximum κ value is given by

$$\kappa_{max} = \frac{\pi}{a}$$

that is,

$$\left(\frac{1}{\lambda}\right)_{max} = \frac{1}{2a}$$

whence

$$n_{max} = \frac{N}{2}$$

But each value of n appears twice because of the $\pm$ sign so that the total number of possible electron states in the first band is N. Note that this is consistent with the qualitative treatment given in Sections 7.4, 7.5, and 7.6 where we had two electron states for two wells or nuclei, three states for three centers, etc. Of course in the kind of sample we can use in practice, N is sufficiently large ($\sim 10^{24}$) that this enormous number of possible κ values is, to all intents and purposes, a continuous distribution. The foregoing result has been obtained for a linear lattice but can be shown to hold also for two or three dimensions where N is the total number of atoms involved. To avoid later confusion, it must be clearly noted at this stage that the previous calculation has given us the number of possible *wave functions* only. We have neglected spin throughout and consequently, in terms of the Pauli Principle, the N states can be occupied by $2N$ electrons.

7.12   Summary

The energy levels of an atom isolated in space are sharp. The influence of adjacent atoms is to spread out the levels into bands. The band spreading is least for inner levels where the range of the electron wave functions is least. The band spreading is greatest for upper levels. Each band so formed is associated with one of the levels of the single atom and is described by the same nomenclature ($2s$, $3d$, etc.).

The momentum state of a particular electron will depend on circumstances and will be one of the N states available in a single band. Given this value of κ, the energy of the electron will be determined by the E, κ relation (or vice versa, the momentum state will be similarly specified by the energy). As κ increases through certain values, discontinuous changes in energy occur from the top of one band to the bottom of the next, provided the bands do not overlap. The κ values defining the discontinuities are the limits of the Brillouin zones.

The properties of electrons in solids depend on the closeness of the associated κ vector to the Brillouin zone boundary, since it is close to the boundary that the departures from the free electron approximation are the most marked.

REFERENCES

L. V. Azaroff, *Introduction to Solids*, McGraw-Hill Book Company, New York, 1960.

A. J. Dekker, *Solid State Physics*, Prentice-Hall, Englewood Cliffs, N.J., 1957.

R. M. Eisberg, *Fundamentals of Modern Physics*, John Wiley and Sons, New York, 1961.

C. Kittel, *Introduction to Solid State Physics*, John Wiley and Sons, New York, 1956.

R. B. Leighton, *Principles of Modern Physics*, McGraw-Hill Book Company, New York, 1959.

N. F. Mott, and H. Jones, *The Theory of the Properties of Metals and Alloys*, Clarendon Press, Oxford, 1936.

M. J. Sinnot, *The Solid State for Engineers*, John Wiley and Sons, New York, 1958.

G. H. Wannier, *The Elements of Solid State Theory*, Cambridge University Press, Cambridge, 1959.

A. H. Wilson, *The Theory of Metals*, Cambridge University Press, Cambridge, 1953.

EXERCISES

1. Ultraviolet light of wavelength 500 Å falls on atomic hydrogen. With what velocity will an ejected electron leave the atom?
2. The electron in a hydrogen atom is in a state with $n = 3$. What is its energy? What are the possible values for its angular momentum? What is the wavelength of the photon emitted in a transition down to the state with $n = 1$?

3. Consider a two-dimensional square lattice of side 3 Å. At what electron momentum values do the sides of the first Brillouin zone come? What is the energy of a free electron with this momentum?

4. Delineate the boundaries of the fourth Brillouin zone for a two-dimensional square lattice.

5. Obtain the equations of the planes bounding the second Brillouin zone for a cubic lattice.

6. Obtain the equations of the planes bounding the first Brillouin zone for a close-packed hexagonal lattice.

8

The Distribution of

Electrons in Atoms and Solids

Chapter 7 is concerned with the behavior of a single electron in the nuclear fields of atoms and solids. We wish now to turn our attention to actual atoms and solids that contain not one but many electrons. It will appear that the differences which are found arise because there are restrictions on the way in which a number of electrons can occupy the available energies in a system. For our purpose the dominant feature is the way in which the electrons are distributed among the various energy levels, and this will be our first concern.

8.1 The Pauli Principle and the Fermi Distribution Function

Distribution functions are of common occurrence in physics. They always arise when we are considering assemblies of large numbers of particles. When we deal with a system containing only a few particles, it is possible to describe the system item by item. For instance, we might say that on a particular billiard table there is one ball at a certain place with a certain velocity, another at another place with its velocity, and so on. In solids with 10^{28} particles per cubic meter such detailed knowledge becomes meaningless and impossible to obtain. It is normally preferable to ask questions about *how many* particles are involved. For example, in considering a mass of gas we might ask how many particles, on the average, are contained in a certain volume, or how many in a certain volume have a particular energy, and so on. Such statistical information is just as useful for determining overall assembly properties as detailed information would be if it were possible to obtain. The application of such statistical methods to gas kinetic theory is probably familiar to the reader in the form first enunciated by Boltzmann and Maxwell.

There exists, however, an essential difference between the distribution of energies among the atoms or molecules of a gas and the distribution of energies among the electrons of atoms or solids. In classical gas kinetic theory there is no restriction on the way in which the available energy can be shared among the molecules. The application of such a simple unrestricted distribution to the electrons in a solid leads, however, to quite obvious contradictions with experimental observation. One of the most striking of these concerns the heat capacity of metals. Gas kinetic theory would predict a contribution to the heat capacity of the metal from each of the mobile electrons of $\frac{1}{2}k$ for each degree of freedom, where k is the Boltzmann constant. This large contribution is not observed. Many other examples of the failure of Maxwell-Boltzmann statistics when applied to electrons in solids could be cited.

The appropriate way of dealing with electrons evolved from a suggestion made by Pauli in 1925 concerning the distribution of energies among the electrons in an atom. The Pauli principle may be stated as follows: *in any particular system no more than two electrons may have the same set of quantum numbers n, l, and m_l, and these two electrons must have opposite spin*. In other words, no more than two electrons in a system can have a particular wave function.

On the basis of this new principle it is possible to work out, in a fashion analogous to gas kinetic theory, the way in which a large number of electrons in a system will be distributed among the available energies. The distribution, derived first by Fermi, will be merely quoted. The probability $F(E)$ for the occupation of a particular energy level is given by

$$F(E) = \frac{1}{e^{(E-E_F)/kT} + 1} \tag{8.1}$$

Here $F(E)$ is called the *Fermi function*, E is the energy of the level, E_F is the *Fermi level* and is a constant for the particular system concerned.

Figure 8.1 shows the shape of the Fermi function at the temperature $T = 0°K$. Function $F(E)$ has the value unity for $E < E_F$ and zero for $E > E_F$. Thus at $T = 0$, all levels with an energy less than E_F will be completely filled and those above E_F will be completely empty. For the special case in which the electrons have a continuous range of energy available to them, E_F has the significance of being the maximum energy of filled states at $T = 0°K$. This will not be true where the electrons do not have a continuous energy range available, that is, if there are gaps in the energy spectrum. Such cases will be encountered later when we discuss semiconductors. Furthermore, E_F is the energy of the highest filled state only at $T = 0°K$; the finite temperature case will be described later. Unless we are dealing with a continuous electron energy distribution at

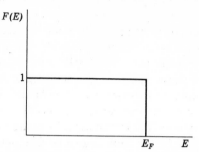

Figure 8.1 The Fermi distribution function at $T = 0$.

$T = 0°K$, the quantity E_F does not have an easily identifiable significance. It is merely a constant of the system which can be evaluated by methods to be discussed later. Notice, however, that at any finite temperature $F(E) = \frac{1}{2}$ for $E = E_F$.

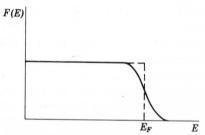

Figure 8.2 The Fermi distribution function at a finite temperature.

It is common to define a temperature T_F by the relation

$$kT_F = E_F \tag{8.2}$$

where k is Boltzmann's constant. Temperature T_F is called the Fermi temperature and is a constant of the system.

Figure 8.2 shows the Fermi function for a finite temperature. The curve differs from that of Fig. 8.1 in the smearing of the drop from value 1 to value 0. In actual fact, the extent of the smearing is very small except for very high temperatures. This can be seen by considering a specific point on the curve, say for $F(E) = 0.2$. The energy E' for this value of $F(E)$ is easily seen to be given by

$$(E' - E_F) = 1.39\, kT$$

Thus the extent of the smearing is of the order of kT whereas the distribution as a whole has a dimension of E_F (or kT_F). Thus the smearing is small in scale compared with the distribution as long as $T < T_F$.

The table of T_F values (Table 8.3) shows that the condition $T \ll T_F$ holds for most materials at room temperature. Only by heating materials into the thousands of degrees does the smearing of the Fermi function become comparable with the scale of the distribution as a whole. It will be seen later, however, that if we are considering the conditions very close to E_F, the very small degree of smearing even at room temperature can become very significant.

If, at a finite temperature, we consider the top of the distribution where we can write

$$E - E_F \gg kT$$

we may be able to ignore the constant of unity in the denominator and write

$$F(E) = e^{-(E-E_F)/kT}$$

This simplified form is identical with the Boltzmann distribution, which is valid for a classical gas. Thus, at high temperatures the top of the Fermi distribution can be approximated by the classical statistics, and this can frequently simplify such calculations. We refer to the "Boltzmann tail" of the distribution.

The Fermi function does not, by itself, give us the number of electrons which have a certain energy, for it gives us only the probability of occupation of an energy state by a single electron. To know the actual number of electrons with a given energy we must also know the number of states in the system which have the energy under consideration. Then by multiplying the number of states by the probability of occupation we get the actual number of electrons. If $N(E)$ is the number of electrons in a system that have energy E and $Z(E)$ is the number of states at that energy, then

$$N(E)\, dE = Z(E)F(E)\, dE \qquad (8.3)$$

$Z(E)$, of course, is a function of the system.

At this point we can see that the value of the Fermi energy E_F can be obtained from the number of electrons in the system and on the distribution of states along the energy scale. For if, at $T = 0$, we start to create the system by adding electrons, the lower states will be filled first, and the energy of the state into which any electron has to go will depend on the number of states at the lower energies and the extent to which they are already filled by electrons. If few states are available at each energy, the energy of the last electrons to be added will rise rapidly. If many states are available, the energy will increase only slowly. Thus if the state distribution function $Z(E)$ is known, the value of E_F can be calculated for a certain total number of electrons. This calculation follows from the relation for N, the total number of electrons:

$$N = \int_0^{E_F} N(E)\, dE$$

$$= \int_0^{E_F} Z(E)F(E)\, dE \qquad (8.4)$$

This relation would give the value of E_F at absolute zero, and for finite temperatures a similar calculation (integrating from $E = 0$ to $E \to \infty$) will yield the appropriate value of E_F. A knowledge of $Z(E)$ is thus of fundamental importance, and this will now be discussed for several systems.

8.2 The Distribution of Electrons in Atoms

To calculate the number of states available in a single, isolated atom, recall the quantum numbers which were obtained for the hydrogen atom. The energy was determined by n and, within each state thus defined, sub-states were defined, first by l which could run from 0 to $n-1$, and second by m_l which could run from $-l$ to $+l$. The theory, of course, said nothing about multielectron atoms, and indeed there exists no general exact solution for these cases. It is possible, however, to systematize the solution for the multielectron atom by using the quantum number notation for the states of the hydrogen atom. The analogy breaks down in several places when applied to multielectron atoms. We will, however, use it and begin by assuming that the energy of the state increases with increasing n.

If only two electrons may be given the same values of n, l, and m_l, the number of states at each energy level (i.e., n value) must follow the scheme laid out in Table 8.1.

Let us now assume that the level density scheme in Table 8.1 can be applied to multielectron atoms. We shall discuss the energies of the various states in a moment, but in the meantime let us concentrate on the way in which the levels are filled up. For a particular multielectron atom the distribution of electrons among the various levels is now obtained by applying the Fermi function, in that at $T = 0$ the lowest states will be filled up far enough to accommodate the electrons, and the higher states will be empty.

Let us take sodium as an example. Sodium has a nuclear charge of eleven times the electronic charge. Let us take a sodium nucleus and build up the atom by adding the outer electrons in turn. The first electron will fall into the lowest state, that is, $n = 1$, $l = 0$, $m_l = 0$. It will be a $1s$ electron. The next will do the same. The third electron is excluded from the $1s$ level by the Pauli principle; it therefore goes into the $n = 2$ shell.

Table 8.1

$n = 1$	$l = 0$	$m_l = 0$		} 2 states
$n = 2$	$l = 0$	$m_l = 0$	2 states	
	$l = 1$	$m_l = -1$	2 states	8 states
		$m_l = 0$	2 states	
		$m_l = 1$	2 states	
$n = 3$	$l = 0$	$m_l = 0$	2 states	
	$l = 1$	$m_l = -1$	2 states	
		$m_l = 0$	2 states	
		$m_l = 1$	2 states	
	$l = 2$	$m_l = -2$	2 states	18 states
		$m_l = -1$	2 states	
		$m_l = 0$	2 states	
		$m_l = 1$	2 states	
		$m_l = 2$	2 states	

So does the next electron and so on until eight electrons are in $n = 2$. We have now accounted for ten electrons. We need to supply one more electron to complete the neutral sodium atom. It must go into the $n = 3$ shell, and it will be a $3s$ electron in its ground state. The result of this process is a sodium atom with two $1s$ electrons, two $2s$ electrons, six $2p$ electrons and one $3s$ electron. Let us now consider the energy levels occupied by these electrons.

The $1s$ electrons find themselves in the field of a nuclear charge of 11. Remembering equation 7.12, we will see that the $n = 1$ shell of sodium is approximately 120 times as tightly bound as the $n = 1$ shell in the hydrogen atom. The electrons in the $n = 2$ shell have wave functions (as shown for the H atom in Fig. 7.4) which are mostly *outside* the wave functions of the $n = 1$ shell. Consequently, the positive nuclear charge is partially neutralized as far as the $n = 2$ electrons are concerned, and this is termed "screening." The $n = 2$ electrons therefore move in a field with an effective nuclear charge of approximately $Z = 9$ (the screening is not complete because of the spread of the wave function, and so the effective nuclear charge is a little over 9). Consequently this $n = 2$ level must be (because of equation 7.12) approximately eighty times as tightly bound as the $n = 2$ level in atomic hydrogen.

The foregoing considerations lead to two conclusions. First, the inner shells of multielectron atoms are tightly bound, and second, the gaps between the inner energy levels are large. For example E_1 for sodium is about -1630 eV and E_2 about -270 eV, and so the photon emitted in a transition between $n = 2$ and $n = 1$ in sodium has an energy of approximately 1360 eV, with a wavelength of about 8 Å. This is in the X-ray region and, in general terms, transitions between the inner levels of multielectron atoms will give radiation in the X-ray region with a wavelength that decreases as the atomic number of the element increases.

X-ray spectroscopists have a nomenclature for the levels which runs

$n = 1$	K shell
$n = 2$	L shell
$n = 3$	M shell
$n = 4$	N shell
etc.,	

Thus the X-rays emitted in the transitions between $n = 2$ and $n = 1$, $n = 3$ and $n = 1$, $n = 4$ and $n = 1$, etc., are known as the K series, the transitions down to $n = 2$ as the L series and so on. Since the energy gaps between the various shells are dependent on Z, the atomic number, the X-ray spectrum is characteristic of the atom producing the X-rays. These characteristic X-rays are the basis of identification of elements by X-ray methods.

For transitions to take place between these normally filled levels of the atom, an electron must first be removed from an inner shell, thus allowing electrons from upper levels to fall into the lower state, emitting parts of the X-ray spectrum as they do so. Such ionization of the inner levels of an atom can be accomplished by bombarding the atom by a sufficiently energetic electron. The probability of such ionization of a particular shell is clearly zero if the energy of the bombarding electron is less than the energy of binding of the electron in the atom. If the energy of the bombarding electron is increased up to the required value, the probability of ionization rises abruptly as shown in Fig. 8.3. Thereafter, further increase of the bombarding electron's energy will, even though there is sufficient energy for ionization, actually give a declining probability of ionization. This curve should be compared with Fig. 2.2, which shows (by the dotted line) the probability of atomic ionization by a photon.

The preceding paragraphs have been concerned with the electrons in the inner levels. The single 3s electron in sodium is in a rather different position. Its wave functions are concentrated outside the $n = 1$ and $n = 2$ shell, giving screening to the extent that the effective nuclear charge is close to one. This electron is therefore, by comparison, very loosely bound at around 5 eV. This electron is responsible for the optical as opposed to the X-ray spectrum of the atom. It produces the optical spectrum by transitions between various excited levels above its $3s$ ground state, where a feature appears that is not found in the X-ray levels. The inner levels are bound so tightly that they are relatively unaffected by differences in l

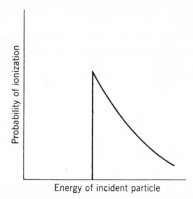

Figure 8.3   The probability that an energetic particle will ionize an atom from one particular shell.

value. Thus all the $n = 2$ levels are approximately at the same energy. But the single outer electron experiences screening (and consequently binding), which depends very much on the detailed shape of the wave functions and consequently the excited levels, are very dependent on the l value of the state. The excited levels for the outer electron of sodium are shown in Fig. 8.4.

The influence of temperature on the sodium atom can be seen by applying the temperature dependence of $F(E)$ illustrated in Fig. 8.2. It is obvious that, in view of the discrete nature of the levels, the system is not going to be affected by temperature until the tail of the Fermi function reaches the next occupiable level. Since the average thermal energy (measured by kT) at room temperature is about 0.025 eV, and the gap between the ground state in sodium and the first excited is about 2 eV, the probability of excitation of a sodium atom at room temperature is effectively zero. It takes a temperature of at least 1000°K to make kT comparable with the energy gap and so to give appreciable excitation.

Thus, to summarize, the electronic system is completely condensed into the lowest states at all normal temperatures, and at higher temperatures the relative populations of the occupied levels can be calculated by use of the Fermi function. This is a satisfactory description of many of the physical and chemical properties of atoms.

The chemical properties, in particular, follow from the dependence of the binding between electron and nucleus on the quantum number state of the electron. In the case of sodium, discussed earlier, the binding of the outermost electron is weak, and it is therefore more readily removed permitting easy chemical reaction. All atoms that have this configuration will share this chemical property. Thus the *alkali metals*, lithium with one

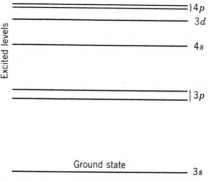

Figure 8.4   The excited optical levels of atomic sodium (not accurately to scale).

electron in $n = 2$, sodium with one electron in $n = 3$, potassium with one electron in $n = 4$, etc., will all be chemically reactive. If, on the other hand, an atom is such that its outermost shell is just full, the nuclear binding is relatively strong. The structure is then such that there is little tendency from such an atom to share electrons with other atoms. The resulting chemical inertness is characteristic of the *rare gases*, helium, neon, argon, etc. Any atom just short of having a complete shell will be chemically reactive. Thus the *halogens*, fluorine with seven electrons in $n = 2$, chlorine with seven electrons in $n = 3$, etc., will tend to share electrons by accepting one to form the stable structure of the closed shell. Electrons are readily shared by the halogens in chemical combination with the alkali metals. The *valence* of the elements arises naturally out of this description as the number of electrons outside a closed shell or the number required to complete a closed shell. The valence of the alkali metals and halogens thus will be one, and for the elements that have a deficiency or excess of two electrons such as magnesium, calcium, oxygen, etc., the valence is two. The tendency of some elements to form ions in gases or solution is again simply the same property. If an electron is easily removed, *positive ions* of unit charge are formed; if a closed shell can be completed by the addition of electrons, *negative ions* are readily formed.

We have seen in Table 8.1 that a simple scheme of allocating electrons in multielectron atoms to particular energy levels results from using the atomic hydrogen quantum number structure. The scheme is a good representation of the levels in elements at the beginning of the periodic table. Let us make a brief survey of the periodic table from this point of view.

In hydrogen and helium the $n = 1$ shell is occupied respectively by one and two $1s$ electrons. In lithium, beryllium, boron, carbon, nitrogen, oxygen, fluorine, and neon the $n = 2$ shell is occupied by $2s$ and $2p$ electrons up to a total of two and six respectively. The $n = 3$ shell is occupied from sodium onward by adding first two $2s$ electrons and then six $2p$ electrons to give finally at argon eighteen electrons in the shell. At this stage we might expect the next electrons to be $3d$, but this does not happen. The energies of this complicated structure containing a nucleus and nineteen electrons are such that the energy of the $4s$ state is then lower than that of the $3d$ state, and in potassium the outermost electron is in a $4s$ state, leaving ten $3d$ states empty. Thus these are two chemical periods of eight elements each when we would expect, on the basis of the quantum-number structure, one of eight and a second one of eighteen elements.

The structure of the elements just past potassium is important. Calcium adds a second $4s$ electron leaving the $3d$ level still empty. Then from scandium onward the elements titanium, vanadium, chromium, manganese, iron, cobalt, nickel, and copper fill up the $3d$ shell until it is just full at copper. The partially filled $3d$ level is responsible for many of the striking properties of the so-called *transition elements*, in particular the high magnetic moment and ferromagnetic character of iron, cobalt, and nickel.

Other unfilled spaces in the quantum number structure exist and account for departures from a simple periodicity in the chemical properties. The most striking of these is in the *rare earth group* in which the $4f$ shell is being filled while eleven electrons are occupying levels ranging from $5s$ to $6p$. Such shielding of the $4f$ shell from the outside of the atom produces almost complete chemical indistinguishability of these elements, although other properties that arise from the $4f$ level, such as the magnetic moment, may be very different.

The evidence for the quantum number structure quoted previously is obtained from spectroscopic magnetic and other measurements and makes it possible to obtain the quantum number structure, even if a detailed theoretical treatment is impossible. The complete electronic structure of the elements is given in Table 8.2.

Table 8.2   The Electronic Structure of Atoms

ATOMIC NUM-BER	ELE-MENT SYM-BOL	NUMBER OF ELECTRONS										IONIZA-TION ENERGY, eV	ATOMIC RADIUS, Å	MAGNETIC SUSCEP-TIBILITY
		K	L		M			N						
		1s	2s	2p	3s	3p	3d	4s	4p	4d	4f			
1	H	1										13.53	0.53	-1.97×10^{-6}
2	He	2										24.47	0.30	-0.47
3	Li	2	1									5.37	1.50	$+0.50$
4	Be	2	2									9.28	1.19	-1.00
5	B	2	2	1								8.25	0.85	-0.69
6	C	2	2	2								11.20	0.66	-0.49
7	N	2	2	3								14.47	0.53	-0.8
8	O	2	2	4								13.55	0.45	$+106.2$
9	F	2	2	5								18.6	0.38	
10	Ne	2	2	6								21.47	0.32	-0.33
11	Na	2	2	6	1							5.12	1.55	$+0.51$
12	Mg	2	2	6	2							7.61	1.32	$+0.55$
13	Al	2	2	6	2	1						5.96	1.21	$+0.65$
14	Si	2	2	6	2	2						8.08	1.06	-0.13
15	P	2	2	6	2	3						11.11	0.92	-0.90
16	S	2	2	6	2	4						10.31	0.82	-0.49
17	Cl	2	2	6	2	5						12.96	0.75	-0.57
18	A	2	2	6	2	6						15.69	0.67	-0.48
19	K	2	2	6	2	6	—	1				4.32	2.20	$+0.52$
20	Ca	2	2	6	2	6	—	2				6.09	2.03	$+1.10$
21	Sc	2	2	6	2	6	1	2				6.7	1.80	
22	Ti	2	2	6	2	6	2	2				6.81	1.66	$+1.25$
23	V	2	2	6	2	6	3	2				6.76	1.52	$+1.4$
24	Cr	2	2	6	2	6	5	1				6.74	1.41	$+3.08$
25	Mn	2	2	6	2	6	5	2				7.40	1.31	$+11.8$
26	Fe	2	2	6	2	6	6	2				7.83	1.22	Ferromag.
27	Co	2	2	6	2	6	7	2				8.5	1.14	Ferromag.
28	Ni	2	2	6	2	6	8	2				7.61	1.07	Ferromag.
29	Cu	2	2	6	2	6	10	1				7.68	1.03	-0.086
30	Zn	2	2	6	2	6	10	2				9.36	0.97	-0.157
31	Ga	2	2	6	2	6	10	2	1			5.97	1.13	-0.24
32	Ge	2	2	6	2	6	10	2	2			8.09	1.06	-0.12
33	As	2	2	6	2	6	10	2	3			10.5	1.01	-0.31
34	Se	2	2	6	2	6	10	2	4			9.70	0.95	-0.32
35	Br	2	2	6	2	6	10	2	5			11.30	0.90	-0.39
36	Kr	2	2	6	2	6	10	2	6	—	—	13.94	0.86	-0.35

(N.B. The magnetic susceptibility values in this table are in cgs units. To convert to mks units, multiply the cgs value by 4π.)

Table 8.2 (continued)

ATOMIC NUMBER	ELEMENT SYMBOL	NUMBER OF ELECTRONS										IONIZATION ENERGY, eV	ATOMIC RADIUS, Å	MAGNETIC SUSCEPTIBILITY
		N				O					P			
		4s	4p	4d	4f	5s	5p	5d	5f	5g	6s			
37	Rb	2	6	—	—	1	—	—	—	—	—	4.16		$+0.21 \times 10^{-6}$
38	Sr	2	6	—	—	2	—	—	—	—	—	5.67		−0.20
39	Y	2	6	1	—	2						6.5		+5.3
40	Zr	2	6	2	—	2						6.92		−0.45
41	Nb	2	6	4	—	1						6.8		+1.5
42	Mo	2	6	5	—	1						7.06		+0.04
43	Tc	2	6	6	—	1						7.1		
44	Ru	2	6	7	—	1						7.7		+0.50
45	Rh	2	6	8	—	1						7.7		+1.11
46	Pd	2	6	10	—	—						8.3		+5.4
47	Ag	2	6	10	—	1						7.54		−0.20
48	Cd	2	6	10	—	2						8.96		−0.18
49	In	2	6	10	—	2	1					5.76		−0.11
50	Sn	2	6	10	—	2	2					7.30		−0.25
51	Sb	2	6	10	—	2	3					8.35		−0.87
52	Te	2	6	10	—	2	4					8.96		−0.31
53	I	2	6	10	—	2	5					10.44		−0.36
54	Xe	2	6	10	—	2	6					12.08		−0.34
55	Cs	2	6	10	—	2	6				1	3.87		−0.22
56	Ba	2	6	10	—	2	6				2	5.19		+0.9
57	La	2	6	10	—	2	6	1			2	5.59		+1.04
58	Ce	2	6	10	2	2	6	—			2	6.54		+15.0
59	Pr	2	6	10	3	2	6	—			2	5.8		+25.0
60	Nd	2	6	10	4	2	6	—			2	6.3		+36.0
61	Pm	2	6	10	5	2	6	—			2	6.3		
62	Sm	2	6	10	6	2	6	—			2	6.6		
63	Eu	2	6	10	7	2	6	—			2	5.64		+22.0
64	Gd	2	6	10	7	2	6	1			2	6.7		Ferromag.
65	Tb	2	6	10	8	2	6	1			2	6.7		
66	Dy	2	6	10	9	2	6	1			2	6.8		Ferromag.
67	Ho	2	6	10	10	2	6	1			2			
68	Er	2	6	10	11	2	6	1			2			
69	Tm	2	6	10	12	2	6	1			2			
70	Yb	2	6	10	13	2	6	1			2	6.2		
71	Lu	2	6	10	14	2	6	1			2	5.0		
72	Hf	2	6	10	14	2	6	2	—	—	2	5.5		

(N.B. The magnetic susceptibility values in this table are in cgs units. To convert to mks units, multiply the cgs value by 4π.)

Table 8.2 (continued)

ATOMIC NUMBER	ELEMENT SYMBOL	NUMBER OF ELECTRONS										IONIZATION ENERGY, eV	ATOMIC RADIUS, Å	MAGNETIC SUSCEPTIBILITY
		O				P				Q				
		$5p$	$5d$	$5f$	$5g$	$6s$	$6p$	$6d$	$6f$	$7s$	$7p$			
73	Ta	6	3	—	—	2	—	—	—	—	—	6.0		$+0.87 \times 10^{-6}$
74	W	6	4			2						8.1		$+0.28$
75	Re	6	5			2						7.85		
76	Os	6	6			2						8.7		$+0.05$
77	Ir	6	9			0						9.2		$+0.15$
78	Pt	6	9			1						8.9		$+1.10$
79	Au	6	10			1						9.20		-0.15
80	Hg	6	10			2						10.38		-0.168
81	Tl	6	10			2	1					6.07		-0.24
82	Pb	6	10			2	2					7.38		-0.12
83	Bi	6	10			2	3					8.0		-1.35
84	Po	6	10			2	4					7.25		
85	At	6	10			2	5					9.4		
86	Rn	6	10			2	6					10.69		
87	Fr	6	10			2	6			1		4.0		
88	Ra	6	10			2	6			2		5.25		
89	Ac	6	10			2	6	1		2				
90	Th	6	10			2	6	2		2			0.95	$+0.11$
91	Pa	6	10			2	6	3		2		5.7	0.91	$+2.6$
92	U	6	10			2	6	4		2		4.0	0.89	$+1.73$
93	Np	6	10	5		2	6	—		2			0.88	
94	Pu	6	10	5		2	6	1		2			0.86	
95	Am	6	10	6		2	6	1		2			0.85	
96	Cm	6	10	7		2	6	1		2				
97	Bk	6	10	8		2	6	1		2				
98	Cf	6	10	9		2	6	1		2				
99	—	6	10	10		2	6	1		2				
100	—	6	10	11		2	6	1		2				

(N.B. The magnetic susceptibility values in this table are in cgs units. To convert to mks units, multiply the cgs value by 4π.)

8.3   The Distribution Function for Free Electrons

In Section 8.2 we have considered the distribution of electrons in a single atom. We now wish to extend this to a solid, but the procedure is not obvious. Our considerations of the binding energy of the various atom shells suggests that for the inner shells we can ignore the spreading of the levels, which arises from the solid structure. We are left then with only the valence electron or electrons to consider. Their looser binding suggests that the Kronig-Penny treatment may be applicable. But the Kronig-Penny treatment given in Chapter 7 referred to a single electron. At this stage we want to consider the distribution among the available energies of a large number of electrons. It was demonstrated in Section 7.10 that the total number of electrons that could be accommodated within the first Brillouin zone was $2N$ where N is the number of nuclei in the sample. For the application of equation 8.3, however, we require not so much the total number of states available as the state density function $Z(E)$. Unfortunately this is not easy to calculate for conditions treated in Sections 7.7 to 7.10. Because of this difficulty we shall perform a simpler calculation and then discuss its relevance to actual solids. The simplification consists of calculating the state density function for an assembly of completely free electrons, which we shall call an electron gas.

The potential function that defines a free electron in a solid is a rectangular well of the dimensions of the sample under consideration. Thus the problem of a free electron gas is just that of an electron in a box, considered in Section 6.4. There it was shown that a single electron confined in one direction to a space a may have energy levels given by

$$E_n = \frac{n^2 h^2}{8ma^2} \tag{8.5}$$

It is clear that the spacing of the levels depends on a. If a is small, the energies E_n rise rapidly as n increases, and the spacing between the levels is large. If, on the other hand, a is large, the spacing is small. This is shown in Fig. 8.5. It will emerge that when a is of sample dimensions, say cms, the number of levels becomes so enormous as virtually to constitute a continuum.

Let us now calculate how many levels there are in a range of energies dE at energy E. The result should be valid for three dimensions so that we write, without proof, the extended form of equation 8.5 applicable to a cube of side a

$$E = \frac{h^2}{8ma^2} (n_x^2 + n_y^2 + n_z^2) \tag{8.6}$$

where n_x, n_y, and n_z are integers. Thus states of the same energy can be constructed by various choices of the values for n_x, n_y, and n_z, and it is this multiplicity that provides a number of states all with the same energy, that is, a state density. We must calculate how many choices of these integers there are to give energies lying within a certain range of energy dE at energy E.

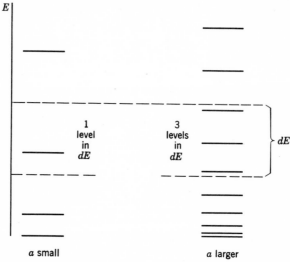

Figure 8.5   The energy levels of an electron in a box as a function of box size.

To perform this calculation, construct a space of points represented by the values n_x, n_y, and n_z. In this space the radius from the origin to a point (n_x, n_y, n_z) is given by n where

$$n^2 = n_x{}^2 + n_y{}^2 + n_z{}^2 \tag{8.7}$$

Each point at this radius gives the same value of E, and so a volume element which is a spherical shell of thickness dn at radius n will give a measure of the number of states in the energy range dE at E. The volume of the shell is clearly $4\pi n^2\,dn$, and since only positive values of n_x, n_y, and n_z have any meaning, the number of states $Z(E)\,dE$ will be given by one-eighth of that volume. Thus

$$Z(E)\,dE = \tfrac{1}{2}\pi n^2\,dn \tag{8.8}$$

Using the value of n from equation 8.5, we obtain

$$dn = \frac{1}{2}\left(\frac{8ma^2}{h^2}\right)^{\!\frac{1}{2}} E^{-\frac{1}{2}}\,dE$$

Hence

$$Z(E)\,dE = \frac{1}{2}\pi\left(\frac{8ma^2}{h^2}\right)E\cdot\frac{1}{2}\left(\frac{8ma^2}{h^2}\right)^{\frac{1}{2}}E^{-\frac{1}{2}}\,dE$$

$$= \frac{\pi}{4}\left(\frac{8ma^2}{h^2}\right)^{\frac{3}{2}}E^{\frac{1}{2}}\,dE \tag{8.9}$$

It should be remembered that the Pauli exclusion principle permits two electrons in each state so that the number of energy states which can be filled is

$$Z(E)\,dE = \frac{\pi}{2}\left(\frac{8ma^2}{h^2}\right)^{\frac{3}{2}}E^{\frac{1}{2}}\,dE \tag{8.10}$$

In terms of the volume V available to the electrons $(=a^3)$ this becomes

$$Z(E)\,dE = \frac{\pi}{2}\left(\frac{8m}{h^2}\right)^{\frac{3}{2}}VE^{\frac{1}{2}}\,dE \tag{8.11}$$

This simple parabolic function is illustrated in Fig. 8.6.

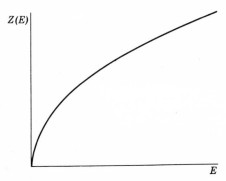

Figure 8.6　The state density for a free electron gas.

The number of states $Z(E)\,dE$ in a volume of $10^{-6}\,\text{m}^3$ lying below an energy of 1 eV will now be calculated.

$$\text{The number of states} = \int_0^E Z(E)\,dE = \frac{\pi}{2}\left(\frac{8m}{h^2}\right)^{\frac{3}{2}}V\int_0^E E^{\frac{1}{2}}\,dE$$

$$= \frac{\pi}{2}\left(\frac{8m}{h^2}\right)^{\frac{3}{2}}V\frac{2}{3}E^{\frac{3}{2}} = 4.6 \times 10^{21}$$

Thus in spite of the exclusion principle, an enormous number of electrons can occupy a volume of $10^{-6}\,\text{m}^3$ before the energy of the top level reaches 1 eV. These state numbers are high enough so that all the valence electrons in a metal can be accommodated without the Fermi energy rising above a few eV in all cases.

We should notice here that, although we do not require the result at the present moment, we can write equation 8.11 in terms of momentum instead of energy. Replacing E by $p^2/2m$ and dE by $p\,dp/m$ we obtain for unit volume

$$Z(p)\,dp = \frac{8\pi}{h^3}\,p^2\,dp. \tag{8.11a}$$

This result will be used in the discussion of thermionic emission in Chapter 9.

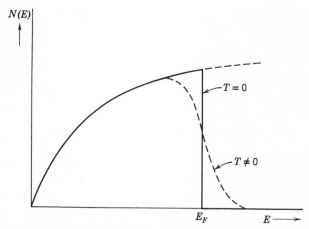

Figure 8.7   The population density for a free electron gas.

The actual number of electrons $N(E)\,dE$ in a given energy range will now be obtained by multiplying the state density $Z(E)\,dE$ by the Fermi function. Thus

$$N(E)\,dE = \frac{\pi}{2}\left(\frac{8m}{h^2}\right)^{3/2} V E^{1/2} \frac{1}{e^{(E-E_F)/kT} + 1} \tag{8.12}$$

This distribution is shown in Fig. 8.7. At absolute zero the distribution is simple, all states up to the Fermi level will be filled and those above E_F will be empty. At higher temperatures the typical tailing appears, the extent of this tailing being, of course, very small compared with the scale of the distribution until very high temperatures are reached.

Whenever the actual state density is known it is possible to calculate the Fermi level. The calculation is possible at any temperature but is particularly simple at $T = 0°$K because of the simple numerical value of $F(E)$.

At $T = 0$ for N free electrons we have

$$N = \int_0^{E_F} N(E)\, dE$$

$$= \int_0^{E_F} \frac{\pi}{2}\left(\frac{8m}{h^2}\right)^{\frac{3}{2}} V E^{\frac{1}{2}} \frac{1}{e^{(E-E_F)/kT} + 1}$$

Remembering that at $T = 0$ the Fermi function has value unity, the integration is easily carried out to yield

$$E_F = \left(\frac{h^2}{2m}\right)\left(\frac{3N}{8\pi}\right)^{\frac{2}{3}} \tag{8.13}$$

if we now specify that N is the number of electrons per unit volume.

Table 8.3

MATERIAL	NUMBER OF FREE ELECTRONS PER m^3	E_F eV	T_F °K
Li	4.6×10^{28}	4.72	5.5×10^4
Na	2.5	3.12	3.6
K	1.3	2.14	2.5
Rb	1.1	1.82	2.1
Cs	0.85	1.53	1.8
Cu	8.5	7.04	8.2
Ag	5.8	5.51	6.4
Au	5.9	5.54	6.4

This Fermi energy is a very important and useful quantity, because whenever we can use the free electron model, which is quite often, the value for E_F obtained gives us (at $T = 0$) the energy at which the topmost electrons will be found.

For example, if we assume that the single-valence electron of sodium is completely free, we can calculate the Fermi energy for sodium. The number N of atoms per unit volume is approximately 5×10^{28} m^{-3} giving a value for E_F of 4.96×10^{-19} joule or 3.1 eV. This energy relates only to the electrons considered to be free, that is, the valence electrons, and is consequently the energy difference between the bottom of the valence levels and the top of the distribution. Values for E_F and T_F for various materials are given in Table 8.3.

8.4 State Densities in Actual Solids

We are now ready to attempt the evaluation of the state densities, and ultimately the electron population, of actual multielectron atoms combined in a solid. We have given a generalized treatment of the energy levels of a single electron in a periodic potential, and this had as its two limiting cases the tightly bound electron with its sharp energy levels characteristic of an isolated atom, and the free electron for where the binding was negligible and the energy level distribution is virtually continuous. We have also considered how the electrons are packed into the available energy levels for the case where large numbers of electrons must be considered. Since there is no general solution to the final problem of actual multielectron atoms in actual solids, our task is to select, for each part of the electron structure, the appropriate model to serve as the best approximation.

The basis for such a choice lies in the binding experienced by the electrons. The electrons in the inner shells will experience strong binding from the nuclear charges whereas the valence electrons will be less tightly bound. For the latter it may be possible to use the free electron approximation.

Most of the considerations listed below have already been discussed, but it is helpful to summarize the whole discussion at this point. Let us consider the energy level distribution in 10^{-3} kg of sodium. There are approximately 10^{23} nuclei each of charge eleven times the electronic charge. The number of electrons is 11×10^{23}. Let us consider the first 10^{23} electrons and assume them distributed one each among the atoms. In the $n = 1$ shell each electron will experience a nuclear charge of eleven and will as a consequence be very tightly bound. From equation 7.12 we saw that the binding energy was proportional to Z^2 and so the inner level electrons in sodium are approximately 120 times as tightly bound as the electron in hydrogen. Transitions into such levels would be well into the X-ray region of wavelength. The next 10^{23} electrons will go into the $n = 1$ shell. Again the wave functions will be those appropriate to the right-hand side of Fig. 8.15 and the energy levels will be sharp.

The $n = 1$ shell is now full and the next 10^{23} electrons must go into the $n = 2$ levels. Here they each experience a nuclear field that is diminished by the screening of the inner two electrons already added. However, the effective nuclear charge is approximately nine and this still constitutes very tight binding. The $n = 2$ level also is thus relatively sharp. As seven more electrons per atom are added the $n = 2$ shell fills, each electron experiencing a nuclear charge of approximately nine and the level remaining sharp. The last 10^{23} electrons to be added must go into the $n = 3$ shell. Here each experiences an effective nuclear charge of approximately one, the binding is no longer tight, and the levels are spread into bands. The complete diagram of the energy levels as a function of lattice spacing is given in Fig. 8.8.

We must still consider the problem of the state density in the band. As we have already pointed out at the beginning of Section 8.3 it is not easy to calculate the state density throughout the whole first Brillouin zone for a bound electron. We have done so, however for a free electron, and this

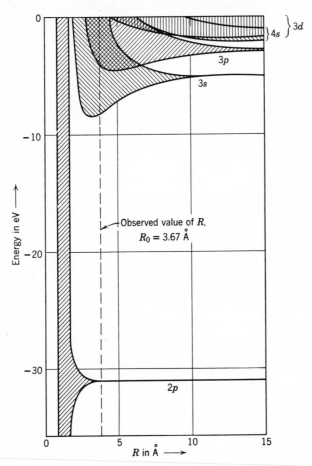

Figure 8.8   The energy level diagram for sodium as a function of lattice spacing.

result will be applicable to the bound case to the extent that the free electron approximation is valid. We have already considered this point in Section 7.9. The free electron approximation is good as long as we can consider the constant energy contours in Fig. 7.25 to be circular. This is the case at the bottom of the band, and so we can conclude that the state density function starts as a parabola at the bottom of the band.

Incidentally, we can write the equation of the parabola as in equation 8.11 because at this stage we are changing the origin of the energy scale. We have hitherto considered all energies in bound states as negative and based on $E = 0$ infinitely far from the system. Now, if we are going to apply the free electron theory, or slight modifications of it, to the valence electron or electrons in the solid, we shall regard them as a separate system and start the energy scale for the valence electrons at $E = 0$ at the bottom of the valence band. Thus the energy of an electron in the valence

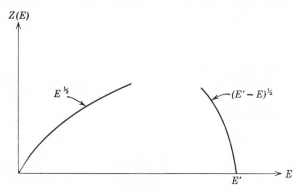

Figure 8.9   The electronic state distribution at the top and bottom of a valence band in a solid.

band, as for example the Fermi energy, will appear as a positive number even although it refers to a bound state.

Let us now consider the circumstances at the top of the band. Again referring to Fig. 7.25, it is clear from the geometry of the first Brillouin zone that the state density must decline to zero at the top of the band because the opportunities for a momentum vector to yield a particular energy diminish as the vector reaches into the corners of the zone. The actual state density function is associated with the form of the constant energy contours, and we have already seen in Fig. 7.25 that, near the corners of the zone, these contours become circles centered on the zone corners. This implies another parabolic function relating state density and energy where, this time, the energy variable is measured from the top of the band. Its equation would be

$$Z(E) = \text{constant } (E' - E)^{\frac{1}{2}} \qquad (8.14)$$

if E' is the energy at the top of the band.

For the two regions so far considered, the state distribution $Z(E)$ is drawn, as a function of E, the energy, for the $n = 3$ electrons of sodium in Fig. 8.9.

The form of the $Z(E)$ curve for the region in the middle of the band cannot be obtained by a simple theoretical treatment. The characteristic feature is a cusp in the middle of the band, arising from a crowding of the states as the radius vector defining the κ value approaches the sides of the

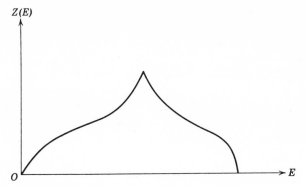

Figure 8.10   The complete density function for a band.

first Brillouin zone (see Fig. 8.10). Experimental evidence from which the actual shape of bands in metals can be obtained is available, and will be considered in Chapter 9.

Whatever the distribution of state density within the band, however, we

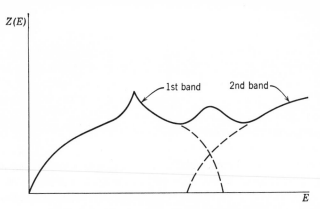

Figure 8.11   Band shapes with overlapping bands.

must remember that the total number of states in the band is given by the quantum number constitution of the band. For example in sodium, the state is 3s, giving two states per atom. If a lump of sodium contains N atoms, there will therefore be room for $2N$ electrons in the valence band.

Sodium has been chosen as an example of the circumstances most favorable to theoretical treatment. The problem is more complicated for atoms with more than one electron per atom in the outer shell and the necessity of considering the occupation of the upper parts of the band involves such matters as the overlapping of the bands. The resultant state density can be shown as in Fig. 8.11. In the overlapping region the resulting state density is the sum of those in the two overlapping bands. Further consideration will be given to such cases in the next section.

8.5   Electron Population Density in Solids and the Fermi Surface

Section 8.4 was concerned only with state densities. We do require electron population densities, however, and these will now be considered. Such electron densities will be determined by the number of valence electrons and by the number of levels in the bands that governs the extent to which the bands are filled.

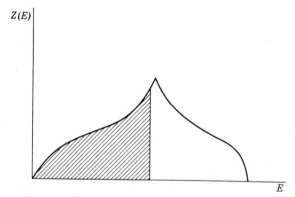

Figure 8.12   The occupation of the valence band of a monovalent metal. The occupied region (at $T = 0°K$) is shaded.

The problem is simple for sodium. The band where the valence electron is found is a 3s band with, therefore, two places per atom. With one valence electron per atom, the band consequently is half full as illustrated in Fig. 8.12. On the basis of this description, we might expect that in the element next up from sodium, magnesium, the 3s band would be just filled. In a way, this is true, but the question of overlapping of the bands must be considered. The occupation would then be as illustrated in Fig. 8.13. On the assumption that the lower band would be just full in the absence of the upper, the extra occupied states at 1 must compensate exactly for those at 2 which will thus remain empty. The case of such occupied, overlapping bands is very important and will be found to account for very many metallic properties. The energy range between the first band and the value $E = 0$ is generally filled with an extremely complex mixture of overlapping bands. It can thus be regarded as a continuum of available energies right up to $E = 0$. Figure 8.14 summarizes the whole sodium structure.

One very important feature of the occupation of the available levels by electrons is the state of affairs at the surface of the distribution. We have been discussing the occupation in terms of energy only. It is constructive now to consider the occupation in momentum space. Consider, for the

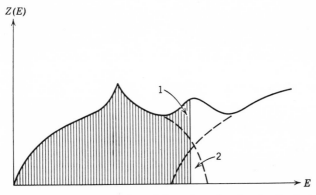

Figure 8.13   The occupation of the valence bands of a divalent metal.

moment, a square lattice with constant energy contours as shown in Fig. 7.25. Remember that these constant energy contours give the momentum values appropriate to a certain energy in the various part of the zone. Whatever the shape of these constant energy contours, one of them must be distinguished by being at the surface of the distribution. In other words, one energy contour must have the value E_F. At $T = 0°$K, therefore, this contour delineates the surface of the electron distribution. Three dimensions give a surface instead of a linear contour, and the surface is known as the Fermi surface.

Clearly for a free electron, the two-dimensional contour is a circle and in three dimensions a sphere—known as the Fermi sphere. The Fermi surface for a monovalent metal may approximate a sphere as shown for two dimensions in Fig. 8.15a, or it may show deviations, particularly if the occupied region touches the first Brillouin zone boundary as shown in Fig. 8.15b. The conditions illustrated in Fig. 8.15a may be found in the alkali metals, particularly in the case of sodium and those illustrated in Fig. 8.15b are found in copper.

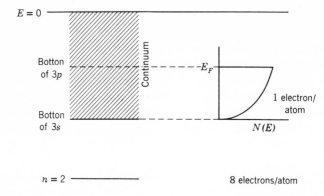

$n = 2$ ———————   8 electrons/atom

$n = 1$ ———————   2 electrons/atom
             Level   Occupation

Figure 8.14   The complete electron population distribution in metallic sodium at $T = 0°K$ (assuming a parabolic state density function for the valence electron).

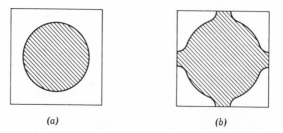

Figure 8.15   The Fermi surface in two dimensions for the case in which it (a) does not touch, (b) does touch, the first Brillouin zone boundary.

Band overlap can also be described in this way. After a situation like that illustrated in Fig. 8.15*b* has been passed, a stage can be reached at which any further electrons that must be added to complete the band may have to go into the second zone to result in an occupation diagram as illustrated in Fig. 8.16. Recent studies of complex materials such as tin have shown Fermi surfaces that penetrate not merely into the second Brillouin zone, but even into the third, fourth, and fifth zones. The Fermi surface is a very important feature in the electronic properties of solids, but further study—including the experimental techniques of delineating the surface—cannot be pursued here. Some aspects of the importance of the Fermi surface in relation to the Brillouin

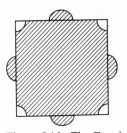

Figure 8.16 The Fermi surface in two dimensions for a divalent metal with overlapping bands.

zones will be considered when conductivities are discussed in Chapter 10. One of the simpler Fermi surfaces is illustrated in Fig. 8.17.

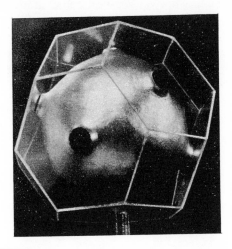

Figure 8.17 The Fermi surface and the first Brillouin zone boundary for copper.

8.6 Summary of the Energy Level Configurations for Typical Materials

Let us now summarize the results for some typical or important materials. The evidence leading to the structure to be described is usually a compound of pure theoretical calculation and of experimental results on a large range of phenomena. The theoretical treatment of the last two chapters is far too elementary to enable any of the following to be predicted, but it does at least serve as a basis for understanding the electron distributions.

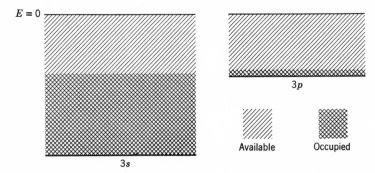

Figure 8.18   The band structure for sodium.

Sodium.   Sodium has one valence electron per atom. It is a state with two places per atom, and the band is half filled. Actually the $3p$ band does overlap the top of the $3s$ band, and this part of the band structure is shown in Fig. 8.18 (the bands are displaced laterally for clarity). Since the nuclear charge is so well shielded by the ten inner electrons, the valence electron is loosely bound and the free-electron treatment holds very well. Conditions similar to these are found in the other alkali metals, lithium with one $2s$ electron, potassium with one $4s$ electron, etc.

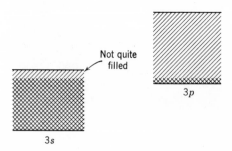

Figure 8.19   The band structure in magnesium.

Magnesium.   Magnesium lies just above sodium in the Periodic Table and so has two $2s$ electrons. This would completely fill the $3s$ band but the overlapping by the $3p$ band prevents this. The energy level structure is shown in Fig. 8.19. Similar situations are found in beryllium with two electrons in $2s$, calcium with two in $4s$, etc.

Copper. Copper lies at the end of the series of elements in which the 3*d* band has been filling while the 4*s* levels are already wholly or partially occupied. In copper the 3*d* band is just full and there is one 4*s* electron. Since there is room for two electrons per atom in the 4*s* band it will be,

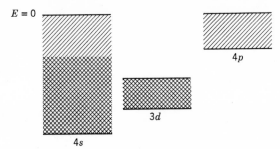

Figure 8.20   The band structure for copper.

as for the alkali metal potassium, half full. The next available state is a 4*p*, and in copper the 4*p* band completely overlaps the 3*s*. The 3*d* electrons are much more tightly bound than the 4*s*, since each experiences an effective nuclear charge of approximately 11 whereas the 4*s* experiences a charge of the order of 1 only. Consequently the 3*d* band is much narrower than the 4*s*. Figure 8.20 shows the copper electron diagram and it is similar to that for the other noble metals; silver with a 5*s* electron above a just completed 4*d* band and gold with a 6*s* electron above the 5*d* band.

Iron. We have discussed copper in which the 3*d* band is full. The transition series of elements, in which this band is filling while the 4*s* is already occupied, have chemical properties which are similar in many

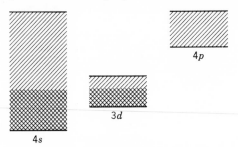

Figure 8.21   The band structure in iron.

respects. Properties, however, such as ferromagnetism, which are dependent on the degree to which the 3*d* band is filled, are different for iron, nickel, and cobalt, where the band is nearly full, from those found in the elements of the series where the band is more empty. Figure 8.21 shows the iron energy band diagram.

Diamond. A band theory treatment for diamond with its strongly directional C—C bands is very difficult. The energy diagram is shown in Fig. 8.22, in which it will be seen that the lower band is completely filled whereas the upper, which is separated from the lower by an energy gap, is completely empty.

$E = 0$ ——————————————————————————

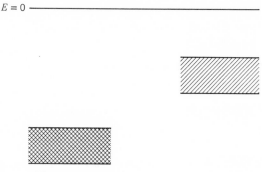

Figure 8.22   The band structure for diamond.

Silicon. Silicon has a type of bond—that is, covalent—similar in nature to that of diamond. The energy diagram is thus like that shown in Fig. 8.22, with the highly significant difference that in silicon the energy gap between the bands is much narrower. In germanium the gap is still less (diamond 6 to 7 eV, silicon 1.1 eV, germanium 0.7 eV). The consequences of this band structure are pursued in Chapter 12.

REFERENCES

L. V. Azaroff, *Introduction to Solids*, McGraw-Hill Book Company, New York, 1960.

A. J. Dekker, *Solid State Physics*, Prentice-Hall, Englewood Cliffs, N.J. 1957.

C. Kittel, *Introduction to Solid State Physics*, John Wiley and Sons, New York, 1956.

H. G. Kuhn, *Atomic Spectra*, Longmans, Green and Company Ltd., London, 1961.

R. B. Leighton, *Principles of Modern Physics*, McGraw-Hill Book Company, New York 1959.

N. F. Mott and H. Jones, *The Theory of the Properties of Metals and Alloys*, Clarendon Press, Oxford, 1936.

M. J. Sinnott, *The Solid State for Engineers*, John Wiley and Sons, New York, 1958.

G. H. Wannier, *Elements of Solid State Theory*, Cambridge University Press, Cambridge, 1958.

H. E. White, *Introduction to Atomic Spectra*, McGraw-Hill Book Company, New York, 1934.

EXERCISES

1. Using the Fermi function, evaluate the temperature at which there is a 1 per cent probability that an electron in a solid will have an energy 0.5 eV above the Fermi energy of 5 eV.

2. Calculate the extent of the energy range between $F(E) = 0.9$ and $F(E) = 0.1$ at a temperature of 2000°K and express it as a fraction of E_F which is 3 eV.

3. Using the Boltzmann function, evaluate the number of H atoms excited to the state $n = 2$ in the atmosphere of the sun at a temperature of 6000°K as compared with the number in the ground state.

4. Calculate approximately the wavelength of copper Kα radiation (i.e., arising from $n = 2 \rightarrow n = 1$) and the potential difference through which an electron must be accelerated in order to excite it.

5. Estimate the ionization energy in magnesium.

6. The sodium and chlorine ions in rock salt are 2.81 Å apart. What is the magnitude of the electrostatic force between them?

7. Assuming the electrons to be free, calculate the total number of states below $E = 5$ eV in a volume of 10^{-5} m^3.

8. Assume that lithium has one electron per atom that can be considered to be free. Calculate the Fermi energy and the Fermi temperature for lithium.

9

Static Electron Properties of Metals

In Chapters 9 and 10 we divide the electronic properties of metals roughly into two groups. The first group includes static electron properties, and the other group involves conduction phenomena. The first group includes the various electron emission properties such as photoemission, thermionic emission, and field emission and properties such as contact potential. These properties can all be treated adequately for our present purpose if we consider only the energy level or distribution of energy levels from which the electrons have come. We consider only the overall potential change of the electron without enquiring too closely into the detailed processes by which the transition has taken place. In general terms, such excitation is quite high energy excitation produced by light photons, thermal energy, strong electric fields, etc. Here the free electron approximation is generally perfectly satisfactory, so that almost all the work of Chapter 9 uses the free electron model with only incidental reference to the bound electron case.

In the second group of phenomena, the conduction effects which will be considered in Chapter 10, we must be concerned with the detailed response of the electron to an external field and so must take into consideration the acceleration properties of the electron. In contrast to the first group, these conduction phenomena generally involve only a very slight perturbation of the electronic distribution.

200

9.1   Photoelectric Phenomena

It is an easily observed phenomenon that there is an interaction between the electrons of a metal and light waves. Charged electroscopes discharge more quickly if the collector plate is irradiated with ultraviolet light, the onset of spark discharges is facilitated if the electrodes are similarly treated, and there are many other similar effects. If the metal surface is placed in an evacuated enclosure and a second electrode sealed in with it as shown in Fig. 9.1, it can readily be found that the effect of the light is to cause the emission of charged particles from the surface; and from the sign of the

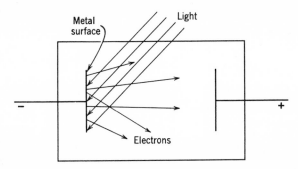

Figure 9.1   The photoelectric effect.

potential required to collect the charges on the collector anode, it is clear that these must be electrons. This effect is called the *photoelectric effect*, and an apparatus such as that illustrated in Fig. 9.1 is called a *photoelectric cell*. The effect is not a big one, and with typical metal surfaces and light wavelengths and intensities, currents in the microamp range are observed. One of the most striking features is the dependence of the emitted current on the frequency and intensity of the incident light. It is found that the energy of the emitted electrons depends on the *frequency* of the light and not on its *intensity*. There exists also a minimum frequency below which no emission occurs. The part played by the light intensity is to influence the *number* of electrons emitted.

A simplified description of the phenomenon in terms of the models developed in Chapters 7 and 8 can be given. Consider a monovalent metal in which we can assume a state density function in the valence band giving an electron distribution illustrated in Fig. 9.2. To the extent that the free electron model is applicable, this function will be a parabola (e.g., for the alkali metals). Anyhow, there will be a continuous occupation of energy levels from the bottom of the valence band up to the Fermi level.

As shown, this is at energy E_F above the energy at the bottom of the valence band. There will then be a gap in the occupied energy spectrum between the Fermi level and the top of the energy scale at the value zero. This gap is usually called the *work function* and will be denoted by ϕ.

Now consider the arrival of a photon at the metal surface. It is obvious that an electron at the top of the distribution will be able to absorb enough

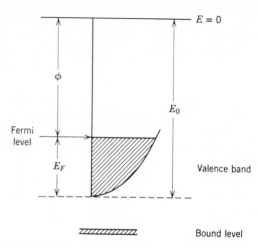

Figure 9.2   The work function in a conducting solid.

energy to escape from the metal, provided the photon has a sufficiently high frequency so that

$$h\nu \geqslant \phi \qquad (9.1)$$

This accounts immediately for the existence of a threshold frequency below which photoelectric emission is not possible. Typical values for ϕ and the corresponding threshold frequency are given in Table 9.1.

If $h\nu$ is greater than ϕ, an electron which is initially at the top of the distribution in the solid will escape from the surface with an energy given by

$$\tfrac{1}{2}mv^2 = h\nu - \phi \qquad (9.2)$$

If the electron has been taken from a point in the distribution below E_F, the energy with which it leaves the surface will be reduced. If the light frequency is increased, the photons can excite electrons from points deeper and deeper in the valence band, giving increasing photoelectron yield up to the frequency at which $h\nu$ is greater than $\phi + E_F$ when no further increase is possible. After this point the yield will actually decline although the photons have more than enough energy to cause excitation. This decline is related to a lessening probability of electron transition out of the original state as mentioned on page 176 and illustrated in Fig. 8.3. The whole spectral sensitivity curves for the alkali metals are shown in Fig. 9.3.

Actually the problem is not quite so simple as is suggested by the elementary energy balance conditions given earlier. It can be shown that the conditions of energy and momentum conservation make it impossible for a free electron in the interior of the material to receive energy in this way. Consequently, most of the emitted photoelectrons came from points very close to the surface where energy and momentum conservation is permitted. The effect is enhanced by the low penetrability of light into

Table 9.1   Photoelectric Constants

ELEMENT	WORK FUNCTION (eV)	THRESHOLD WAVELENGTH (Å)
Li	2.46	5040
Na	2.28	5430
K	2.25	5510
Cs	1.94	6390
Mg	3.70	3350
Fe	4.63	2680
Cu	4.48	2770
Ag	4.70	2640
Zn	4.27	2900
Ge	4.62	2680
Si	3.59	3450

most solids and the inability of low energy electrons to escape from points deep in the solid. Thus altogether the photoemission is very sensitive to surface conditions as regards both magnitude of emitted current and threshold frequency. One consequence of this sensitivity is that although the measurement of the threshold frequency offers a very tempting possibility of measuring the work function ϕ, such measurements must be made only with very careful attention to surface conditions if reliable results are to be obtained.

One further factor of practical importance is the spectral response of the surface. This is seen from Fig. 9.3 to involve a peaked response. The position of this peak determines the uses in which the cathode may be employed. For example, many everyday applications require maximum sensitivity in the visible region, whereas special purposes may call for cathodes sensitive in the ultraviolet or infrared regions.

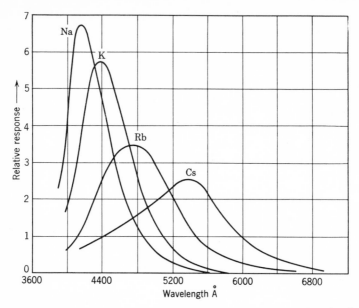

Figure 9.3 The spectral sensitivity of the photoelectric effect in the alkali metals.

The manufacture of cathodes to meet specific requirements is something of an art, since the details of the physical mechanisms involved may not be clearly understood. The conditions to be filled include high quantum yield (number of photoelectrons produced per quantum of incident light) and low work function. Commercially manufactured cathodes are sometimes made of pure alkali metals (lithium, sodium, potassium, rubidium, or cesium) which have been "sensitized" by a glow discharge in hydrogen

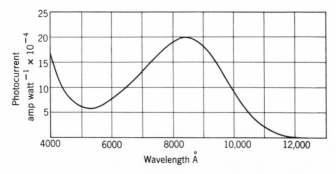

Figure 9.4 The spectral sensitivity of the photoelectric effect in the silver-oxygen-cesium photocathode.

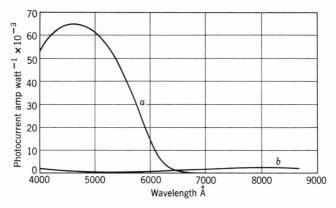

Figure 9.5 (*a*) The spectral sensitivity of the photoelectric effect in the antimony-cesium photocathode. (*b*) The curve of Fig. 9.4 for silver-oxygen-cesium redrawn on the same scale for comparison.

(which acts to produce hydrides at the emitting surface) inside the phototube. Sometimes composite cathodes are used. Among the more common of these is a silver-oxygen-cesium layer structure which has a response curve extending conveniently into the infrared as illustrated in Fig. 9.4, and the antimony–cesium compound whose response curve is illustrated in Fig. 9.5. This last cathode has the amazing quantum yield of 20 per cent at the peak value, which is to be compared with the figures of 10^{-3} to 10^{-2} per cent for pure alkali metals. For a detailed study of materials and preparation methods for photoelectric emitters, reference should be made to the text by Zworykin in the bibliography.

The actual collection of the photoelectons by the anode is related to the geometry of the cell electrodes. A photoelectric cell is shown in Fig. 9.6. A fraction (*a*) of the photoelectrons will be emitted in such a direction as to strike the anode. When a positive potential is applied to the anode an additional fraction (*b*) will be attracted and as the potential is increased more and more electrons will contribute to the current. The increase will continue, however, only until all the emitted electrons are attracted to the anode, and thereafter a higher potential will not increase the current. The current-voltage relation is illustrated in Fig. 9.7. A

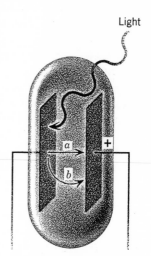

Figure 9.6 The collection of photoelectrons by a positive electrode.

phototube is normally operated in the saturation region where it is insensitive to small changes in anode potential.

If a *negative* potential is applied to the anode, electrons will be retarded as they approach it. With a sufficiently high potential they may even be prevented from reaching the anode. The potential at which this happens depends on the energy with which the electron left the emitting surface. Clearly, therefore, the shape of the current curve in the negative potential region contains information about the number of electrons being emitted with a certain energy. Furthermore, with careful control over surface

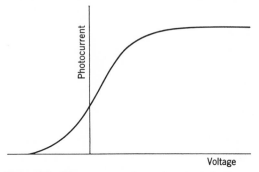

Figure 9.7   The current-voltage characteristic for a typical phototube.

conditions and electrode geometry, this method has been used to obtain experimentally the distribution of state density in the valence band of the alkali metals.

One of the chief problems in interpreting such curves, even with favorable geometry, arises from the fact that in practice we are dealing, not with a single electron, but with many electrons. Consequently those electrons which are traveling after emission toward the collector constitute a "space charge" which reduces the accelerating potential experienced by an electron that has just left the emitting surface. This electron, in turn, influences the shape of the current-potential curve, giving, at any particular potential, lower currents than would otherwise be expected.

9.2   Transitions between Internal Energy Levels

The possibility exists that an electron may be excited into unoccupied energy levels by a light quantum or energetic incident electron *without leaving* the metal. Such a transition would normally be difficult to detect in view of the effectively unquantized structure of levels in the valence band.

But if there is any preference for the electrons to come from a particular region of the valence energy band, the selective nature of the phenomenon might give it detectable characteristics. Such is apparently the case, for example, in copper where excitation from the densely occupied $3d$ levels results in preferential absorption of blue wavelengths in the incident light, resulting in the familiar red concentration in the reflected light.

Transitions between the inner tightly bound electron shells of an atom generally fall in the X-ray region. Such levels are usually sharp and unaffected by the proximity of neighboring atoms. Thus X-ray spectroscopy

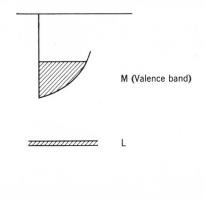

Figure 9.8   The levels giving rise to the soft X-ray spectrum of sodium.

is generally unaffected by the physical state of the material. If we consider transitions involving the upper regions of the bound energy levels, however, then the X-ray spectrum is sensitive to the broadened nature of such levels found in solids. Consider the level diagram given in Fig. 9.8. The X-ray spectrum is excited by removing an electron from an inner shell of the atom. As electrons from the upper levels make transitions downward to fill the gap, quanta are emitted to constitute the X-radiation. If the K shell was ionized initially, the X-ray line corresponding to the L to K radiation will be relatively sharp but the transitions from M (here the valence band) to L will cover a range of energies, depending on the point in the valence band from which the electron made its transition. The spectrum of this radiation, that is, the intensity at each frequency, will thus be a direct measure of the number of electrons at each level of the valence band. A slight correction to the shape is necessary because of possibly varying transition probabilities, but this is only a small effect and does not affect the character of the results. This *soft* X-ray spectrum should therefore be closely associated with the nature of the energy bands. Such spectra have been obtained by Skinner and are illustrated in Fig. 9.9. In this diagram *a* refers to a monovalent metal and should be compared with the band structure of Fig. 8.12, whereas *b* illustrates the case of a divalent metal for comparison with Fig. 8.13. Such experimental confirmation of the general results of band theory is very reassuring and enables measurements of quantities such as the energy width of an occupied band to be made in cases

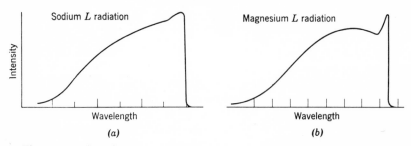

Figure 9.9   The soft X-ray band shapes for (*a*) a monovalent and (*b*) a divalent metal. (After Skinner).

where the calculation from fundamental theory would be very difficult. Thus, for example, the valence band in aluminum is about 12 eV in width, in lithium is 4.2 eV, and in sodium is 3.0 eV.

9.3   Thermionic Emission

It was first observed by Edison that heating a wire filament in a vacuum caused an electrical current to pass between it and an electrode if an external voltage was applied to make the wire negative with respect to the electrode. No current is observed if the voltage is applied the other way. The current is interpreted as resulting from the emission of electrons from the wire and the phenomenon is called *thermionic emission*, which can be described by simple application of the free electron model. The Fermi function at temperature zero gives a sharp cutoff in the electron energy distribution at an energy E_F. At finite temperatures the tail in the distribution curve extends to higher values of energy E and may, if the temperature is high enough, bridge the whole gap from $E = E_F$ to $E = 0$. When this happens some electrons are free to leave the surface to constitute thermionic emission. The condition that an individual electron can leave the surface is that its energy (measured from the bottom of the valence band in accordance with the considerations on page 190) must be at least equal to the value E_0 or $E_F + \phi$ (see Fig. 9.2). Although this condition is necessary, it is not sufficient because the electron must not only have enough energy but must be traveling in the right direction. If we take the x direction perpendicular to the surface of the emitting solid, we can write an expression for p_{x_0}, the critical value of the electron's momentum in the x direction, so that it *just* escapes from the surface.

Since

$$\frac{p_{x_0}^2}{2m} = E_F + \phi$$

$$p_{x_0} = \sqrt{2m(E_F + \phi)} \tag{9.3}$$

The actual thermionic current at a certain temperature will then be the product of the electronic charge and the number of electrons having a momentum in the x direction greater than this critical value, which in unit time arrive at unit area of the surface. Let us suppose that the number of electrons per unit volume with values of momentum in the x direction lying between p_x and $p_x + dp_x$ is given by $N(p_x)\, dp_x$. Its value will be calculated below.

Since the velocity of arrival of an electron of momentum p_x is given by p_x/m, the number arriving at unit area of the surface in unit time with a value of momentum greater than the critical value is given by

$$\int_{p_{x_0}}^{\infty} \frac{p_x}{m} N(p_x)\, dp_x$$

The thermionic current j is thus given by

$$j = \frac{e}{m} \int_{p_{x_0}}^{\infty} p_x N(p_x)\, dp_x \tag{9.4}$$

Our task is now to calculate $N(p_x)$. It will be given by the product of the number of possible states of momentum p_x and the probability that an electron is in each state.

The number of states in a certain momentum range dp at momentum p has already been obtained as equation 8.11a. It was

$$Z(p)\, dp = \frac{8\pi}{h^3} p^2\, dp$$

This result refers to momentum values of p in any direction, however, and we must be concerned with momenta in the x direction specifically. We must, therefore, calculate the number of electrons that have a momentum lying in the range dp_x at p_x while the p_y and p_z values are unrestricted. It is illuminating to consider this problem in a geometrical fashion. Suppose we construct as in Fig. 9.10 a plot in "momentum space" in which each position represents a particular combination of the momentum components p_x, p_y, and p_z. A spherical shell of radius

$$p = p_x{}^2 + p_y{}^2 + p_z{}^2$$

and thickness dp has been drawn. Each quantum state with momentum between p and $p + dp$ lies in this shell. The fraction of states at momentum p which have a momentum lying in the interval p_x to $p_x + dp_x$, p_y to

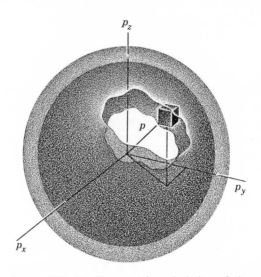

Figure 9.10 To illustrate the calculation of the number of states within certain momentum ranges. The volume element $dp_x\,dp_r\,dp_z$ is supposed to be contained in the thickness of the spherical shell between p and $p + dp$.

$p_y + dp_y$, p_z to $p_z + dp_z$ is therefore given by the ratio of the volume $dp_x\,dp_y\,dp_z$ to that of the spherical shell of thickness dp at radius p. Thus

$$\text{fraction of states in } dp_x\,dp_y\,dp_z = \frac{dp_x\,dp_y\,dp_z}{4\pi p^2\,dp} \tag{9.5}$$

Therefore the actual number of states lying in the interval $dp_x\,dp_y\,dp_z$ is the product of the foregoing fraction with the total number of states in the momentum interval dp at momentum p. Thus

$$Z(p_x p_y p_z)\,dp_x\,dp_y\,dp_z = \frac{8\pi}{h^3}\,p^2\,dp\,\frac{dp_x\,dp_y\,dp_z}{4\pi p^2\,dp}$$

$$= (2/h^3)\,dp_x\,dp_y\,dp_z. \tag{9.6}$$

This is the number of states per cubic meter with momentum component in the x direction lying between the values p_x and $p_x + dp_x$ and similarly for p_y and p_z.

The fraction of these states which is occupied by electrons is given by the Fermi function $F(E)$ of equation 8.1. That is,

$$F(E) = \frac{1}{e^{(E-E_F)/kT} + 1}$$

We thus come to the value of $N(p_x)\,dp_x$ which is

$$N(p_x)\,dp_x = \frac{2}{h^3}\,dp_x \int_{p_y=-\infty}^{\infty} \int_{p_z=-\infty}^{\infty} \frac{dp_y\,dp_z}{e^{(E-E_F)/kT} + 1} \tag{9.7}$$

Since ϕ is of the order of a few electron volts, the quantity $E - E_F$ is much bigger than kT (k has a value of 8.6×10^{-5} eV per degree) even at temperatures in the thousands of degrees. We can therefore ignore the 1 in comparison with $e^{(E-E_F)/kT}$. Hence the Fermi function reduces to the Boltzmann function $e^{-(E-E_F)/kT}$.

On making this simplification and remembering that

$$E = \frac{1}{2m}(p_x^2 + p_y^2 + p_z^2)$$

equation 9.7 becomes

$$N(p_x)\,dp_x = \frac{2}{h^3}\,dp_x e^{E_F/kT} e^{-p_x^2/2mkT} \int_{-\infty}^{\infty} e^{-p_y^2/2mkT}\,dp_y \int_{-\infty}^{\infty} e^{-p_z^2/2mkT}\,dp_z$$

The integrals have a standard form with value

$$\sqrt{\pi 2mkT}$$

each. Thus finally,

$$N(p_x)\,dp_x = \frac{4\pi mkT}{h^3} e^{E_F/kT} e^{-p_x^2/2mkT}\,dp_x \tag{9.8}$$

On substituting this value in the equation for the thermionic current, we obtain

$$j = \frac{e}{m} \int_{p_{x0}}^{\infty} \frac{4\pi mkT}{h^3} e^{E_F/kT} e^{-p_x^2/2mkT} p_x\,dp_x$$

$$= \frac{4\pi mek^2}{h^3} T^2 e^{-\phi/kT} \tag{9.9}$$

This equation is commonly written

$$j = AT^2 e^{-\phi/kT}$$

where

$$A = \frac{4\pi mek^2}{h^3} = 120 \text{ amp cm}^{-2} \text{ deg}^{-2} \tag{9.10}$$

This is the Richardson-Dushman equation. The equation gives only the total current produced. There will, of course, be an energy distribution among the thermionic electrons arising from the part of the Boltzmann tail of the Fermi distribution that has reached out beyond a value of $E_0 = E_F + \phi$.

There are several auxiliary conditions that modify this result either theoretically or in practice. These conditions are now briefly discussed.

1. There is a certain probability that an electron approaching the metal surface will suffer reflection even though it has enough energy to escape. Consequently, this reflectivity slightly reduces the emitted current.

2. It has been assumed in the treatment that we are considering the passage of a single electron into a vacuum outside the metal. In practice the electrons emitted may, if not removed very quickly by a collector with a high positive potential, constitute a space charge which, in effect, increases the value of ϕ. This space charge again acts to decrease the current.

3. A large applied electric field can be arranged to remove space charge effects, but the field itself effectively reduces the values of ϕ. This is discussed in Section 9.4.

4. The work function ϕ is often dependent on the crystal orientation relative to the emitting direction. In a polycrystalline material, therefore, an averaged value of ϕ is appropriate.

5. Just as was the case in photoelectric emission, the thermionic current is strongly dependent on surface conditions. Contamination—accidental or deliberate—may have a large effect on the ϕ value, and because of the exponential function may greatly modify the thermionic current.

The choice of materials for the practical application of thermionic emission is dominated, as it was for photoelectric phenomena, by the necessity for a small value of ϕ. One other consideration is necessary here which was not found in the previous case because the material must be stable at relatively high temperatures. It must not therefore be too volatile, and thus the alkali metals and compounds mentioned previously are not suitable. Materials combining adequate emissivity and low volatility include the alkali earth oxides (BaO, CaO and SrO) and adsorbed thin films of cesium, barium, thorium, or lanthanum on tungsten. In particular, thoriated tungsten is very frequently used. If emission at a very high filament temperature is desired, a pure tungsten filament may be used. Values for the thermionic constants of typical materials are given in Table

9.2. Further information regarding the practical application of thermo-emissive materials may be found in the texts by Seeley, Ryder, and Egli in the Bibliography. In practice, of course, the thermionic current must be generated and collected in some kind of evacuated system in a manner

Table 9.2 Thermionic Constants

MATERIAL	$\overset{\text{Å}}{(\text{amp cm}^{-2\circ}\text{K}^{-2})}$	WORK FUNCTION (eV)
W	~75	4.5
Ta	60	4.1
Thorium on tungsten	4.0	2.7
BaO	0.1–60	1.4–1.5
SrO	100	2.2
Thorium carbide	100	3.2

similar to that employed for photoelectric emission. Space charge characteristics similar in nature to those previously discussed are again found.

9.4 Field Emission and the Schottky Effect

Field Emission. We can observe that it is possible to remove electrons from a metal surface by the action of an electric field alone, provided only that the field is strong enough. The phenomenon is called *field emission*. It is important in cases such as the onset of a spark discharge and is also the basis of the *field emission microscope*. This is a tool of importance in the study of solid surfaces and is described later.

The phenomenon can be described by the free electron model if we consider the total potential energy experienced by the electron. The free electron model treats the solid as a box with a potential energy which is constant inside the box and which rises discontinuously to zero at the boundaries of the material. This is illustrated in Fig. 9.11 (note the inversion of the potential scale because electrons are conventionally negative).

If now a field is applied, the potential, measured from zero at the surface of the solid at $x = 0$, can be considered to increase linearly with distance from $x = 0$. The total potential experienced by the electron is thus as illustrated in Fig. 9.12.

The top of the electron distribution can be considered to be at A in Fig. 9.12. The free space potential is thus seen to take on the character of a *barrier* whose height depends on ϕ and whose width depends on the steepness of the rise of the potential curve, that is, on the field strength. The behavior of an electron wave as it meets a rectangular potential barrier has already been discussed in Section 6.3 and a value for the transmission probability obtained. The barrier involved in the present discussion is not

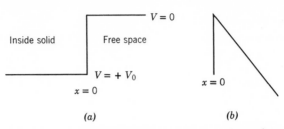

(a)   (b)

Figure 9.11   (a) The potential distribution at the surface of an idealized solid in the absence of an external electric field. (b) The potential distribution outside a solid in the presence of an external electric field.

rectangular but triangular so that the previous result is not applicable. The result remains usable, however, to the extent that the transmission probability depends on the thickness of the barrier in an exponential fashion (the standing wave amplitude was proportional to $e^{-\gamma x}$ in Section

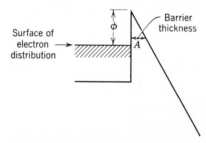

Figure 9.12   The total potential at the surface of a solid in the presence of an external electric field.

6.3. It is obvious from Fig. 9.12 that the barrier thickness is inversely proportional to the electric field strength so that we may expect terms of the form

$$e^{-\text{constant/field}}$$

in the expression for the transmission current. The complete expression for the current (the Fowler-Nordheim equation) is similar in form to the Richardson-Dushman equation with the exception that in the former the field strength occupies the place of the temperature in the latter.

Very high field strengths are necessary to provide substantial emission through the foregoing mechanism. For a ϕ value of 3 eV, fields of the order of 10^9 v m^{-1} are necessary. Such fields are normally found only near very sharp points. The mechanism is thus of great importance, as stated earlier, in initiating spark breakdown between electrodes at high potentials. Unless the electrodes are atomically smooth, minor defects in the surface give field concentrations that lead to field enhanced emission of electrons.

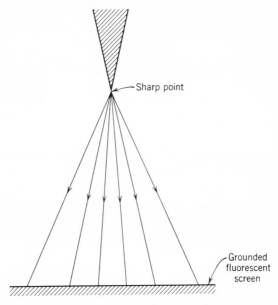

Figure 9.13   Field lines and electron paths in the field emission microscope.

Field emission can be used to study surface detail in the *field emission microscope*. Consider a sharp point of metal to which is applied a high negative potential as in Fig. 9.13. The field is made uniform around the point by a grounded enclosure. If the field is high enough and the point sharp enough, field emission of electrons takes place. Because of the approximately spherical geometry, the electrons are accelerated radially to strike a fluorescent screen. Since only radial movement is involved, the image on the fluorescent screen will represent the intensity with which electrons were given off in that particular direction, and can give a greatly magnified image of work function variations over the specimen point. Such a picture for a single crystal of tungsten is shown in Fig. 9.14. The dark spots correspond to points of high work function, and these can be correlated with specific directions in the crystal. This method has since been extended to use positive ions reflected from the surface instead of electrons for image production. This instrument is called an *ion emission microscope*. With it the magnification and resolution have been improved to the extent that it is now possible to "see" individual atoms in the solid surface (see the paper by Muller in the Bibliography).

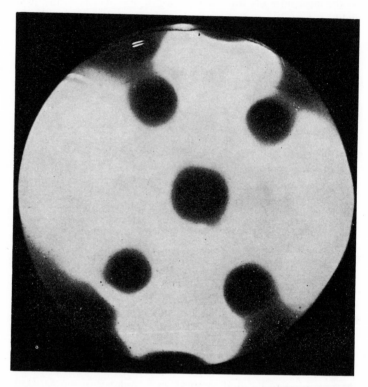

Figure 9.14   A field emission microscope picture giving the variation of work function over a tungsten point.

The Schottky Effect. Another mechanism exists whereby electrostatic fields can influence the electron emission of solids. In the case of field emission, the presence of the field provided the possibility for tunneling without change of the actual value of the work function. Now if we consider a slightly more detailed model of the potential function near the surface of the metal, we shall find that the work function itself is changed by the external field. The refinement which we wish to add to the potential function is the inclusion of the force on an electron outside the metal surface. Any charge when placed near the surface of a conductor experiences a force arising from the polarization of the conducting material.

It can be simply shown that the force is equal to that which would be experienced if the conducting surface were replaced by a charge equal in magnitude but opposite in sign to the original charge at a point as far behind the surface as the original charge was in front of it. In view of

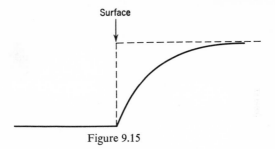

Surface

Figure 9.15

this feature the force is known as an "image" force. To obtain the complete potential function for the electron at the surface of the metal, therefore, we must add in the contribution of the image force. The potential for the image force must be

$$V_{\text{image}} = -\frac{1}{4\pi^2\epsilon_0}\frac{e^2}{4x} \tag{9.11}$$

where x is the distance between the surface and the charge and e is the value of the charge. This potential is shown in Fig. 9.15.

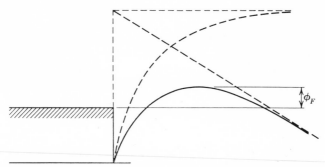

Figure 9.16   The total potential at the surface of an idealized metal including both image forces and an external electric field.

Now if an external electric field $\mathscr{E}_x$ is applied, the potential experienced by the charge is the sum of the image potential and the applied potential. The total potential is shown in Fig. 9.16.

The most important feature of this result is that the work function in the field ϕ_F is smaller than that without the field. If the field is strong enough it is clearly possible for ϕ_F to vanish completely. When this happens the top of the electron distribution is free to leave the metal without the necessity for tunneling. This reduction in work function is known as the *Schottky effect*.

To obtain the actual value for the reduction in work function we write the total potential

$$V = - \frac{e^2}{16\pi^2\epsilon_0 x} - e\mathcal{E}_x \qquad (9.12)$$

We require the maximum value of V. This is obtained by differentiating V

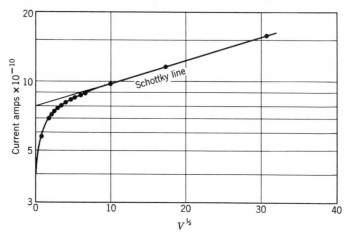

Figure 9.17   The Schottky effect in tungsten.

with respect to x from which the value of x for which V is a maximum is easily shown to be

$$x_{V_{max}} = \frac{1}{4\pi\sqrt{\epsilon_0}} \sqrt{e/\mathcal{E}_x} \qquad (9.13)$$

and the actual value of V at this value of x is

$$V_{max} = - \frac{1}{2\pi\sqrt{\epsilon_0}} e\sqrt{e\mathcal{E}_x}$$

This quantity is the value of the reduction in work function. At a particular temperature, then, we can obtain the actual emitted current as a function of field by substitution of the modified value of ϕ into the Richardson-Dushman equation. We obtain

$$j = AT^2 e^{-\left(\phi - \frac{1}{2\pi\sqrt{\epsilon_0}} e\sqrt{e\mathcal{E}_x}\right)/kT} \qquad (9.14)$$

This is normally represented by a graph of $\log j$ vs $\sqrt{\mathcal{E}_x}$ or $\sqrt{V}$ which gives a straight line known as the Schottky line, and is illustrated in Fig. 9.17.

Deviations occur at low $\mathscr{E}_x$ where small scale influences on the value of ϕ itself might be expected to be important.

The effect on ϕ is not large ($\Delta\phi \simeq 1.2 \times 10^{-2}$ eV for $\mathscr{E}_x = 10^5$ v m^{-1}), but the effect on the emitted current can be appreciable. It is important, for example, for a diode rectifier at high voltages.

9.5   Contact Potential

Consider two metals with different work functions ϕ_1 and ϕ_2 and allow them to become electrically connected. The state of affairs just after they

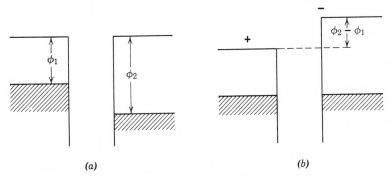

(a)   (b)

Figure 9.18   The Fermi levels and potentials of two metals (a) before electron transfer has taken place, and (b) after electron transfer has generated the contact potential.

have been brought into contact but before any electron transfer has taken place is illustrated in Fig. 9.18a.

If electron flow is possible, it will take place only from left to right since (at $T = 0$) there are no empty states below E_F. Anyhow, the electrons can lower the overall energy of the system by flowing from metal 1 to metal 2, and they will continue to do so until the two Fermi levels are the same. The consequence of this flow is an excess of electrons in one metal and a deficiency in the other which can be observed as a potential difference between the two metals called a *contact potential*. The contact potential is commonly represented by a spacing between the "$V = 0$" levels as shown in Fig. 9.18b. The value of the contact potential is clearly the difference between the two work functions.

Contact potentials can be measured by making the two metals the opposite plates of a capacitor. If the plates are connected, the contact potential difference gives rise to charges on the electrodes. If now the distance between the plate is suddenly changed, a voltage pulse is produced in the connecting circuit because of the sudden change in capacitance. An external potential can be applied to the plates and adjusted so that with the distance between the plates in continuous oscillation the voltage pulse is reduced to zero. The applied potential must then just equal the contact potential which is thus measured. Once the work function is known for one of the plates, the value of other unknown work functions can be easily obtained by substitution.

Contact potentials are important in practice if we wish to know to high precision a potential such as an accelerating potential between a cathode and an anode. The actual accelerating potential difference is that between their Fermi levels which differs from that between the metal surfaces by an amount equal to the contact potential. Since contact potentials can be seen from Table 9.2 to often amount to 2 or 3 volts, this may be an important correction in precise work.

The concept of the lining up of the Fermi levels in two materials in contact will prove to be of the greatest importance in the semiconductor work described in Chapter 11, since most semiconductor applications involve junctions of one sort or another.

9.6   The Effect of Surface Conditions on the Work Function

Frequent reference has been made to the influence on the work function of surface conditions, particularly the presence of an adsorbed surface layer of foreign atoms. There are many different mechanisms whereby surface conditions can affect work functions, and many of these are used in the preparation of surfaces for photoemission and thermionic emission. Only one mechanism will be discussed here, but it will serve as an example of the type of phenomenon in question.

Consider an atom close to a metal surface. If that atom has an easily removable electron that can join the metal at a lower energy than it had in the atom, a positive ion will be formed. Electrostatic attraction between the negatively charged metal surface and the positive ion will cause it to adhere to the surface. If we now consider a complete monatomic layer covering the metal surface, we shall have a double sheet of charge as illustrated in Fig. 9.19. This gives rise to no external field, but there is a field in the space between the two charge sheets. Thus if we extract an electron from inside the metal, the amount of work we must do is reduced because of the assistance provided by this internal field in the surface layer. In other words, a monolayer of electropositive atoms *reduces* the work function of the surface. This is the case for alkali atoms and alkali earth atoms adsorbed on metals like tungsten. On the other hand, a layer of negative ions will increase the work function, and this is found, for example, with oxygen on tungsten.

To calculate the change in work function we must write down the field in the space between the double layer. It is

$$\mathscr{E} = \frac{\sigma}{\epsilon_0}$$

where σ is the surface charge density. If the two charge sheets are separated by a distance d, the potential difference across the space will be

$$\Delta\phi = \frac{\sigma}{\epsilon_0} de$$

If the charge density σ arises from N ions per unit area each with charge e, we have finally

$$\Delta\phi = \frac{Ne^2d}{\epsilon_0}$$

For a monotomic layer, values of $\Delta\phi$ of about 1 eV can arise quite easily.

The foregoing is only one aspect of the effect of surface contamination on the work function. In spite of the technological importance of the topic, however, its great complexity precludes further discussion here.

9.7 The Heat Capacity of an Electron Gas

One further property remains to be described in the class of phenomena that depend, in general, only on the distribution of electrons among available energy levels. This is the heat capacity of electrons in a metal. It is not an important topic from the point of view of the everyday use of metals, but it becomes a dominant property at very low temperatures. It is also one of the properties whose treatment by classical methods gave strikingly wrong results and whose satisfactory description by wave mechanics was one of the early triumphs of the new theory.

To evaluate the heat capacity of the electrons in a metal we must first calculate their total energy as a function of temperature. If $N(E)\,dE$ is the

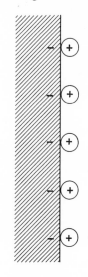

Figure 9.19   The contribution to the work function of an adsorbed layer of atoms on the surface of a solid.

number of conduction electrons per kilogram atomic weight having energies lying between E and $E + dE$, we can write the total electron energy as

$$u = \int_0^\infty EN(E)\,dE \qquad (9.15)$$

Just as in Section 9.3, we can write $N(E)\,dE$ in terms of the Fermi function and the state density function and then integrate. The electronic heat capacity C_v per kilogram atomic weight at constant volume is then obtained as

$$C_v = \frac{\partial u}{\partial T} \qquad (9.16)$$

The actual integration of (9.15) is rather complex and will not be given here. It is, in any case, possible to make an order-of-magnitude estimate of the heat capacity by an elementary argument. First of all it is clear that the heat capacity is going to be small. Only a very few conduction electrons at the top of the distribution will have empty states sufficiently close to them into which they can be thermally excited by normal temperatures. This contrasts with the classical view in which all particles in an assembly would be able to absorb energy and so contribute to the heat capacity.

At a temperature close to $T = 0$, consider an energy range between $E_F - kT$ and E_F. It is obvious from the graph of the Fermi function in Fig. 8.1 that the fraction of conduction electrons contained in this energy range is, ignoring tailing, kT/E_F. If all the conduction electrons behaved like gas molecules, the energy absorbed by the electrons per kilogram atomic weight in raising the temperature to T would be of the order of $\mathcal{N}kT$ where $\mathcal{N}$ is the number of electrons per kilogram atomic weight. Since, however, it is only those electrons in the small energy range we are considering that can gain energy the value of u is given by

$$u \simeq \mathcal{N}kT\left(\frac{kT}{E_F}\right) \qquad (9.17)$$

Hence

$$C_v \simeq \mathcal{N}k\frac{kT}{E_F} \qquad (9.18)$$

At normal temperatures $kT \ll E_F$, thus providing the expected small value of C_v. The value which is given by the complete theory differs from the above value only by a constant and is

$$C_v = \left(\frac{\pi^2}{2}\right)\mathcal{N}k\left(\frac{kT}{E_F}\right) \qquad (9.19)$$

This is commonly written

$$C_v = \gamma T \tag{9.20}$$

One of the features of this result, the linear dependence on T, has the consequence that in spite of the smallness of the electronic specific height at normal temperatures as compared with the lattice specific heat, the electronic heat capacity at low temperatures decreases more slowly than the lattice heat capacity which decreases as T^3, and can become a sufficiently large fraction of the total heat capacity to be measurable. Measurements of γ are of considerable interest in relating theory to the properties of actual metals.

REFERENCES

A. J. Dekker, *Solid State Physics*, Prentice-Hall, Englewood Cliffs, N.J., 1957.

P. H. Egli, *Thermoelectricity*, John Wiley and Sons, New York, 1960.

C. Kittel, *Introduction to Solid State Physics*, John Wiley and Sons, New York, 1956.

J. Millman and S. Seely, *Electronics*, McGraw-Hill Book Company, New York, 1951.

N. F. Mott and H. Jones, *The Theory of Metals and Alloys*, Clarendon Press, Oxford, 1936.

E. W. Muller, Study of the Atomic Structure of Metal Surfaces in the Field Ion Microscope, J. Appl. Phys., **28**, 1 (1957).

J. D. Ryder, *Electronic Fundamentals and Application*, Prentice-Hall, Englewood Cliffs, N.J., 1956.

W. H. B. Skinner, The Soft X-ray Spectroscopy of the Solid State Reports on Prog. Phys. 5, 257 (1938).

A. Sommer, *Photoelectric Tubes*, Methuen, London, 1951.

R. L. Sproull, *Modern Physics*, John Wiley and Sons, New York, 1956.

V. K. Zworykin and E. G. Ramberg, *Photoelectricity and its Applications*, John Wiley and Sons, New York, 1949.

EXERCISES

1. Calculate the photoelectric threshold for tungsten which has a work function of 4.5 eV.
2. Light from a mercury vapor lamp passes through a filter to isolate the 5461 Å line and falls on a cesium surface with an intensity of 10^{-2} watt m^{-2}. Assuming a quantum yield of 10^{-4}, calculate the photocurrent produced. What retarding potential would have to be applied to the collector to reduce the current to zero?
3. Show that a photon cannot give up all its energy to an electron isolated in space. [The momentum of a photon is E/c where E is its energy and c the velocity of light].
4. Calculate the thermionic current emitted by a tungsten filament 0.05 m long and 10^{-4} m in diameter which is at a temperature of 2000°K in no external field.

5. Repeat the calculation of exercise 4 for the case in which an electric field at the surface of the filament is 5×10^5 volts m^{-1} and state the amount by which the work function has been reduced.

6. What is the contact potential between silver and tungsten?

7. Calculate the heat capacity of the electron gas at room temperature in copper assuming 1 free electron per atom. Compare this with the value of 2.4×10^4 joule (Kg mole)$^{-1}$ deg^{-1} for the total heat capacity.

10

Electrical and Thermal
Conductivities in Metals

In Chapter 9 we were concerned with those properties of solids, and in particular of metals, which can be treated by using only the distribution of electrons in the energy bands. We gave only an elementary treatment which ignored the detailed mechanisms whereby the electrons were accelerated. We wish now to describe the properties of metals that depend in detail on the changes in electron velocity.

10.1 Electrical Conduction

It was known from the early days of experimenting with static electricity that certain materials possessed the property of conducting electric charge from point to point under the influence of an electric field.

In many instances it is found experimentally that the current density j is proportional to the field $\mathscr{E}$ between the ends of the conductor. If we specify that this observation is to be made under certain conditions (uniform temperature of conductor to avoid thermoelectric contributions to $\mathscr{E}$, freedom from external magnetic fields to avoid resistance contributions from bending of electron trajectories, etc.) we can write Ohm's Law

$$j = \sigma \mathscr{E} \tag{10.1}$$

where σ is the *conductivity* or the reciprocal of the *resistivity* ρ. The aim of any theory of conductivity must therefore be a prediction of Ohm's Law in the cases where it is appropriate, and also the value of the resistivity of the material, that is the resistance per unit length per unit cross-sectional area.

The ease with which materials conduct electricity varies widely, giving an empirical classification into good conductors (metals) whose resistivity is of the order of 10^{-7} ohm m, "non" conductors (insulators) with resistivities of about the order of magnitude of 10^{13} ohm m, and a group of

Table 10.1

ELEMENT	RESISTIVITY (ohm m)	TEMPERATURE OF MEASUREMENT
	METALS	
Ag	1.6×10^{-8}	20°C
Al	2.83×10^{-8}	20°C
Cu	1.69×10^{-8}	20°C
Au	2.44×10^{-8}	20°C
Fe	8.85×10^{-8}	0°C
Hg	95.8×10^{-8}	20°C
Ni	7.24×10^{-8}	20°C
Na	4.3×10^{-8}	0°C
	SEMICONDUCTORS	
Ge	0.47	
Si	3×10^3	
In Sb	$\sim 2 \times 10^4$	
	INSULATORS	
Mica	9×10^{14}	
Quartz	3×10^{14}	
Diamond	10^{14}	

materials with a wide range of intermediate resistivity values called semiconductors. Typical values of resistivities are given in Table 10.1

The occurrence of this phenomenon of conductivity can be given an elementary description in terms of the band models we have been using. Consider a solid subject to an electric field. The electrons would like to move up the field direction, thereby gaining energy. However, the opportunity for any particular electron to gain energy is governed by whether or not there is an *available* and *empty* energy level at the new energy. If there is a level that can be occupied by the electron in its excited state, the electron will move under the influence of the field. If there is no available level, the electron cannot obtain energy from the field and so will not respond to it. The consequence of this argument is that, under the low energy kind of excitation involved in conductivity phenomena, the question of whether or not the material will conduct depends on whether or not the electrons at the *top* of the distribution can accept energy. If they can and do, they will leave spaces lower in the distribution into which electrons from deeper in the distribution can be excited, and so on. Thus the requirement of available states at the top of the distribution means that conductivity will occur only in an unfilled band, as in sodium (see Fig. 8.18), or in a filled band only if it overlaps the next higher unoccupied band, as in magnesium (see Fig. 8.19). If a band is just filled, as for example in

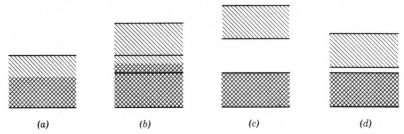

Figure 10.1   Electron occupation in various band configurations; (a) and (b) conductors, (c) insulator, and (d) semiconductor.

diamond (see Fig. 8.22), in general no response to a field will be possible. If, however, the energy gap between the filled band under discussion and the next higher unfilled band is not large, the possibility exists of excitation of electrons over the gap. This excitation could take place either because of thermal energy or field energy. In such a case conductivity would be observed, but its value would be a function of the degree of excitation between the two bands, that is, of the temperature or field. It will be seen in Chapter 11 that this is the situation in a semiconductor. The various possibilities are summarized in Fig. 10.1.

The response to an electric field can also be described in terms of the Fermi surface. In Fig. 10.2 the densely shaded sphere represents the Fermi surface in the absence of an external field. Electrons have velocities in all directions but no net current flows because the distribution is spherically symmetrical. Now consider the application of an electric field. On the assumption that the electrons all acquire an average velocity $v_{\mathscr{E}}$ in the $-x$ direction in the field, the altered distribution will be shown as the displaced sphere in Fig. 10.2. The distribution is no longer symmetrical about $v = 0$ and so net current flow will occur. Normally the energy supplied to electrons by a field is much smaller than the energy at the top of the distribution and the displacement indicated in Fig. 10.2 is a greatly exaggerated representation of a small perturbation. Other mechanisms for conductivity exist, for example, in "insulators," but these will be considered later.

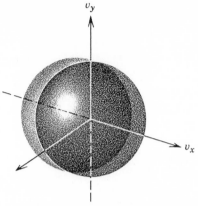

Figure 10.2   The displacement of the Fermi surface in a conductor carrying a current.

10.2   The Effective Mass of the Electron

To calculate the value of the conductivity it is necessary to consider the acceleration of an electron in the field applied to the material. One difference between the behavior of electrons bound in a solid and electrons in free space is immediately obvious. Electrons in free space are accelerated indefinitely by an applied field, but in a metal, even though we talk about "free" electrons, some process must be operative to restrict the current to the observed values. We shall discuss later the mechanism by which this limiting process works, but for the present it will suffice merely to say that the situation can be described by ascribing to the electron a time, τ, called the relaxation time, during which it can be accelerated. At the end of time τ the electron is "scattered" into a new state, thereby losing all the momentum gained in the field direction. Clearly such an assumption constitutes a modification of the standard Krönig-Penney model treatment (Section 7.8). In that treatment an electron will remain in its particular momentum state indefinitely, that is, τ is infinite.

Consider now an electron in a conductor in an electric field $\mathscr{E}$. The electron will be accelerated in the field direction. It is not too easy to see what value the acceleration should have on the basis of the treatment of the electron in a periodic lattice given in Chapter 7, because the motion of such an electron was shown not to obey the simple relations which hold for a free particle in classical mechanics. The classical mechanics energy-momentum relation for a free particle is simply

$$E = \frac{p^2}{2m} \qquad (10.2)$$

and the acceleration a of a charge e in a field $\mathscr{E}$ is

$$a = \frac{e\mathscr{E}}{m} \qquad (10.3)$$

For the electron in the periodic lattice, however, the energy-momentum relation turned out to be a most complicated function whose graph appeared in Fig. 7.22. This means that for this relation we no longer calculate velocities or accelerations from energy changes using the simple formulation of Newtonian mechanics.

To discuss this problem of the velocity of a particle in wave mechanics we refer to the statement in Section 6.2 that the *group velocity of the de Broglie waves is equal to the velocity of the particle which the wave is describing.* Let ω be the angular frequency of the de Broglie wave and κ its wave number. Then the group velocity v_g is $\dfrac{d\omega}{d\kappa}$.

Thus for the electron $\qquad v = \dfrac{2\pi}{h} \dfrac{dE}{d\kappa} \qquad (10.4)$

This relation now provides a means of calculating the velocity of an electron in the band model and consequently the acceleration. The acceleration is simply

$$a = \frac{2\pi}{h} \frac{d}{dt}\left(\frac{dE}{d\kappa}\right)$$

$$= \frac{2\pi}{h} \frac{d^2E}{d\kappa^2} \frac{d\kappa}{dt} \qquad (10.5)$$

Since we have the quantity $\dfrac{d^2E}{d\kappa^2}$ from the E, κ relation, all we have to do now is to find the value of $\dfrac{d\kappa}{dt}$ under the influence of an applied field $\mathscr{E}$.

Consider an electron to be acted on by a field during a time dt. If the velocity of the electron is v, the distance travelled in dt is $v\,dt$ so that

$$dE = e\mathscr{E} \cdot v\,dt$$

$$= e\mathscr{E} \frac{2\pi}{h} \frac{dE}{d\kappa}\,dt$$

that is, $\qquad \dfrac{d\kappa}{dt} = \dfrac{2\pi e\mathscr{E}}{h} \qquad (10.6)$

Combining equations 10.5 and 10.6 gives us, finally, for the acceleration

$$a = \frac{4\pi^2 e\mathscr{E}}{h^2}\frac{d^2E}{d\kappa^2} \tag{10.7}$$

Now compare this result with equation 10.3 for a free, classical particle. It is obvious that the two are identical in form if we define a new quantity.

$$m^* = \frac{h^2}{4\pi^2}\left(\frac{d^2E}{d\kappa^2}\right)^{-1} \tag{10.8}$$

so as to write in all cases

$$a = \frac{e\mathscr{E}}{m^*} \tag{10.9}$$

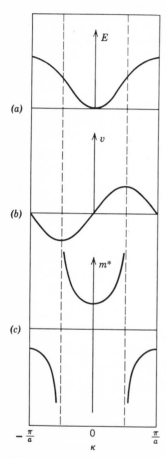

(a)

(b)

(c)

$-\dfrac{\pi}{a}$ 0 $\dfrac{\pi}{a}$

κ

Figure 10.3   The E, κ relation and effective mass in the first Brillouin zone of a linear lattice.

The quantity m^* is called *the effective mass of the electron*. It serves to take into account the nonclassical properties of the electron in the periodic lattice and consequently to enable us always to use the simple form of the acceleration equation.

The graphs of E, $dE/d\kappa$ and $d^2E/d\kappa^2$ in the first Brillouin zone of a linear lattice are given in Fig. 10.3. These graphs illustrate some surprising properties of the electron. From a constant value at $\kappa = 0$, m^* rises rapidly as the κ value (and the momentum) of the electron increases. Then m^* passes through a singularity and thereafter is clearly negative up to the top of the first zone. For a particular metal, of course, the actual behavior of the electrons will depend on the Fermi energy, that is, on how far out in the zone the electron distribution reaches. Some values of m^*/m for particular metals are given in Table 10.2.

The values given in Table 10.2 can be understood by reference to the appropriate E, κ relation. In Chapter 7 we did not write down an E, κ relation explicity but drew only the graph shown in Fig. 7.22. It is possible, however, to obtain an expression for E as a function of κ (see the text by Wilson in the Bibilography) which shows that, as the binding of electrons (i.e., the height V_0 of the potential barrier) increases, the steepness of the dependence of E on κ also increases. Consequently metals like the transition metals which have their Fermi energy falling in a tightly bound band like the 3d band will show relatively high values of $dE/d\kappa$ and $d^2E/d\kappa^2$. These are represented by the very high values of m^*/m for metals such as nickel and αFe. Lower values of m^*/m arise for cases where the valence electrons are less tightly bound and are governed merely by the position of the Fermi energy in the E, κ diagram.

Table 10.2

METAL	m^*/m
Ni	28
Fe	12
Pd	43
Pt	22
Cu	1.47
Mb	1.33
Ti	3.15
Zr	2.24
Cr	2.93
Li	1.53
Na	0.94
K	0.58
Be	1.62

It is worth taking some trouble to consider the physical basis of the somewhat surprising behaviour represented by the v-κ and m^*-κ curves.

For an electron near the middle of a zone and of low energy, the de Broglie wavelength is large compared with the lattice spacing. This allows the wave to be propagated comparatively freely through the lattice. (This would also happen of course for a high energy particle in which the wavelength is much *less* than the lattice spacing.) However, in the intermediate range in which the de Broglie wavelength is of the same order as the lattice spacing interference properties appear. Consider first the situation in which an electron has a κ value that coincides with the value at the top of the first zone of a linear lattice, that is, using equation 7.23,

$$\frac{1}{\lambda} = \frac{1}{2a} \qquad (10.10)$$

As has already been pointed out, this condition corresponds to Bragg reflection of the electron waves. It is particularly easy to see this for the linear lattice because the double journey from one lattice site to the next and back again after reflection constitutes one wavelength retardation. The direct and reflected waves are therefore in phase; this is the condition known as a "standing" wave, and is characterized by the fact that its amplitude modulation is stationary in space which gives us the $v = 0$ value at the top of the zone (remembering that it is the *group* velocity of the electron wave, i.e., the velocity of the amplitude modulation, which corresponds to the velocity of the electron). Now if we consider an electron with an energy in the upper part of the band, the wavelength of the de Broglie wave is greater than it was at the top of the band, and so the wave reflected from an adjacent lattice site is no longer exactly in phase with the direct wave. This results in an amplitude modulation which is not stationary and so corresponds to a finite velocity of the electron. However, it is a velocity which diminishes as the energy of the electron increases to make the wavelength closer to the "standing" wave value. This argument makes plausible the descending part of the v, E curve in the upper part of the zone. Apparent violations of Newton's second law do not occur because we are considering the response to the field of only part (the electron) of a compound system (the electron + the lattice).

The argument can be extended to cover the case of m^* corresponding to a point of inflection on the E, κ diagram. This value occurs at a wavelength that is twice as great as that at the top of the zone. The returning reflected wave is then exactly *out of phase* with the direct wave leading to the singularity represented by an infinite value of m^*.

We have by no means proved that the use of m^* in the classical acceleration equation is justified. It turns out in practice, however, that it is an almost invariably satisfactory way of taking the electron-lattice interaction into account without the necessity for considering each problem in terms of the the appropriate E, κ relation. In this way we can almost always take a result which is valid on the free electron model and make it valid for the periodic potential by substituting m^* for m. This is a great convenience. It must be noted carefully, however, that our simple treatment has used only a linear lattice. A real metal in three dimensions may be anisotropic, and the values of m^* appropriate to the three coordinate directions may differ. An arbitrary direction for the electron momentum would then require a tensor representation for m^*.

The influence of the band structure on the electrical properties of solids will therefore be seen whenever the mass of the electron enters an equation. In this way even static properties like the heat capacity are influenced because, as equation 9.19 shows, the electronic heat capacity is inversely proportional to the Fermi energy which is, in turn, inversely proportional to the electron mass. A similar situation holds for the paramagnetic properties of the electron gas and this is discussed in Chapter 12. The influence of the effective mass concept on properties like conduction is obvious and are taken up in this chapter as the necessity arises.

10.3   The Value of the Conductivity

We are now in a position to evaluate the conductivity of a conductor that depends on electrons for the transport of charge. Assuming a value for the acceleration of an electron under the influence of a field $\mathscr{E}$ from equation 10.9, we obtain for the velocity gained in time τ the value $v_{\mathscr{E}}$

where
$$v_{\mathscr{E}} = \frac{e\mathscr{E}}{m^*} \cdot \tau \qquad (10.11)$$

Note that this velocity $v_{\mathscr{E}}$ constitutes a drift velocity along the field direction. It is superimposed on the ordinary random velocities of the electrons that make no contribution to the current.

The current j is then the rate of flow of charge across unit area of the conductor perpendicular to the current flow; that is,

$$j = Nev_{\mathscr{E}} \qquad (10.12)$$

where N is the number of conduction electrons per unit volume. Thus,

$$j = \frac{Ne^2\tau}{m^*}\mathscr{E} \qquad (10.13)$$

Thus we have achieved our objective in obtaining Ohm's law, $j \propto \mathscr{E}$, as a consequence of the theory, and the conductivity is

$$\sigma = \frac{Ne^2\tau}{m^*} \qquad (10.14)$$

It should be noted that τ will differ for electrons from different parts of the conduction band. However, Fig. 10.2 shows that the perturbed distribution due to the field can be constructed by rearranging only those electrons near the surface of the distribution. Thus even though all the electrons in the valence band contribute to the current, the value of τ appropriate to equation 10.14 can be taken as that for the electrons near E_F. Using this condition we can define a mean free path l for the electrons as

$$l = v_F\tau \qquad (10.15)$$

where v_F is the velocity of the electrons near the Fermi surface. The conductivity equation then becomes

$$\sigma = \frac{Ne^2l}{m^*v_F} \qquad (10.16)$$

At this stage the question arises regarding the value of N to be used. On the free electron assumption this may be obvious as, for example, in sodium, where it would be fair to guess that the number of free electrons should be very close to one per atom. For more complicated atoms, however, the extent to which the band is filled becomes important because, as we shall see on page 241, some of the electron distribution can be blocked from participation in the response to the electric field. In this case we cannot say immediately what the number of conduction electrons should be and we talk about N_{eff}, the effective number of free electrons per atom. This number is the subject of either very detailed calculation or of measurement. Typical values of N_{eff} l, v_F, and τ are given in Table 10.3.

Table 10.3

METAL	N_{eff} (electrons per atom)	v_F (m sec^{-1})	τ (sec)	l (m)	σ (Ohm^{-1} m^{-1})
Na	~1	1.07×10^6	31×10^{-15}	6.7×10^{-8}	2.09×10^7
Cu	~1	1.58×10^6	27×10^{-15}	8.4×10^{-8}	5.76×10^7
Ag	~1	1.40×10^6	41×10^{-15}	11.4×10^{-8}	6.12×10^7
Au	~1	1.40×10^6	29×10^{-15}	8.1×10^{-8}	4.37×10^7
Ni	0.6	1.34×10^6	10×10^{-15}	2.7×10^{-8}	1.36×10^7
Fe	0.2	0.91×10^6	24×10^{-15}	4.4×10^{-8}	1.01×10^7
Pt	0.6	1.23×10^6	9×10^{-15}	2.2×10^{-8}	0.92×10^7

The actual value of the conductivity is therefore governed by the quantities N, m^*, and l (or τ). The parameter l plays the dominating role in determining the conductivity. No matter what value of l is found, however, the value of m^* will influence the conductivity. For instance the high values of m^* for the transition metals contribute to the low conductivity seen in Table 10.1, and the low m^* values for the alkali metals and for metals like silver and copper contribute to high conductivity.

10.4 Sources of Resistance

In the band theory of Krönig and Penney there is no provision for any alteration of the electron state of energy and momentum. In fact, it has been proved by Bloch that, in an ideal, perfectly periodic lattice an electron would, in the absence of external influences, remain in its state of energy or momentum indefinitely. The existence of the finite relaxation time τ in a certain state which is necessary in the description of conductivity must therefore be the consequence of departure of the lattice from perfect periodicity.

Such departures from perfection can be imagined to include:

1. The vibration of lattice atoms through temperature excitation
2. The presence of mechanical or chemical defects such as vacancies, interstitial atoms or impurities, dislocations, grain boundaries, etc.

In fact the variation of resistivity of a material with temperature shows features that we can identify with each of the foregoing mechanisms. The

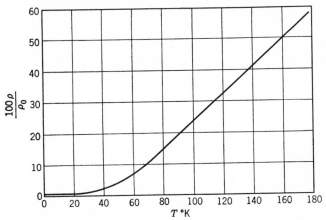

Figure 10.4   The temperature variation of the resistivity of copper. The resistivity is expressed as a fraction of that at 0°C. The curve is linear above a temperature of about 70°K, and the resistance is effectively constant at the residual value below about 15°K.

curve for copper is shown in Fig. 10.4. The curve shows the presence of a temperature-dependent contribution to the resistance which is approximately linear with temperature. This resistance we identify with that arising from lattice vibrations. The curve also shows a constant contribution to the resistance at a temperature low enough for the lattice vibration contribution to be neglected. This latter resistance is called the *residual resistance* and is assumed to arise from the second class of lattice imperfections.

At a finite temperature we must consider the presence of the two contributions simultaneously, that is, we must calculate the probability of scattering from one mechanism *or* the other. Since we can say that the scattering probability is proportional to $1/\tau$ we have

$$\frac{1}{\tau_{\text{total}}} = \frac{1}{\tau_R} + \frac{1}{\tau_T} \tag{10.17}$$

where τ_{total} is the effective relaxation time for the whole process, and τ_R and τ_T refer respectively to the relaxation time for scattering by defects and thermal vibrations. Thus we obtain for the total resistivity

$$\rho = \frac{m^*}{Ne^2}\left(\frac{1}{\tau_R} + \frac{1}{\tau_T}\right) \tag{10.18}$$

The presence of the two contributions can be seen in the resistivity of copper-nickel alloys shown in Fig. 10.5. Here the temperature-dependent

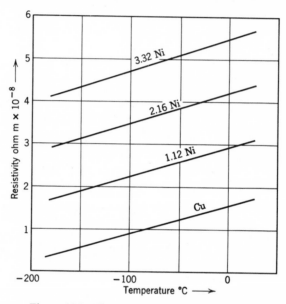

Figure 10.5 The resistivity of copper-nickel alloys showing the existence of the same temperature dependent resistivity superimposed on varying amounts of residual resistance.

resistance is added to the residual resistance, the latter increasing as the copper lattice is progressively distorted by the addition of impurities.

Finally we should observe that the relaxation time τ which we have been discussing is related to the response time of the electron distribution. This response time can be defined if we consider the electron distribution to be in equilibrium just prior to the switching off of the field. When the field is switched off the average drift velocity of the electrons will start to decay in a manner that can be assumed to be exponential so that we can write

$$v_\mathscr{E} = v_{\mathscr{E}0}e^{-t/\tau} \tag{10.19}$$

as illustrated in Fig. 10.6.

Equation 10.19 depends on the scattering being isotropic so that an electron has an equal probability of meeting a scattering center in any direction. Relaxation times are very short so that they affect only physical properties in which the electron distribution is very rapidly distorted.

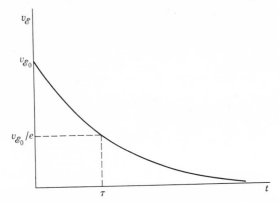

Figure 10.6   The relaxation of the average electron drift velocity.

10.5   The Lattice Vibration Contribution to the Resistivity

Experiment shows that the temperature variation of resistance is closely linear over a wide range of temperature. This linearity breaks down at low temperatures before the resistance falls to its residual value. The low temperature region is illustrated in Fig. 10.7. The linearity also breaks down at high temperatures as illustrated in Fig. 10.8. These departures will be discussed later, but in the meantime we shall confine our attention to the middle temperature range.

Let us consider that the effect of temperature on a solid is to make each atom oscillate between its neighbors with simple harmonic motion. The differential equation for such an oscillation will be

$$M\ddot{x} + cx = 0 \qquad (10.20)$$

where M is the mass of the atom, c is the restoring force for unit displacement, and x is the displacement. The frequency of vibration f is then given by

$$4\pi^2 f^2 = \frac{c}{M} \qquad (10.21)$$

This frequency f is used to define a temperature Θ through the equation

$$hf = k\Theta \qquad (10.22)$$

(k is Boltzmann's constant). The quantity Θ is called the *characteristic temperature* for the lattice because it depends specifically on the atomic masses and interatomic forces of the particular solid. In its role of governing lattice vibrations the characteristic temperature is an important constant of the solid, and values will be found in Table 10.4. It must be stressed that this model of the vibrational properties of the solid is grossly

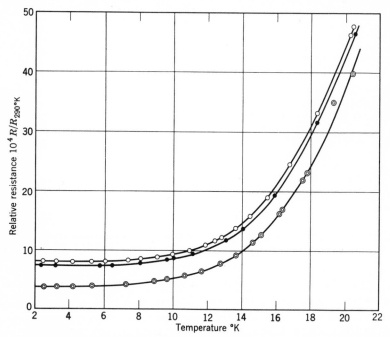

Figure 10.7   The resistance of three samples of sodium. (After MacDonald and Mendelssohn).

oversimplified. It is much more likely that, instead of having just one frequency of atomic vibration, there should be a whole spectrum of frequencies. In fact such an assumption enables us to calculate very satisfactorily the heat capacity of solids. The single frequency model carries the name of Einstein and the frequency spectrum model that of Debye. The divergences between the two are apparent only for $T < \Theta$ and we are, at present, discussing the resistance at higher temperatures.

To return to the problem of electron scattering, it can be shown rigorously that the probability that an electron will be scattered from such a displaced atom is proportional to the square of the displacement. This is a very plausible result because the probability of scattering should depend on the distortion of the potential seen by the electron. This distortion

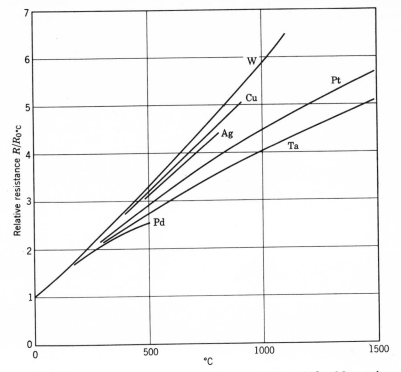

Figure 10.8   The high-temperature resistance of metals. (After Mott and Jones).

Table 10.4

ELEMENT	Θ (°K)
Ag	229
Al	375
Au	164
Cu	343
Fe	355
Hg	75
Mg	342
Na	160
Pb	96
Pt	233

depends on the energy of the displaced atom, which is proportional to the square of the displacement. Hence the resistivity contribution should be proportional to the mean square displacement of the scattering atom. Other factors may enter, but we shall restrict ourselves to the simple calculation.

Let us assume

$$\rho \propto \overline{x^2} \tag{10.23}$$

Now we can calculate the value of $\overline{x^2}$ because it is the quantity that appears in calculating the potential energy of a body vibrating under elastic forces. In fact

$$\overline{cx^2} = \text{average potential energy in one cycle}$$
$$= \text{one-half maximum potential energy}$$
$$= \text{one-half total energy of vibration}$$

This last statement arises because in oscillation the energy is shared alternately between kinetic and potential forms whereas the total is constant.

The law of equipartition of energy states that the total energy per degree of freedom per atom is $\frac{1}{2}kT$, so that, assuming a one-dimensional oscillation,

$$\overline{cx^2} = \frac{1}{2}kT \tag{10.24}$$

or

$$\overline{x^2} = \frac{1}{2}\frac{k}{cT}$$

Hence using equations 10.21 and 10.22 it is easy to show that

$$\overline{x^2} = \frac{kh^2}{8\pi kM\Theta^2} \cdot T \tag{10.25}$$

and thus

$$\rho \propto \frac{T}{M\Theta^2} \tag{10.26}$$

Equation 10.26 summarizes all the important aspects of the temperature-dependent scattering. It contains the result we wanted that, within a suitable temperature range (whose limits will be discussed shortly), the resistance is linearly dependent on the temperature. It also suggests that the mass and elasticity properties of the lattice are described by the $M\Theta^2$ term. Therefore, if we wish to isolate the factors *other* than the temperature that contribute to the absolute value of the conductivity of the metal, that is, those contained in the constant of the proportionality in equation 10.26, the quantity we should discuss is $\rho M\Theta^2$ or $\sigma/M\Theta^2$. The other factors in question would be quantities such as the electron's momentum at the Fermi surface, the effective number of conduction electrons, and the actual value for the probability of scattering at any displaced atom.

The influence of the latter factors is illustrated in Fig. 10.9. This curve demonstrates first the high conductivity of the alkali metals and the copper, silver, gold group which arises from low scattering probability. Second, it

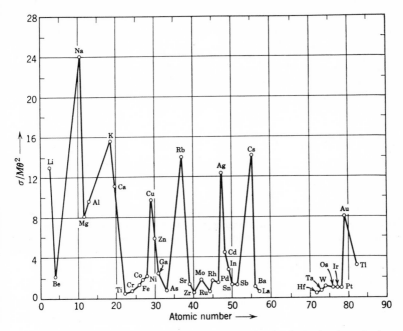

Figure 10.9   The variation of electron scattering by the lattice through the periodic table.

shows the much lower conductivity that is characteristic of the divalent metals, the reason for this probably being associated with the almost complete occupation of the first band. Nearly filled bands contribute very little to the conductivity because so much of the electron distribution is in contact with the zone boundary as illustrated for a square lattice in Fig. 10.10a. This situation cannot be perturbed much by an electric field because such a small fraction of the Fermi surface has adjacent and empty states that the electrons can occupy. These are conditions close to the completely filled band, which does not respond at all to the electric field. Even though the common divalent metals do show a certain degree of penetration of the Fermi surface into the second zone as shown in Fig. 10.10b, considerable areas of the Fermi surface can still be blocked by

Brillouin zone boundaries against perturbation by the field. Thus, although there are twice as many electrons per atom as in the monovalent metals, the value of N_{eff} may be considerably less than one per atom. The electron distribution for a monovalent metal with its complete freedom to deform under an electric field is shown in Fig. 10.10c for comparison.

The last feature illustrated in Fig. 10.9 is the low conductivity exhibited by the transition metals. Here the reason is a high scattering probability. It is a general result of quantum mechanical scattering theory that scattering probabilities are proportional to the state density in the energy region to

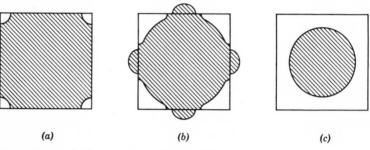

(a)   (b)   (c)

Figure 10.10   (a) The occupation of the first Brillouin in a case for which it is almost filled. (b) The complete occupation diagram for a divalent metal with band overlap. (c) The Fermi surface for a monovalent metal.

which the particle is scattered. In the transition elements the conduction is dominated by s electrons with an m^* value not far from unity, whereas the electrons in the $3d$ band will contribute less to the conductivity because of their high m^*. Because of the high state density in the d band, however, the probability of scattering from the s band to the d band is high and the conductivity correspondingly low.

The deviations that arise at high and low temperatures are the consequence of breakdown of the assumptions regarding the frequency of the lattice vibrations. At low temperatures, that is, when $T < \Theta$ the assumption of a single frequency as in the Einstein model becomes invalid. A more detailed treatment involving the actual spectrum of lattice vibration yields the result that the resistance should be proportional to the fifth power of the temperature.

At high temperatures the single frequency assumption is reasonably satisfactory, but the actual value of the appropriate frequency may be temperature dependent. This is because at temperatures of hundreds of degrees, thermal expansion reduces the magnitude of the atomic restoring forces. A lower frequency means a lower Θ and a resistivity greater than that expected on the basis of a simple proportionality with T. This is the case illustrated in Fig. 10.8. The figure also shows that in other metals such as palladium, platinum, and tantalum, the resistance lies *below* the linear variation with T. This is probably because of a change in the scattering probability with temperature. The scattering is of s electrons into the d band, but as the temperature rises the top of the electron distribution approaches the top of the d band where the state density is falling very sharply. This provides less opportunity for the higher energy electrons to be scattered, thus yielding a lower resistivity.

The value of the Debye Θ is also affected by external stress since the frequency of the atomic vibrations must be influenced by any extra contributions to the forces between the atoms. The resistivity of a material is therefore stress-dependent, a feature which forms the basis of strain gauge operation.

It may be mentioned in concluding the discussion of lattice scattering of electrons that a quantum description of the lattice vibrations is possible. Just as it was necessary to construct a quantum picture for apparently continuous electromagnetic waves, so it is possible to describe the lattice vibrations by quanta of sound waves. These are given the name *phonons*, and the problem of lattice scattering of electrons becomes one of electron-photon interactions. This interpretation becomes most significant at low temperatures.

10.6　The Residual Resistivity

It has been pointed out already that the resistivity resulting from contributions other than the lattice vibrations can be studied at temperatures below about 10–15°K (see Fig. 10.7). The most important source of such a resistivity is impurity in the metal lattice. Provided the concentration of impurity atoms is not too high, the impurity resistivity turns out to be independent of temperature.

The value of ρ_{impurity} is obviously dependent on the fraction of impurity atoms, and Fig. 10.5 shows how the contribution from ρ_{impurity} rises with increasing concentration of nickel atoms in copper. Note that at these fractions of nickel, the added atoms can be regarded as an impurity in an otherwise pure matrix. The case where two components are present in roughly equal proportions to constitute an alloy will be considered later.

Yet another contribution to the residual resistance is provided by lattice defects. Unfortunately at present the theory of scattering from such defects is far from satisfactory. In any case the contribution to the resistivity from point defects or dislocations is small and is significant only for very pure materials at low temperatures. It becomes of practical importance at

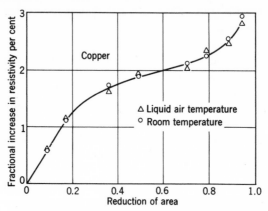

Figure 10.11   The increase in resistivity caused by cold work. The lattice distortion was effected by drawing the material through a die.

normal temperatures only after relatively severe working of the metal or after irradiation by high energy particles. Figure 10.11 shows resistivity changes brought about by lattice distortion.

Experimentally the contributions from the various types of defect can be studied by creating a variety of defects in the lattice at a very low

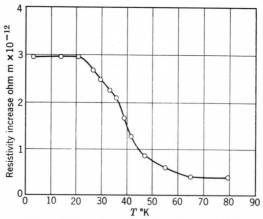

Figure 10.12   The annealing out of radiation-produced sources of resistance. The specimen was first irradiated at the low temperature. The experimental points were then obtained by pulse heating the specimen and holding it for 10-minute periods at successively higher temperatures; each 10-minute annealing being followed by a resistivity measurement at 4.2°K.

temperature. This is commonly done by irradiating the specimen at liquid hydrogen or liquid helium temperatures using a nuclear reactor or a particle accelerator. As the specimen is allowed to warm up gradually the excess resistivity disappears, frequently in sudden jumps at well-defined temperatures as shown in Fig. 10.12. The temperatures at which the jumps take place are those at which certain types of defect become mobile and so anneal out. Since the activation energies for the movement of defects are known to some extent, it then becomes possible to identify each part of the excess resistivity with the various kinds of defect, interstitial-vacancy pairs, dislocations, etc.

10.7 The Resistivity of Alloys

In Section 10.6, mention was made of the resistance contribution to a pure solid from a second constituent. The additive was there treated as an

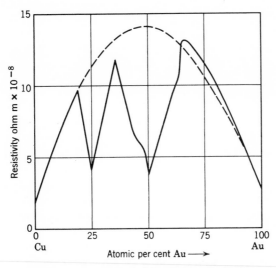

Figure 10.13   The resistivity of copper-gold alloys. The full line refers to annealed samples and the dashed line to quenched samples.

impurity. However, in a genuine alloy in which the constituents are present in roughly equal proportions, we must be concerned with the structure of the lattice as a whole rather than with the presence of a few impurity atoms in an otherwise perfect matrix.

Figure 10.13 shows typical behavior in copper-gold alloys. At each end of the curve there is a smooth increase in resistivity since this is the condition of a small amount of impurity distributed in an otherwise perfect lattice. The dashed curve represents the resistivity for disordered quenched alloys. However, annealed alloys can form the ordered structures Cu_3 Au and Cu Au and these have the minima of resistivity at the appropriate values of concentration.

10.8   High-Frequency Conduction Effects

All standard books on electrodynamics show that alternating electric fields differ from static electric fields in that they do not penetrate uniformly through a conductor but decay in magnitude exponentially from the surface inward. The decay can be described by a *penetration depth*, which is the distance from the surface at which the field strength has been reduced by a factor of $1/e$. The penetration depth increases with increasing wavelength and also depends on the resistance of the material being greater for poor conductivity materials. Typical values for copper are:

Wavelength	1 cm	1 m	100 m	10 km
Penetration depth	2.4×10^{-4} cm	0.024 mm	0.24 mm	2.4 mm

The electromagnetic theory from which these values are calculated is valid only in the region $T > \tau$ where T is the period of the alternating electric field and τ is again the relaxation time of the electron distribution. Other treatments are necessary at higher frequencies where relaxation effects are important. A simplified treatment is given below. It turns out that a typical value of the penetration depth for metals in the optical region is 200 Å.

To consider the optical properties of metals we shall first treat the simple case which neglects resistivity effects. This is equivalent to the assumption that $T < \tau$. Remembering the values of τ from Table 10.3, this restriction puts us in the visible and ultraviolet region.

The equation of motion of a free electron (no binding forces) under the influence of a periodic electric field $\mathscr{E} = \mathscr{E}_0 e^{i\omega t}$ of angular frequency ω can be written

$$m\ddot{x} = -e\mathscr{E}_0 e^{i\omega t} \tag{10.27}$$

which, on solving, gives

$$x = - \frac{e\mathscr{E}_0 e^{i\omega t}}{m\omega^2} \tag{10.28}$$

The displacement of electrons represented by this equation gives an electronic polarization P (see Chapter 13), per unit volume, of magnitude nex where n is the number of electrons per unit volume.

Thus

$$P = \frac{Ne^2 \mathscr{E}_0 e^{i\omega t}}{m\omega^2} \tag{10.29}$$

The dielectric constant ϵ_r is defined in equation 13.7 as

$$\epsilon_r = 1 + \frac{P}{\epsilon_0 \mathscr{E}}$$

and thus the dielectric constant due to electronic polarization is

$$\epsilon_r = 1 + \frac{Ne^2}{\epsilon_0 m\omega^2} \tag{10.30}$$

It is a simple consequence of the definitions of refractive index, n_0 and dielectric constant, and of their relations with the velocity of electromagnetic radiation that

$$\epsilon_r = n_0^2$$

Thus the refractive index of the solid is

$$n_0^2 = 1 - \frac{Ne^2}{\epsilon_0 m\omega^2} \tag{10.31}$$

There are two cases to consider:

1. When $Ne^2/\epsilon_0 m\omega^2 > 1$.

Here the right-hand side of equation 10.31 becomes negative and the refractive index is imaginary. This condition is shown in texts on optics to correspond to total reflection of the wave from the surface. This is the normal condition in metals in the visible region, and if the reflection is not completely perfect it is because of dissipative effects to be considered later.

2. When $Ne^2/\epsilon_0 m\omega^2 < 1$.

Here n_0 is real and this is the condition, familiar through experience with glass and other dielectrics, of transparency. This condition does actually happen in metals for which the foregoing treatment is valid (i.e., for really *free* electrons) provided the frequency of the radiation is high enough. The effect is observed in the alkali metals in the ultraviolet beyond the critical wavelength λ_0, which is given by the condition

$$\frac{Ne^2}{\epsilon_0 m\omega^2} = 1 \tag{10.32}$$

Critical wavelengths are given in Table 10.5.

When the period of the applied electric field approaches the relaxation time of the electron distribution, the electrons' motion gets a little out of phase with the applied field. Relaxation absorption is observed. This will not be discussed. We will merely list a few of the mechanisms which contribute to absorption.

The most obvious contribution to scattering of the electrons is by the lattice. This dissipates the reradiation from the electron that constitutes the reflected wave. Energy can also be absorbed by the electrons directly from the incident wave, that is, by excitations of electrons to states higher in the

Table 10.5

METAL	λ_0 OBSERVED	λ_0 CALCULATED
Cs	4400	3600
Rb	3600	3200
K	3150	2900
Na	2100	2100
Li	2050	1500

conduction band. This effect is known as the internal photoelectric effect and is particularly prominent in transition metals. For example, excitation of the $3d$ electrons in copper absorbs blue light preferentially, leaving the red to be reflected. In the metals in which the $3d$ band is only partly full, the corresponding transition lies toward the infrared, and so *all* visible wavelengths are poorly reflected. Similar internal photoelectric transitions are responsible for the yellow color of gold and the well-marked absorption by silver in the ultraviolet.

10.9　Cyclotron Resonance

One important type of experiment in which high frequency radiation is absorbed is called *cyclotron resonance*. The technique is well known for ions in free space but has only recently been studied for electrons in solids.

Consider a charge q to move with velocity $\mathbf{v}$ in a plane perpendicular to a field of magnetic induction $\mathbf{B}$. The path is circular with a radius r given by the equilibrium condition

$$Bev = \frac{mv^2}{r}$$

or

$$r = \frac{mv}{Be} \tag{10.33}$$

The time for the circuit is

$$T = \frac{2\pi r}{v}$$

or

$$T = \frac{2\pi m}{Be} \qquad (10.34)$$

Notice that the time is independent of r, a feature on which the operation of the cyclotron particle accelerator is based. If energy is supplied in the form of an alternating field of the correct frequency, energy will be absorbed by the charge regardless of the radius of the path.

In the solid state the phenomenon is particularly important. The frequency at which absorption will take place is given by an equation like (10.34) but for such an application we must use the effective mass m^*. The resonant frequency v is therefore

$$v = \frac{Be}{2\pi m^*} \qquad (10.35)$$

This phenomenon is therefore suitable for making a direct measurement of effective mass. If a single crystal specimen is used, the effective mass tensor for the various crystal axes can be determined by using different orientations of **B**. To observe the cyclotron resonance absorption signal it is necessary that the electron be able to traverse a significant fraction of the whole circular path before being scattered. This normally restricts the observation of the effect to very pure materials at liquid helium temperatures. A simple calculation will show that, for typical values of m^*, magnetic inductions of the order of webers per square meter require frequencies in the tens of thousands of megacycles. If both electrons and holes (see page 265) are present in a specimen, they will both resonate, and two separate resonance frequencies will be observed.

The measurement of m^* gives, of course, the value of $dE/d\kappa$ at the top of the electron distribution. By using varying orientations of orbit for a single crystal specimen, the shape of the whole constant energy surface for a material may be evaluated.

10.10   The Conduction of Heat by Electrons and the Lattice

In metals electrons are the principal carriers of heat energy. This they do by being excited by energetic scattering centers (usually atoms) and carrying the extra energy to yield it up at another scattering center in a cooler part of the metal. The heat conductivity will obviously behave like the electrical conductivity, and will be high or low according as the conductor is a good or bad conductor.

We shall write the energy transferred by electrons between two planes spaced apart at a distance of one electronic mean free path in a solid containing a thermal gradient. Suppose we consider a metal with a thermal gradient. Let us try to write an expression for the thermal

Table 10.6

ELEMENT	THERMAL CONDUCTIVITY AT ROOM TEMPERATURE (watts $m^{-2}(°K\ m^{-1})^{-1}$)
Al	208
Ag	421
Au	295
Cu	384
Fe	67
Hg	6.3
Mg	157
Na	134
Pb	35
Pt	69
Glass	0.7
Ice	2.1
NaCl	7.1
Sapphire	2.5
Ge	59
Si	84

conductivity between two planes spaced apart a distance of one electronic mean free path. Since the heat is carried by the free electrons, this problem is directly analogous to that of the thermal conductivity of a gas and the standard texts give an expression for the conductivity K:

$$K = \tfrac{1}{3}Cv\lambda \tag{10.36}$$

where C is the heat capacity of the gas, v is the average velocity of the gas molecules, and λ is the mean free path. If we apply this result directly to our case of a free electron gas we must use the electron heat capacity (equation 9.19) for C, v_F the Fermi velocity for v (since only electrons near the surface of the distribution are affected by scattering processes), and the electronic mean free path l of electrons near the Fermi energy.

With these substitutions we obtain an expression for the thermal conductivity due to electrons in metals, namely

$$K = \frac{\pi^2}{3} \frac{\mathcal{N} k^2 l T}{m^* v_F} \qquad (10.37)$$

In metals the thermal conductivity due to electrons is much larger than the lattice conductivity due to the vibrational motion of the ions (which will be considered later) and accounts for the familiar high thermal conductivity of metals. Typical values are given in Table 10.6.

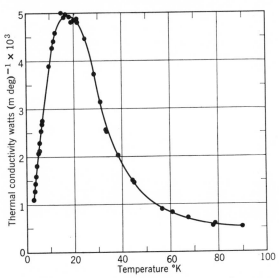

Figure 10.14   The temperature variation of thermal conductivity in copper.

The temperature dependence of K is not obvious. Certainly it contains a simple T term, but we must not forget that the electronic mean free path is also a function of temperature. Insofar as $\rho \propto T$, l will be proportional to $1/T$ and the thermal conductivity should be independent of temperature. At lower temperatures, however, the balance breaks down. The complete curve is shown in Fig. 10.14. The conductivity, of course, has to go to zero at very low temperatures because l becomes constant and the T term remains.

From equation 10.14 which gave the electrical conductivity, and from (10.37) which gave the thermal conductivity, we can find the ratio of the two, namely

$$\frac{K}{\sigma} = \frac{\pi^2}{3} \left(\frac{k}{e}\right)^2 T \qquad (10.38)$$

This linear dependence of κ/σ on T is known as the *Law of Wiedemann and Franz*. The constant multiplying number is called the *Lorenz number L*, that is,

$$L = \frac{\pi^2}{3}\left(\frac{k}{e}\right)^2$$

$$= 2.45 \times 10^{-8}\,\text{watt ohm deg}^{-2} \tag{10.39}$$

In the region in which $\rho \propto T$, that is, for $T > \Theta$, the value of $\kappa/\sigma T$ should be a constant for all conductors. Values of the Lorenz number obtained from various materials are given in Table 10.7.

Table 10.7

ELEMENT	LORENTZ NUMBER (watt ohm deg^{-2})
Al	2.23×10^{-8}
Ag	2.37×10^{-8}
Cu	2.33×10^{-8}
Fe	2.47×10^{-8}
Pb	2.56×10^{-8}
Pt	2.60×10^{-8}

Although the electronic contribution to the heat conductivity in metals is by far the larger, we must not forget that the lattice, too, conducts heat. Indeed the relative abilities of the electrons and the lattice to conduct heat is apparent in the familiar and perceptible difference between the thermal conductivities of metals and insulators. We do not intend to pursue the topic of lattice thermal conductivity further, and we shall say merely that, in essence, the theoretical treatment deals with the probability of scattering of lattice waves. Values for the thermal conductivities of insulators are also given in Table 10.6. Note how they compare with those for metals. Naturally, in a metal the two mechanisms exist side by side, and comparison of the values in the two tables will show the extent to which the electronic factor predominates.

The thermoelectric effect is a phenomenon related to the thermal conductivity of electrons in that it too is a consequence of the drift of electrons under a thermal gradient. There are two aspects to thermo-electric phenomena. The first is the Seebeck effect in which a temperature difference between the two junctions of two dissimilar materials gives rise to an emf in the circuit. The second is the Peltier effect in which, if a current is circulated in a circuit consisting of two dissimilar materials, heat is liberated at one junction and absorbed at the other. Both effects are the subject of considerable study because of their practical applications. The generation of electrical power using the Seebeck effect offers the desirable freedom from moving parts, and similar advantages are available in the use of the Peltier effect in refrigeration. In either case one of the chief considerations is the size of the effect, which is a consequence of the detailed electronic structure of the two materials, and a simple theoretical treatment is not available. It emerges, however, that the parameters of the material which are significant in this respect are the same as for the conductivity—namely the effective mass of the electrons and the relaxation time. Thermoelectric effects of either sign can be observed, depending mainly on whether electron effects or hole effects (see page 265) are predominant. By careful selection of the parameters using doped semi-conductors, thermoelectric power supplies now have efficiencies approach-ing 20 per cent (vs. $\sim$ 40 per cent for conventional steam plants) and thermoelectric refrigerators have been built which can maintain a tempera-ture 50°F below room temperature.

10.11 Superconductivity

We have stated earlier that if the temperature of a metal is lowered, the resistance diminishes until, at temperatures below about 10–15°K it levels out at the residual value. This is true of many of the metals we have been discussing, the alkali metals, the transition elements and metals like copper, silver, and gold. It was discovered by Kammerlingh Onnes in 1911, however, that a totally new phenomenon can be observed at tem-peratures in the liquid helium range. It appeared that at a certain tem-perature and within a very narrow temperature range the resistance of many metals could become zero, as illustrated in Fig. 10.15. The name *superconductivity* was given to the phenomenon.

Superconductivity has now been observed in 23 metals and over 450 alloys and compounds. Transition temperatures for the metals and some of the more significant alloys and compounds are given in Table 10.8. Note that in the search for materials that can become superconducting at higher temperatures, temperatures of over 18°K have been found for niobium–tin alloys. Further mention will be made later of some of these alloys.

The crystal state of a material is important in determining the super-conducting properties. In some cases one phase is superconducting and another not. Gray and white tin is an example of this. White tin, the normal variety, is tetragonal and is superconducting; gray tin is cubic and is apparently not superconducting. In other cases, two different phases have different transition temperatures. Examples are mercury, lanthanum, and uranium and these are found in Table 10.8. Sometimes an element becomes superconducting only in the highly specialized structure which results from condensation from the vapor at low temperatures. Beryllium, for example, is superconducting only when so deposited in thin films. One other circumstance is illustrated by bismuth, which becomes superconducting in bulk form only under pressure. A rough classification exists between "soft" superconductors like tin, mercury, and indium and "hard"

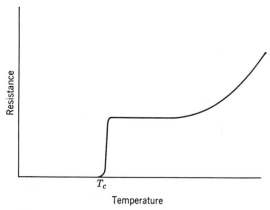

Figure 10.15 The form of the superconducting transition.

superconductors like tantalum, vanadium, and niobium. The distinction between their properties will be brought out as we describe them.

We shall now describe some of the more important properties of superconductors. There is no doubt that superconductivity is a state of genuinely zero resistance and not merely one of very small resistance. It is possible to induce a permanent current in a closed loop of superconducting wire. Any trace of resistance in the material would be detectable by decay of this current. Such currents have been allowed to persist by Dr. Collins of M.I.T. for a period of several years without detectable decay, thus suggesting the complete absence of resistive mechanisms.

It is possible to destroy the superconducting state by the application of a magnetic field. If a long thin superconducting wire is placed in a longitudinal field, the critical field is found to be different for various superconductors and is, furthermore, a function of temperature. The form of the temperature variation is close to being parabolic as represented by

$$H_c = H_0\left[1 - \left(\frac{T}{T_c}\right)^2\right] \tag{10.40}$$

where H_c and H_0 are the critical fields at temperatures of $T°$K and $0°$K respectively, and T_c is the critical temperature. The critical field curve for some superconductors is illustrated in Fig. 10.16. The soft superconductors tend to have lower critical fields than the hard superconductors.

A related effect is observed when the current through a superconducting wire is increased in the absence of any external field. A critical current is

Table 10.8

ELEMENT OR COMPOUND	TRANSITION TEMPERATURE (°K)
Al	1.17
Hg α	4.15
Hg β	3.95
In	3.4
La α	∼5.0
La β	5.95
Nb	9.2
Pb	7.2
Sn	3.72
Ta	4.4
Ti	0.4
V	5.0
Zn	0.8
NbN	15.6
Nb$_4$Sn	18.2
Au$_2$Bi	1.7

observed at which the resistance of the wire is suddenly partially restored, tending to the full value as the current is increased further, as shown in Fig. 10.17. Silsbee's hypothesis states that the critical current i_c is the current that produces, at the surface of the wire, a field equal to the critical value H_c. That is,

$$H_c = \frac{2i_c}{10a}$$

or

$$i_c = 5aH_c \qquad (10.41)$$

where a is the radius of the wire. (These equations are written in terms of the following units, a in cm, H_c in oersted, and i_c in amp.) The critical current and critical field obviously have the same temperature dependence.

The destruction of superconductivity by a field is rather different when a bulk specimen is used rather than the long, thin specimen oriented parallel to the field we have so far envisaged. The problem arises in the following

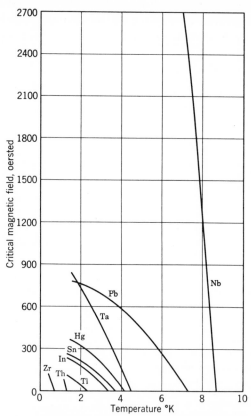

Figure 10.16 Critical field curves for some superconductors. (To conform with current usage in this subject, the fields are measured in oersted. To convert oersted to amp m^{-1}, see the Appendix.)

way. It is a simple deduction from electromagnetic field theory that perfect conductivity leads to the condition

$$\frac{\partial B}{\partial t} = 0 \tag{10.42}$$

where B is the field of magnetic induction threading the material and t is time. The condition can be rewritten

$$B = \text{constant}$$

The constant value of B should be the one used at the time when the perfectly conducting state was initiated. Suppose then that we take a cylindrical sample of superconductor at a temperature below T_c and impose on it a small transverse magnetic field. The initial value of B inside the superconductor was zero so B must remain zero as the field

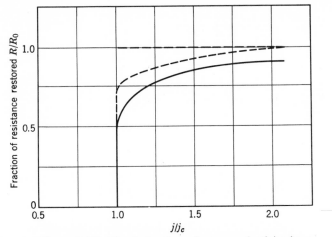

Figure 10.17   The destruction of superconductivity by a current. The full line represents the theoretical result and the dashed line is an experimental curve for tin.

grows. The material is thus behaving perfectly diamagnetic, and the flux lines outside it will be as shown in Fig. 10.18.

The concentration of the flux lines at the points X and X means that the field is higher there than it is at a great distance from the superconductor. Thus if we increase the value of the field, it will reach a value H_c at points X and X before the field at infinity has this value. In fact, for a cylinder the field at X and X would be H_c whereas it would only be $\frac{1}{2}H_c$ at great distances. The critical condition just described is, in fact, adequate to initiate the transition from superconducting to normal conditions. From then on the specimen exists in a rather complex mixture of superconductive and normal regions known as the *intermediate state*. If the field is increased further the proportion of normal material grows at the expense of that of the superconductive material until, when the external field equals H_c the material is wholly normal and the transition is complete.

If we now remove the external field, a rather surprising phenomenon can be observed. The superconductor does not behave like a perfect conductor in which the flux stays at the value it had on initiation of the state. Instead the flux is actually ejected to a greater or lesser extent. If a pure, strain-free material is used, the flux ejection can be almost complete and the phenomenon is called the *Meissner effect*. If the conditions given earlier are not filled, the ejection of flux can be incomplete, leaving a certain fraction of the flux as *trapped flux*. Hard superconductors and alloys tend to trap flux more than soft superconductors. However, the effect is used to specify a condition for the superconducting material that

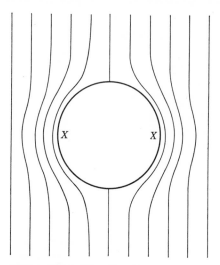

Figure 10.18 The flux lines around a superconducting cylinder.

the flux value in it is not merely constant but is identically zero. Thus the experimental conditions defining the superconducting state are:

$$\mathscr{E} = 0 \text{ (from the absence of resistance)}$$
$$B = 0 \text{ (from the Meissner effect)}$$

By using thermodynamic arguments, it is possible to relate the thermal and magnetic properties of superconducting materials. This will not be pursued here since enough description has now been given to provide a basis for understanding the practical application of superconductivity.

Theoretical treatments of the mechanisms leading to superconductivity were unsatisfactory until very recently. In 1956 a theoretical model was proposed by Bardeen, Cooper, and Schrieffer. The essence of any successful treatment of superconductivity must be a modification of the old single-electron treatment, exemplified by the Krönig-Penny model, to take into account electron-electron interactions. That such interactions are responsible for the onset of superconductivity is strongly suggested by many experiments which are interpreted in terms of *correlation* of electronic momenta. By using this approach, the Bardeen-Cooper-Shrieffer theory does give an electron occupation spectrum which, below a certain temperature enables the electrons to settle in a gound state separated from the other available states by an energy gap. This energy gap provides the required freedom from scattering. The energy available is not enough to carry the electron over the gap and so no scattering transition is possible. A description will now be given of two ways in which superconductivity has become of practical importance.

It was early recognized that superconductivity could be used in gating circuits, and the main initial development was worked out by Buck who

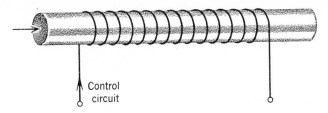

Control
circuit

Figure 10.19   The cryotron in its original form.

invented the term "cryotron." In reference to Fig. 10.19, we see that a current in the control circuit can destroy superconduction in the longitudinal wire, thus closing the gate. By appropriate choice of materials it is possible to use a small current to control a larger one, thus providing the equivalent of a relay. In actual fact the long time constant of the control circuit in the original form illustrated in Fig. 10.19 made the device too slow for the applications in computers, etc., for which it was otherwise well suited. This objection has now been overcome by the use of thin film techniques as shown in Fig. 10.20. In this configuration the lowered inductance provides time constants as low as 10^{-9} sec. This constant is amply low for computer applications. Using similar techniques, we can build bistable elements, thus providing the opportunity for storage of one "bit" of information. The technique provides the opportunity to construct the memory and logic elements necessary in computer work. The advantage, of course, lies in the extremely low power dissipation of a superconducting element. Electrical energy is degraded into thermal only during actual switching, and even then the amount is low. The disadvantage is the necessity for continuous refrigeration, but the availability of liquid helium from commercial sources means that this is no longer the serious problem it would have been even in 1939 when only about ten laboratories in the world had liquid helium available.

The second application of superconductivity is concerned with the production of high magnetic fields. The early discovery that hard super-conductors and alloys had critical fields much higher than those of soft

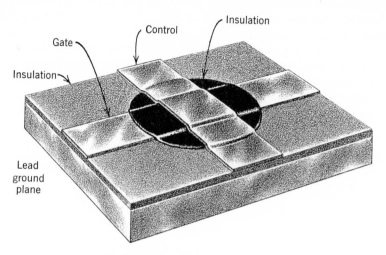

Figure 10.20   The thin film cryotron.

superconductors raised a hope that these could be used to carry resistance-free currents to provide high magnetic fields. This freedom from degenera-tive dissipation of energy would be a useful feature. For fields above about 2 webers m⁻² there is little point in using iron-cored magnets, because the core is completely saturated and contributes nothing more to

Table 10.9

COMPOUND	FIELD B IN WHICH SUPER-CONDUCTING IS STILL OBSERVED (webers m^{-2})
Nb₃Sn	18.5
Mo₃Re	1.8
NbZr	4.8
TiMo	3.0

the magnetic induction. Fields above this range are commonly produced by solenoids using a brute-force technique of high currents. Even with conductors that may be copper strips of centimeter dimensions, the resistance in a solenoid can lead to power dissipation in the range of hundreds of kilowatts within a region of maximum dimension less than a meter. This poses a cooling problem and leads to pulsed field techniques in which the experiment lasts about a millisecond. It was therefore a disappointment when the high critical field alloys turned out to have critical currents which were not correspondingly high. This violation of Silsbee's hypothesis apparently precluded any use of superconducting materials for high magnetic field production. It has recently been found however, that certain alloys and compounds do retain some kind of super-conducting paths both for very high fields and also for very high current densities. Such techniques have revolutionized high magnetic field work. Systems are now available commercially which can produce fields up to 6 webers m^{-2} continuously and involving no power dissipation at all.

REFERENCES

L. V. Azaroff, *Introduction to Solids*, McGraw-Hill Book Company, New York, 1960.

H. A. Boorse, Some Experimental Aspects of Superconductivity, *Am. J. Phys.* **27**, 47, 1959.

J. W. Bremer, *Superconductive Devices*, McGraw-Hill Book Company, New York, 1962.

L. N. Cooper, Theory of Superconductivity, *Am. J. Phys.* **28**, 91, 1960.

A. J. Dekker, *Electrical Engineering Materials*, Prentice-Hall, Englewood Cliffs, N.J., 1959.

A. J. Dekker, *Solid State Physics*, Prentice-Hall, Englewood Cliffs, N.J., 1957.

C. Kittel, *Introduction to Solid State Physics*, John Wiley and Sons, New York, 1956.

F. London, *Superfluids*, Vol. 1, John Wiley and Sons, New York, 1950.

N. F. Mott and H. Jones, *The Theory of the Properties of Metals and Alloys*, Clarendon Press, Oxford, New York, 1936.

D. Shoenberg, *Superconductivity*, Cambridge University Press, Cambridge, 1952.

G. H. Wannier, *Elements of Solid State Theory*, Cambridge University Press, Cambridge, 1959.

A. H. Wilson, *The Theory of Metals*, Cambridge University Press, Cambridge, 1953.

EXERCISES

1. Calculate the velocity of the conduction electrons at the Fermi surface of aluminum for which $E_F = 11.7$ eV.

2. The resistivity of a piece of silver at room temperature is 1.6×10^{-8} ohm m. The effective number of conduction electrons is 0.9 per atom and the Fermi energy is 5.5 eV. Estimate the mean free path of the conduction electrons. Calculate the electronic relaxation time and the electronic drift velocity in a field of 100 vm^{-1}. The density of silver is 1.05×10^4 kg m^{-3}.

3. The critical wavelength for transparency in sodium is 2100 Å. Calculate the number of free electrons per atom which this implies.

4. Cyclotron resonance has been observed in lead at a frequency of 8900 Mc sec^{-1} and a field of 0.24 webers m^{-2}. What result does this give for the effective mass of electrons in lead?

5. Using the data of exercise 2, evaluate the thermal conductivity of the silver sample.

6. By using the data of Fig. 10-16, calculate the current required to destroy superconductivity in a lead wire 10^{-3} m in diameter at a temperature of 4°K.

11

Semiconductors

In Chapter 10 we have seen how the electrons in metals carry current when influenced by an electric field, the limitation to the current for any particular metal being caused by imperfections in the metal lattice. In semiconductors the situation is quite different. Unlike that for metals, the *number* of conducting electrons in semiconductors varies with temperature and field, giving rise to conductivities whose dependence on temperature and field is quite characteristic. The numbers of current carriers in useful semiconductors at room temperature are such that the conductivities lie in value between those of metals and insulators.

The crystalline structure of the best known semiconductors silicon and germanium has been described in Chapter 1. This structure, the diamond cubic, is characterized by bonds between the atoms in which the neighboring atoms share electrons. Certain of these bonds must be broken before electrons are released to carry current. The agency that breaks the bond is usually thermal agitation. At zero temperature, therefore, a semiconductor will have no broken bonds and will have the electrical characteristics of an insulator. We begin this chapter by reminding the reader of the nature of the band structure in semiconductors and then go on to make calculations of the number of charge carriers, which at a certain temperature are in the conduction band, and the variation in that number with temperature and voltage.

11.1   The Band Structure of Intrinsic Semiconductors

An intrinsic semiconductor is one in which the conduction is a property of the pure crystal. Chapter 8 gave a description of the band structure of diamond and pointed out that in silicon and germanium the nature of the bands were similar, with the highly significant difference that the energy gap between the valence and conduction band was much narrower than in diamond. Figure 11.1a gives the band scheme for an intrinsic semiconductor showing the filled valence band separated from the conduction band, the latter being empty at zero temperature. Table 11.1 gives the values of the energy gap for a number of semiconductors.

Table 11.1 Values of the Energy Gap Between the Valence and Conduction Bands in Semiconductors, at Room Temperature

CRYSTAL	E_g (eV)	CRYSTAL	E_g (eV)
Diamond	6	ZnSb	0.56
Si	1.10	GaSb	0.78
Ge	0.68–0.72	PbS	0.34–0.37
Sn (gray)	0.08	PbSe	0.27
InSb	0.18	PbTe	0.30
InAs	0.33	CdS	2.42
InP	1.25	CdSe	1.74
GaAs	1.4	CdTe	1.45
AlSb	1.6–1.7	ZnSe	2.60
InSe	(1)	AgI	2.8
GaP	2.25	Ag_2Te	0.17
α-Mg_3Sb_2	0.82	Cu_2O	2.1
Ca_2Si	0.9	Mg_2Si	0.7
Ca_2Sn	0.9	Mg_2Ge	0.7
Ca_2Pb	0.46	Mg_2Sn	0.3

11.2   The Number of Electrons in the Conduction Band

In an intrinsic semiconductor such as germanium, the energy gap is narrow enough so that at room temperature electrons may be thermally excited from the valence band across the gap into the conduction band. Quantum states in the valence band which were filled at 0°K are thus emptied. Such empty quantum states in a normally filled valence band

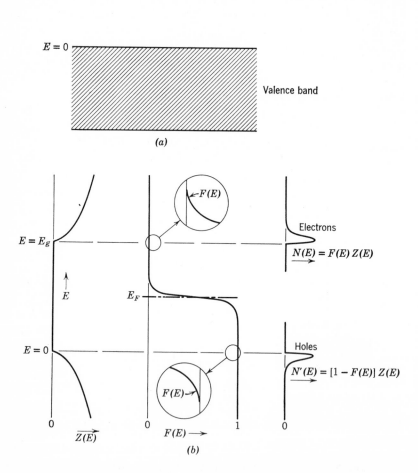

$E = E_g$ —————————————————   Conduction band

$E = 0$

Valence band

(a)

Figure 11.1   (a) The valence and conduction bands in an intrinsic semiconductor at $T = 0°$K. (b) The density of states $Z(E)$, the Fermi function $F(E)$, and densities of electrons $N(E)$ and of holes $N'(E)$ at a temperature above zero. (After Sproull) will behave like positive charges. For this reason the empty quantum state is called a *positive hole* or simply a *hole*. Our first task is to calculate the number of electrons in the conduction band and hence free to migrate through the crystal. The number of holes also free to migrate will follow as a direct consequence of the electron calculation.

As outlined in Chapter 8, we must calculate the density of states function $Z(E)$ and the Fermi function $F(E)$. The product of these two functions will then give us $N(E)$, the actual number of electrons of a given energy E in the conduction band. A plot of $F(E)$ and $N(E)$ is also made in Fig. 11.1b. An expression for $Z(E)$ has been already derived in equation 8.11. At the bottom of the conduction band where $E = E_g$, the expression is, for unit volume,

$$Z(E)\, dE = \frac{\pi}{2}\left(\frac{8m}{h^2}\right)^{3/2}(E - E_g)^{1/2}\, dE \qquad (11.1)$$

In Fig. 11.1b, $Z(E)$ is plotted against E.

We have now to find the Fermi level E_F at a temperature T which is above zero. A hole in the valence band is produced for each electron that is thermally excited into the conduction band. This implies that the probability of finding an electron at the energy value E_g is equal to that of finding a hole at the energy value $E = 0$. Thus

$$F(E_g) = 1 - F(0) \qquad (11.2)$$

We now insert the total expression for the Fermi function given in equation 8.1. This gives

$$\frac{1}{e^{(E_g - E_F)/kT} + 1} = 1 - \frac{1}{E^{-E_F/kT} + 1} = \frac{e^{-E_F/kT}}{e^{-E_F/kT} + 1}$$

$$e^{-E_F/kT} + 1 = e^{-E_F/kT}[e^{(E_g - E_F)/kT} + 1]$$

$$1 = e^{(E_g - 2E_F)/kT}$$

that is, $$E_F = \frac{E_g}{2} \qquad (11.3)$$

Thus in an intrinsic semiconductor the Fermi level lies midway between the top of the valence bond and the bottom of the conduction band. Hence the number of electrons in the conduction band (or holes in the valence band) is proportional to $e^{-E_g/2kT}$.

We can now complete the calculation of the number N_n of electrons in the conduction band. It is convenient to introduce an "effective density of states in the conduction band" which we will designate Z_c. This quantity is defined by writing N_n, the total number of electrons per unit volume in the conduction band, as the product of Z_c and the Fermi function *evaluated at the bottom of the band.* That is,

$$Z_c F(E_g) = \int_{E_g}^{\infty} N(E)\, dE = \int_{E_g}^{\infty} Z(E)\, F(E)\, dE \qquad (11.4)$$

Since $E_g - E_F$ is greater than a few times kT, we can write

$$F(E_g) = \frac{1}{e^{(E_g - E_F)/kT} + 1} \simeq e^{-(E_g - E_F)/kT} \qquad (11.5)$$

Thus

$$Z_c e^{-(E_g - E_F)/kT} = \int_{E_g}^{\infty} Z(E)\, F(E)\, dE$$

$$= \int_{E_g}^{\infty} \frac{\pi}{2} \left(\frac{8m}{h^2}\right)^{3/2} (E - E_g)^{1/2} e^{-(E_g - E_F)/kT}\, dE \qquad (11.6)$$

Equation 11.6 uses the substitutions given in (11.1) and (11.5). The integration gives the expression for Z_c, namely,

$$Z_c = 2\left(\frac{2\pi m k T}{h^2}\right)^{3/2}$$

that is,
$$Z_c = 4.83 \times 10^{21}\, T^{3/2} \qquad (11.7)$$

The total number of electrons per cubic meter in the conduction band, that is, N_n, is thus given by

$$N_n = 4.83 \times 10^{21}\, T^{3/2} F(E_g) \qquad (11.8)$$

and the total number of holes per cubic meter in the valence band, that is, N_p, is given by

$$N_p = 4.83 \times 10^{21}\, T^{3/2} [1 - F(0)] \qquad (11.9)$$

$$= N_n \text{ for an intrinsic semiconductor}$$

For an intrinsic semiconductor with an energy gap of 1 eV, the value of the Fermi function at room temperature is approximately e^{-20}. Thus the number of electrons in the conduction band, that is N_n, is given by

$$N_n = 4.83 \times 10^{21} \times 300^{3/2}\, e^{-20} = 10^{17}\, \text{m}^{-3}$$

Since the number of atoms per cubic meter may be of the order 10^{28}, only a small fraction of the valence electrons are excited into the conduction band.

11.3   Conduction by Electrons and Holes

If an electric field is applied to the intrinsic semiconductor in the x direction, the electrons receive momentum, and there is a drift velocity of electrons in the $-x$ direction superimposed on their random movement.

This means that a positive current flows in the $+x$ direction. The field also imposes a drift velocity in the $+x$ direction on the random movement of the holes. Thus positive charge is also carried by the holes in the $+x$ direction. Based on the definition of the drift velocity given in Section 10.3, the mobility μ can be defined as the drift velocity per unit electric field. In an ideal intrinsic semiconductor the mobility is determined by scattering of the electrons (and holes) by thermal waves in the lattice. At low enough temperatures, however, where the "mean free path" of the electrons becomes long, scattering by impurity atoms sets a limit to the mobility attained. The successful use of semiconductors had to await the development of the zone-refining technique (see Section 3.6) before sufficiently high purities were attainable to give useful values of mobilities.

The total conductivity σ by electrons and holes in an intrinsic semiconductor is then given by

$$\sigma = N_n e \mu_n + N_p e \mu_p \qquad (11.10)$$

where μ_n and μ_p are the mobilities of electrons and holes respectively and e is the electron charge. Finally by combining equations 11.8 and 11.9 with equation 11.10, we obtain

$$\sigma = 4.83 \times 10^{21} T^{3/2} e(\mu_n + \mu_p) e^{-E_g/2kT} \qquad (11.11)$$

The temperature dependence of conductivity in an intrinsic semiconductor is dominated by the exponential term, the $T^{3/2}$ factor varying relatively slowly. Thus in the intrinsic range a plot of log σ against $1/T$ will be linear, the slope of the line giving the value of $E_g/2k$.

In germanium at temperatures above about 150°C, most of the electrons in the conduction band come for the valence band in the manner already envisaged. This is the intrinsic semiconductor region. At lower temperatures impurities in the germanium contribute in a major way to the supply of electrons and holes. This process is called *impurity* or *extrinsic semiconduction*.

11.4   The Band Structure of Extrinsic Semiconductors

The conductivity of a semiconductor may be increased by several powers of ten by the addition of a fraction of one per cent of certain chemical impurities. If we take germanium or silicon as our typical semiconducting elements, the chemical additions which are commercially used are either from Group V or Group III of the periodic table. Let us consider in some detail the effect of adding elements such as lead, arsenic, or antimony to germanium. An arsenic atom contains five valence electrons, and if it occupies a normal germanium lattice site, only four of its valence electrons will form electron-pair bonds with the neighboring atoms. Thus four positive charges of the As^{5+} core are compensated by the four germanium neighbors leaving only one positive charge to bind the extra electron. The field of the positive charge in which the electron moves is further weakened because the surrounding medium is germanium which is polarized with a dielectric constant of $\epsilon_r = 16$ (see Chapter 13). The charge cloud of the fifth arsenic electron is therefore extended around the impurity center. The electron may be easily removed from the impurity and can migrate as a conduction electron. For this reason impurities like arsenic act as *donors* of electrons.

As may be seen from equation 7.12, the energy required to remove an electron from the field of a proton is inversely proportional to the square of the dielectric constant of the medium in which the electron moves. Thus since the ionization energy of hydrogen is 13.5 eV, the ionization energy of the arsenic atom in the germanium medium will be approximately $13.5/16^2$, that is, 0.05 eV. The approximation is not good and ionization energies of impurities phosphorus, arsenic, and antimony in germanium should be taken as 0.01 eV.

An essentially similar argument can be carried through for a substitutional impurity from Group III. Typical impurities are boron, aluminum, gallium, or indium. Such an impurity has one too few electrons to complete the covalent bands. The vacant state or *hole* is extended as was the extra electron and the calculation of the binding energy of the hole to the impurity or *acceptor* site is similar to the calculation of the binding energy of the electron to the donor. These energies are also approximately 0.01 eV for boron, aluminum, gallium, and indium in germanium. Germanium containing donor impurities is referred to as *n-type* while germanium containing acceptor impurities is called *p-type* and semiconductors in which the conduction electrons or holes are supplied by impurities are called *extrinsic*.

Our next task is to calculate the Fermi level just as we did for the intrinsic semiconductor. Before doing so it is important to emphasize a fundamental difference between the wave functions of electrons in the conduction band and those in *donor* levels. We saw in Chapter 8 that the wave functions of the conduction band are of the form of propagating waves, and the probability of finding the electron in a certain location is distributed over all the lattice cells. The wave function of the donor level, on the other hand, is concentrated around the donor site in a localized cloud. Similar considerations apply to holes. Figure 11.2a shows an arsenic donor in the germanium lattice, and Fig. 11.2b shows the corresponding energy band model.

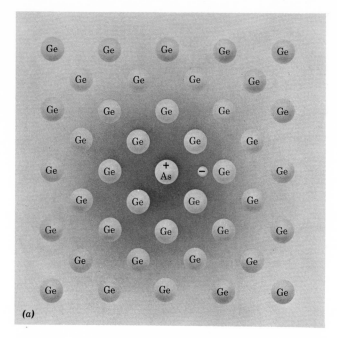

Figure 11.2*a* Substitution of an arsenic atom for a germanium atom. The charge cloud of the extra arsenic electron is extended around the impurity site. (After Spenke)

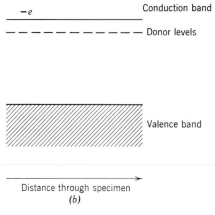

Figure 11.2*b* Band model of an extrinsic semiconductor showing donor levels. The donor levels are drawn as short dashes near the particular impurity to signify the localized nature of an electron in this energy level.

269

11.5   Ionization of Donor and Acceptor Levels in Extrinsic Semiconductors

In Section 11.2 we calculated the number of electrons in the conduction band in an intrinsic semiconductor. The calculation began with an estimate of the Fermi level. In Fig. 11.3 we show the valence, conduction, and donor levels in n-type germanium. The donor level is $E_g - 0.01$ in

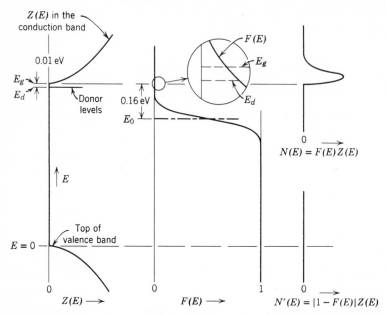

Figure 11.3   The density of states $Z(E)$, the Fermi function $F(E)$, and the densities of electrons $N(E)$ and holes $N'(E)$ in n-type germanium. (After Sproull)

the figure. From equation 11.8 the number of electrons N_n in the conduction band is given by

$$N_n = 4.83 \times 10^{21} T^{3/2} e^{-(E_g - E_F)/kT} \qquad (11.12)$$

If there are N_d donor atoms per cubic meter the number of vacant donor states is

$$N_d[1 - F(E_g - 0.01)] = N_d[1 - e^{-(E_g - 0.01 - E_F)/kT}] \qquad (11.13)$$

To simplify the calculation, let us assume $T = 300°K$ and $N_d = 5 \times 10^{22}$. If all the electrons in the conduction band come from the donors, which means that all the donors are ionized, the number of electrons in the conduction band is obviously equal to N_d, and from equation 11.13,

$e^{-(E_g-0.01-E_F)/kT}$ is much less than unity. Let us begin by making this assumption. Obviously from equations 11.12 and 11.13

$$4.83 \times 10^{21}(300)^{3/2} e^{-(E_g-E_F)/1.38 \times 10^{-23} \times 300} = 5 \times 10^{22} \quad (11.14)$$

This gives $E_g - E_F = 0.16$ eV. The number of electrons from the valence band (or holes in the valence band) is given by equation 11.9. It is

$$4.83 \times 10^{21} \cdot 300^{3/2} e^{-(0.72-0.16)/300 \times 1.38 \times 10^{-23}} \simeq 10^{16} \quad (11.15)$$

This number is much less than the number of electrons in the conduction band which come from the donor levels, and thus the assumption used in the calculation of E_F is justified.

The quantity $e^{-(E_g-0.01-E_F)/kT}$ is negligible if E_F lies more than a few kT below E_g. This is the condition for complete ionization of the donors. In such a condition electrons are the "majority" carriers and "holes" the minority, and the conductivity σ is given simply by

$$\sigma = N_d e \mu_n \quad (11.16)$$

Table 11.2   Conductivity of n- and p-Type Germanium*

CHEMICAL ADDITIVE	CONCENTRATION (atoms/m^{-3})	CONDUCTIVITY AT 300°K	
		TYPE	MAGNITUDE, (mho/m^{-1})
No intentional impurity		Intrinsic	2
Arsenic	8×10^{19}	n	5
Arsenic	1.5×10^{21}	n	90
Arsenic	5×10^{22}	n	2000
Gallium	9×10^{19}	p	3
Gallium	8×10^{20}	p	30
Gallium	1×10^{22}	p	300

* From P. P. Debye and E. M. Conwell, *Phys. Rev.* **93**, 693 (1954).

The Fermi level thus lies below the donor level but above the value $E_g/2$ associated with intrinsic semiconduction. From the development of equation 11.14 we see that the Fermi level is closer to E_g if N_d is larger or if T is lower.

If only acceptors are present in p-type material, the Fermi level lies below the value $E_g/2$. The acceptors are ionized at room temperature, and the calculation of σ is similar to that for n-type material. Holes are then the "majority" carriers. Table 11.2 shows the conductivity of n- and p-type germanium.

Figure 11.4 shows the variation of N_n and σ with T. The two curves do not have the same shape because of the variation of μ_n with T. In n-type material at high enough temperatures the number of electrons coming from the valence band exceeds the number from the donor levels, and the

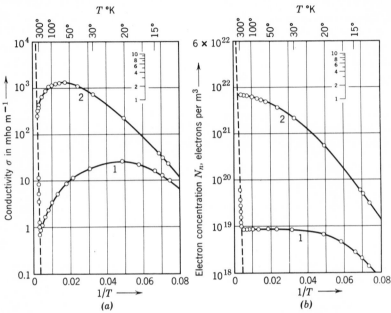

Figure 11.4   (a) Log σ vs. $1/T$ for specimens 1 and 2 of germanium. (b) Log N_n vs. $1/T$ measured by Hall experiments. Specimen 1, donor concentration 10^{19}; acceptor concentration 10^{18}. Specimen 2, donor concentration 7.5×10^{21}; acceptor concentration 10^{20}. (After Debye and Conwell)

semiconduction becomes intrinsic with the Fermi level falling to $E_g/2$. The conduction type, that is, n or p, is determined by the relative numbers of donors and acceptors.

11.6   Hall Effect

It is possible to determine the density and type of charge carrier in metals and semiconductors by measuring the *Hall effect*. We will discuss the experiment in terms of an n-type semiconducting material or a metal where the charge carriers are also electrons. In Fig. 11.5 a rectangular slab of material is subjected to a *horizontal electric* and *vertical* magnetic field. The applied electric field $\mathscr{E}_x$ is in the $+x$ direction, and thus the flow of electrons is in the $-x$ direction. In the presence of the magnetic field of magnetic induction **B**, each electron is subject to a Lorentz force **F** given by

$$\mathbf{F} = e\mathbf{v} \times \mathbf{B} \tag{11.16}$$

where **v** is the velocity of the electron. In the presence of the electric field $\mathscr{E}_x$ the conducting electrons have a small drift velocity $\Delta\mathbf{v}$ superimposed on

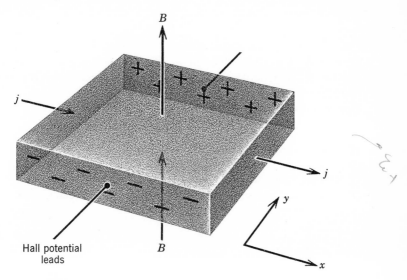

Figure 11.5   Hall effect in an n-type semiconductor.

their otherwise random motion. The magnitude of $\Delta\mathbf{v}$ is given by

$$\Delta v = \mu\mathscr{E}_x \tag{11.17}$$

which follows from the definition of mobility μ. Thus the Lorentz force **F** is in the $-y$ direction and is of magnitude

$$F_y = -eB\Delta v = -eB\mathscr{E}_x\mu \tag{11.18}$$

The electrons are deflected toward the $-y$ face of the slab (toward the reader) and produce a positive charge on the back face and a negative charge on the front face. Thus a potential difference, called the *Hall potential*, is built up between these faces, and this voltage may be measured at the leads. If $\mathscr{E}_y$ is the transverse field (= voltage/slab width), the transverse force $-e\mathscr{E}_y$ on each electron must just balance the Lorentz force.
Hence

$$\mathscr{E}_y = \frac{B\mathscr{E}_x}{\mu} \tag{11.19}$$

The *Hall coefficient* R is defined by

$$R = \mathscr{E}_y/Bj \qquad (11.20)$$

where $j = \sigma \mathscr{E}_x$ is the current density in amperes per square meter in the x direction. We may measure R experimentally. Since $\sigma = Ne\mu_n$ where N is the number of charge carriers, it follows also that

$$R = -\frac{1}{eN} \qquad (11.21)$$

Thus if the charge carriers are electrons, the Hall coefficient is negative and an experimental determination of R gives the density of conducting electrons. The polarity of the voltage measured across the Hall potential bands is reversed if the charge carriers are holes, and again the density of carriers may be determined.

11.7 Recombination and Trapping of Electrons and Holes

We have now discussed the factors affecting the production of electrical charge carriers in semiconductors. An important related process takes place whereby the number of electrons and holes may be reduced. This is

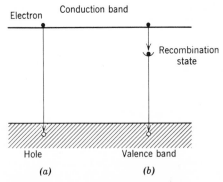

Figure 11.6 (*a*) Direct recombination of electron and hole with the emission of a photon. (*b*) Electron first trapped in recombination state before recombining with hole.

the process of *recombination*. Recombination is especially important in systems where the numbers of carriers are not in equilibrium. Such systems, as for example the *p-n* junction, will be treated later.

When an electron is separated from a hole they may be united by (*a*) direct recombination or (*b*) recombination through trapping states. Both processes are indicated in Fig. 11.6*a* and *b*. In 11.6*a* the electron drops directly into a hole and emits a photon. In 11.6*b* the electron is first held in a trap and later drops out of the trap into a hole.

The direct process is rather unlikely since the electron and hole must pass within a close distance ($\simeq 10^{-11}$ m) in order to attract one another strongly enough to recombine. The statistical chance of this is low and it can be calculated that an electron or hole would exist for times of the order of one second if direct recombination were the only process of annihilation. Lifetimes of many orders of magnitude less than this are observed in germanium.

If either the electron or the hole is immobilized, the chance of recombination is much greater than if both move. Let us examine the nature of

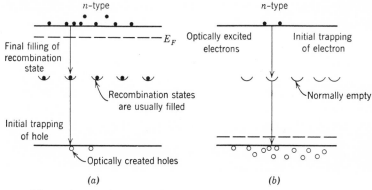

Figure 11.7   (*a*) Recombination process in *n*-type material. (*b*) Recombination process in *p*-type material.

immobilization of electrons and holes in two types of material, namely, strongly *n*-type and strongly *p*-type.

In strongly *n*-type material the Fermi level is close to the conduction band, and traps at lower energies will be nearly filled by electrons. These traps or recombination states then have electrons available to recombine with or trap holes. If an electron-hole pair is first formed in the way we have described earlier, the hole may be trapped in this way. The lifetime of the hole is nearly inversely proportional to the density of trapping centers. When the hole is trapped, the trap that has lost an electron in the process then becomes a localized state into which a migrating electron can fall to complete the annihilation of the original electron-hole pair.

In strongly *p*-type material the Fermi level is near the valence band, and traps are normally empty of electrons. When an electron-hole pair is produced, electrons fall into the traps. Once trapped, the electron recombines with one of the many available holes in a very short time to complete the annihilation of the original electron-hole pair. Figure 11.7 shows the recombination process for *n*- and *p*-type material.

In *recombination through traps* the rate of decay of *excess* carriers is proportional to the carrier density, whereas in *direct recombination* of electrons and holes the rate of recombination is proportional to the square of the electron (or hole) density.

At this point sufficient fundamental theory of semiconductors has been developed to enable us to discuss some of the practical applications.

11.8   Semiconducting Rectifiers

There are three types of important solid state rectifiers. These are (*a*) the *point-contact diode*, (*b*) the *metal rectifier* of which copper oxide and selenium are the best known examples, and (*c*) the germanium or silicon *junction diode*.

In the point-contact diode (*a*), a fine metal wire contacts a semiconductor, which is often *n*-type. It is believed that the action of forming the contact

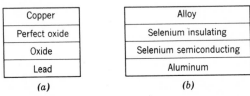

Copper
Perfect oxide
Oxide
Lead

(a)

Alloy
Selenium insulating
Selenium semiconducting
Aluminum

(b)

Figure 11.8   (*a*) Construction of copper oxide rectifier. (*b*) Construction of selenium rectifier.

converts a small portion of the *n*-type into *p*-type so that an *n-p* junction exists at the contact. As we will see later, such a junction can behave as a rectifier. Large currents may not be carried by this rectifier because of the point contact, but the capacitance is low and the device may be used at radio and centimetric wavelengths. We will not study this rectifier in detail since it is of lessening importance. The rectifying action of an *n-p* junction will be discussed under (*c*). The copper oxide rectifier (*b*) was developed in 1923 and has been extensively used for instrument rectifiers. It is not now so generally employed as the selenium rectifier. Figure 11.8 shows the construction of the copper oxide and selenium rectifier. Copper oxide rectifiers are made by first oxidizing Chilean copper in a furnace at a temperature of about 500°C. The oxide coating is red cuprous oxide Cu_2O. The specimen is then sliced in two, making two rectifier disks. The oxide placed in contact with the copper forms an insulating layer of "perfect" oxide. The lead coating is simply to provide electrical contact.

In the selenium rectifier molten selenium is first pressed on an aluminum base. When selenium is solidified, it is an insulator. If, however, it is annealed at a temperature just below the melting point, the selenium changes to the crystalline semiconducting form with an insulating layer on the surface. An alloy contact is spread on the insulating layer. Many details of the processes for making these rectifiers are trade secrets, since empirical factors are of great importance. The metal rectifiers can carry large currents of tens or even hundreds of amperes. The capacitance however is usually so great that the devices are limited to the low frequencies used in power engineering.

We will now discuss in a little more detail the rectifying action of a metal-semiconducting junction. The theory we will present is only qualitatively true of some of the metal rectifiers and fails to account for

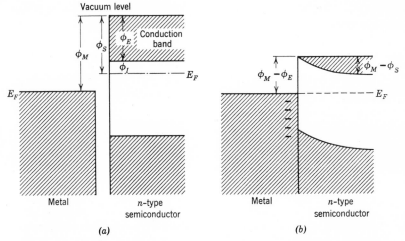

Figure 11.9   Electron energy bands in a metal and n-type semiconductor when $\phi_M > \phi_S$. (a) Before contact of metal and semiconductor. (b) After contact of metal and semiconductor.

the detailed behavior in particular of the rectifying action of metal-germanium or metal-silicon rectifiers. When a metal and semiconductor are brought into contact, a potential barrier arises, (a) because of the difference in thermionic work function of semiconductor and metal or (b) from the existence of localized electron states on the surface of the semiconductor. We now discuss the nature of the first possibility for the case of a metal n-type semiconductor junction. We first give a qualitative discussion, and later when we come to discuss junction diodes, we will apply the equations giving carrier densities that we have already developed. Figure 11.9a shows the energy level diagrams of a metal and n-type semiconductor *before* contact is made between them. The *work function for the metal is* ϕ_M and is the energy required to remove a free electron from the metal. The *work function* ϕ_S *for the semiconductor* can be regarded as the sum of two parts, namely the *internal work function* ϕ_I, which is the energy difference between the Fermi level and the bottom of the conduction band, and the *external work function* ϕ_E, which is the energy required to remove a free electron. Figure 11.9a refers to the case when $\phi_M > \phi_S$.

Figure 11.9b shows the redistribution of the energy levels after the metal and semiconductor have been brought into contact. Electrons occupying levels in the conduction band of the semiconductor have flown into the metal. As discussed in Chapter 9, *equilibrium is reached when the Fermi level of both metal and semiconductor is at the same energy value.* The surface of the metal has received electrons whereas the surface of the semiconductor is depleted in electrons. The metal surface is thus negatively charged with respect to the surface of the semiconductor. The electrons

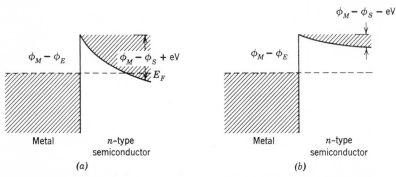

Figure 11.10 Electron energy bands in metal and *n*-type semiconductor when in contact. Again $\phi_M > \phi_S$. (*a*) When a positive voltage V is applied to the semiconductor, that is, reverse bias. (*b*) When a positive voltage V is applied to the metal, that is, forward bias.

that have flown from the *n*-type semiconductor into the metal have come from donors near the surface of the semiconductor. This transfer produces a layer in the semiconductor close to the surface which is depleted of electrons. This layer is an insulating region often called the *barrier layer*. Viewed from the metal side, the height of the barrier between metal and semiconductor V_{M_s} in volts is obviously given by

$$eV_{M_s} = \phi_M - \phi_E \qquad (11.22)$$

Electrons do continue to cross this barrier from both sides, but in equilibrium the numbers are equal and no net current flows.

Suppose now that an electric potential V is applied to the system in a direction such that in Fig. 11.10a the semiconductor is positive. The energy levels in the semiconductor are *lowered* with respect to the metal. The barrier volts for electron flow from the semiconductor is now *increased* to V_{S_M} where

$$eV_{S_M} = \phi_M - \phi_S + eV \qquad (11.23)$$

while the barrier height for electron flow from metal to semiconductor remains at the value eV_{M_S}. The electron flow from semiconductor to metal is consequently reduced from the equilibrium case, and the junction is said to be operating under *reverse bias*.

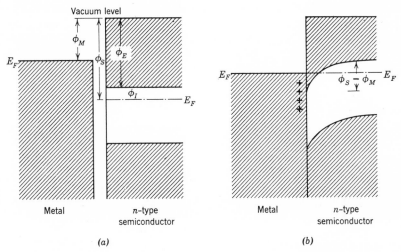

(a)   (b)

Figure 11.11   Electron energy bands in a metal and *n*-type semiconductor when $\phi_M < \phi_S$. (*a*) Before contact of metal and semiconductor. (*b*) After contact of metal and semiconductor.

If the applied voltage V is in the opposite direction such that the negative pole of the battery is connected to the semiconductor, the junction operates under *forward bias*. As is seen in Fig. 11.10*b*, the barrier height for electron flow from semiconductor to metal is reduced to the value V_{S_M} where

$$eV_{S_M} = \phi_M - \phi_S - eV \qquad (11.14)$$

and the flow of electrons increased. It should be emphasized at this part that when $\phi_M > \phi_S$, electron flow in both directions is *opposed* by a potential barrier, the height of the barrier being different when viewed from metal or semiconductor. It is this difference in height that gives rise to the rectifier action.

Now let us suppose that the work function of the metal is less than that of the *n*-type semiconductor, that is $\phi_M < \phi_S$. Figure 11.11*a* and 11.11*b* respectively show the energy level diagrams before and after contact is made. Here electrons flow from the metal into the semiconductor, which makes the metal surface positive and the semiconductor surface negative. The negative surface charge depresses the bottom of the conduction band near the contact surface of the semiconductor.

The application of an electrical voltage to the n-type semiconductor-metal combination is shown in Fig. 11.12a and b, the metal being respectively negatively and positively biased. The method of constructing Fig. 11.12 is similar to that used in Fig. 11.10, and the complete explanation need not be repeated. There is, however, one important difference

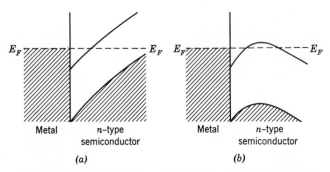

Metal n-type semiconductor   Metal n-type semiconductor

(a)   (b)

Figure 11.12 Electron energy bands in metal and n-type semiconductor when in contact. $\phi_M < \phi_S$ (a) When a positive voltage is applied to the semiconductor. (b) When a positive voltage is applied to the metal.

between the two figures. *No potential barrier* to electron flow is presented in Fig. 11.12. The magnitude of the current is completely dependent therefore on the voltage applied and is governed by Ohm's Law. The contact between metal and n-type semiconductor is thus *rectifying* if $\phi_M > \phi_S$ and *ohmic* if $\phi_M < \phi_S$.

Let us complete our consideration of contact between metals and semiconductors by briefly discussing the situation for p-type semiconducting material. The situations are exactly reversed. When $\phi_M > \phi_S$ and contact is made between the metal and a p-type semiconductor, positive charge is left at the semiconductor surface and a negative at the metal. Holes are the majority carriers in the p-type material and *holes* can flow *uphill* on an electron energy diagram just as *electrons* flow *downhill*. Raising or lowering the energy levels on the right hand side by applying a voltage in either direction does not change the condition that for current flow by holes there exists no potential barrier. The contact is therefore

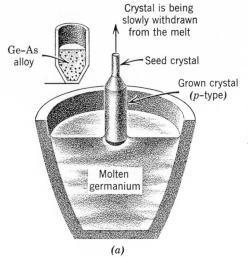

Figure 11.13 (*a*) Growth of a germanium crystal containing a *p-n* junction. (*b*) The preparation of an alloyed *p-n* junction.

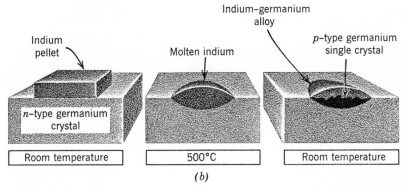

ohmic. Finally, if $\phi_M < \phi_S$, a barrier potential is presented to current flow by holes, and thus the contact will rectify if coupled to an applied voltage.

Let us now discuss the rectifying action of a junction between *p*- and *n*-type semiconducting material. A *p-n* junction is not an external, but is an *internal boundary* within a single crystal on one side of which donors are in excess and on the other side acceptors. There are two kinds of junction, the *abrupt* junction and the *graded* junction, characterized by the width over which the conductor changes from *n*-type to *p*-type. Typical of graded junctions is the *grown* junction, the principles of the construction of which will now be given.

Figure 11.13*a* shows a *p*-type germanium single crystal being grown from a germanium melt which contains, say, gallium in the proportion of a few parts per million. After a certain length of *p*-type crystal has been grown, a donor impurity such as arsenic is added in greater concentration than the acceptor gallium. The part of the crystal subsequently grown is *n*-type and a *p-n* junction is thus obtained.

The other method of fabricating a *p-n* junction, shown in Fig. 11.13*b*, gives a more abrupt junction. A small pellet of indium is placed on a single crystal of *n*-type germanium and melted under hydrogen. The

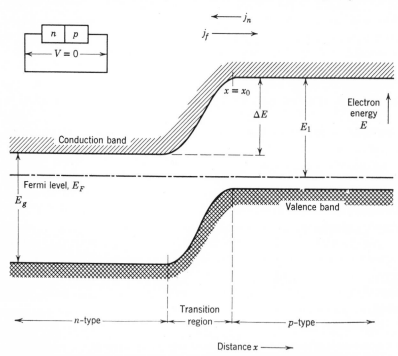

Figure 11.14   Electron energy diagram of a *p-n* junction in equilibrium. When the applied voltage is zero, no net current flows. (After Sproull)

temperature is raised to about 500°C, at which point the indium forms a germanium-indium solution alloy which is steadily enriched in germanium until the melting point equals the operating temperature. When cooled, a single-crystal layer of germanium forms between the germanium crystal and the alloy. This recrystallized layer is heavily doped with indium, that is, it is *p*-type.

Let us now consider the rectifying action of a *p-n* junction. Figure 11.14 shows the energy diagram of a junction in equilibrium. The density of electrons being greater in the *n*-type region, electrons diffuse into the *p*-type region where they recombine with free holes. The *p*-side thus becomes progressively negatively charged with respect to the n-side, and the barrier so formed stops further diffusion. The region over which the barrier is formed is called the *space charge* or *transition region*. Once more the Fermi levels on both sides of the transition are aligned.

Considering at first only the electron currents, it is obvious that the current j_n to the left at the point $x = x_0$ in the diagram is proportional to the number of electrons in the conduction band of the p-type, that is, to $e^{-E_1/kT}$, where E_1 is equal to $E_g - E_F$ on the p-side. This small number of thermally excited electrons flow "downhill" into the n-type region. At the same time the current to the *right* at $x = x_0$ consists of electrons that have climbed the hill from the n-side. The number of electrons in the conduction band on the n-side of the junction is proportional to $e^{-(E_g - E_F)/kT}$ on the n-side. Not all of these electrons can climb the hill, and the fraction able to do so is $e^{-\Delta E/kT}$. The current j_f is thus proportional to $e^{-(E_g - E_F)/kT} \; e^{-\Delta E/kT}$. Since $E_1 = E_g - E_F + \Delta E$, then j_f is proportional to $e^{-E_1/kT}$ and is equal in magnitude to j_n, which is the expected condition at equilibrium.

Let us now suppose that an external voltage V is applied to the junction so that the p-type region is made more negative with respect to the n-type region. This is called *reverse bias*, and the energy diagram is shown in Fig. 11.15a. The barrier energy has been *increased* from ΔE to $\Delta E + eV$ and very few electrons can climb the hill from the n-type to the p-type, which makes the current j_f now very small. The current j_n, however, is very little different from the equilibrium value under reverse bias since the rate of arrival at the bottom of the hill is essentially that of arrival at the top. The values of the currents are now $j_f = j_n e^{-eV/kT}$ with $V < 0$ and j_n. The net current of electrons to the right is thus

$$j = j_f - j_n = j_n(e^{eV/kT} - 1) \tag{11.25}$$

If eV is more negative than about $-4\,kT$, the current is constant at the saturation value j_n.

Forward bias is shown in Fig. 11.15b. Equation 11.25 also applies with, of course, the difference that V in this case is positive. The forward current j_f is increased above its equilibrium value by a factor $e^{eV/kT}$. A net current of electrons to the right results from the increased concentration on the n side. Note that we have assumed that the electrons in excess of the equilibrium value do not recombine in the transition region but travel into the p-type material.

It may easily be shown that an expression similar to equation 11.25 accounts for the current due to the flow of holes. If, therefore, j is the total

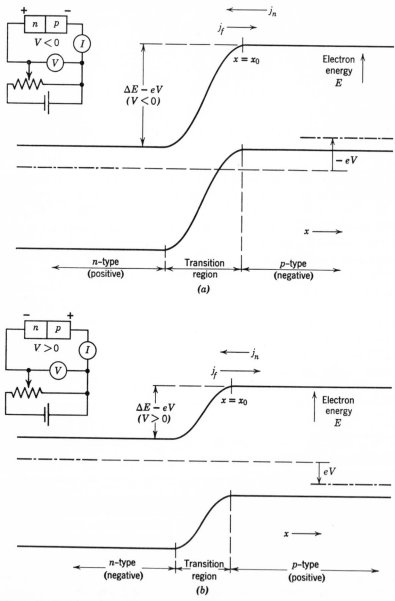

Figure 11.15 (a) A *p-n* junction with *reverse* bias. Electron currents only are shown.
(b) A *p-n* junction with forward bias. (After Sproull)

current due to electrons and holes and j_0 is the saturation value of this current, the equation relating current and voltage for a *p-n* junction is

$$j = j_0(e^{eV/kT} - 1) \tag{11.26}$$

This equation accounts very well for the rectifying behavior of a *p-n* junction and is plotted in Fig. 11.16.

Before we leave the discussion of the *p-n* junction, let us speculate for a moment on the subsequent behavior of the electrons and holes after they have actually crossed the transition region. Equation 11.26 gives us the

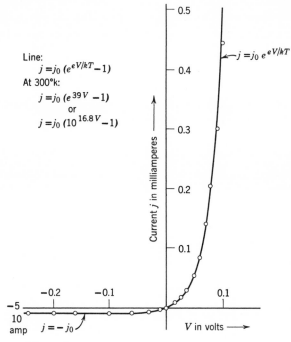

Figure 11.16 Current voltage relationship for a *p-n* junction. (After Sproull)

current that arises because of these carriers, but obviously such a current cannot be maintained were there not a sink for the electrons and holes to fall into beyond the transition region. The process of recombination provides such a sink. The penetration of minority carriers (e.g., electrons into the *p*-type) into regions in excess of their equilibrium density is called *current injection* of minority carriers. Such penetration could arise in two ways. It could arise because of conduction beyond the transition region owing to the driving electric field set up by the voltage V. This is not the case since the field on both sides is "short circuited" by the large density of majority carriers. At a distance beyond the junction the penetration is actually a consequence of diffusion. A concentration gradient must exist. With forward bias, for example, the concentration of electrons at the p-side of the junction, that is, $N_n{}^p$, is in excess of the equilibrium value N_n^{equ}.

In fact,

$$N_n{}^p = N_n^{\text{equ}}\, e^{-eV/kT} \quad \text{at} \quad x = x_0. \tag{11.27}$$

The concentration of electrons N_n at any point x falls from the value $N_n{}^p$ to N_n^{equ} as the distance from $x = x_0$ increases. The excess concentration of electrons at any point x can be related to the distance by an equation

$$N_n - N_n^{\text{equ}} = N_n^{\text{equ}}(e^{eV/\kappa T} - 1)e^{-(x-x_0)/L_n} \tag{11.28}$$

Here L_n is the *diffusion length* for electrons and gives the distance from $x = x_0$ at which recombination has reduced the electron density by a factor

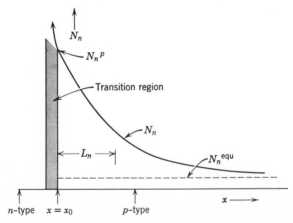

Figure 11.17   The concentration N_n of electrons on the p side of a forward biased p-n junction plotted as a function of the distance x from the junction. (After Sproull)

of $1/e$. Equation 11.28 is plotted in Fig. 11.17. A reduction in L_n will obviously increase the concentration gradient of electrons. From our former discussion of diffusion in Chapter 4, it follows that the diffusion current will be increased. Thus trapping and recombination processes that tend to reduce the lifetime and diffusion length of electrons beyond the junction will result in increased forward current at low voltages.

11.9   The Junction Transistor

The semiconductor device of greatest commercial importance is the *junction transistor*. This consists of two *p-n* junctions within a single crystal. Transistors may be used for amplification of electrical signals and many of the other electronic applications of thermionic tubes. Their small size and increasing reliability make them ideal for electronic miniaturization.

The principle of operation of the junction transistor will be illustrated with reference to the *n-p-n* junction. As with the *p-n* junction diode, the characteristic property is the fact that voltages are taken up in the space charge layer and the effect of the electric field exerted on the carriers responsible for the current is negligible. The only means of transfer across

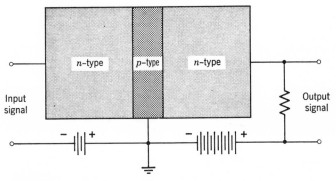

Figure 11.18   An *n-p-n* junction with the left *n-p* junction forward biased and the right *p-n* junction reverse biased.

the junction, at least for small voltages, is by diffusion. Figure 11.18 shows an *n-p-n* transistor wired so that the *left n-p* junction, called the *emitter*, is *forward biased*, and the right junction, called the *collector*, is reverse biased. The actual dimensions of the transistor are small, typical sizes being about 0.020 inch square section with the *p*-type region or *base* about 0.001 inch in thickness. In operation, charge is transferred from the low impedance input circuit to the high impedance output circuit, thus resulting in power gain.

Figure 11.19 shows the energy-level diagram for an *n-p-n* transistor biased as in Fig. 11.18. Consider first the emitter junction. The input signal voltage is applied across the junction. The height of the potential hill varies according to the input signal, and the current varies according to equation 11.26. In practice, the donor concentration is made much higher than the acceptor concentration in the base, and thus almost all the emitter current is a current of electrons to the right with very few holes to the left. The base is made very thin, less in thickness than the diffusion length L_n, and thus almost all electrons entering the base from the emitter slide down the potential hill to the collector. Once across the collector junction these electrons are accelerated by the reverse bias to the collecting electrode. The collector current j_c is only slightly less in value than the emitter current. Figure 11.20 shows the collector current j_c plotted as a function of collector voltage V_c. An analogy exists between the junction transistor and the negative grid triode electronic tube. The emitter and collector act like

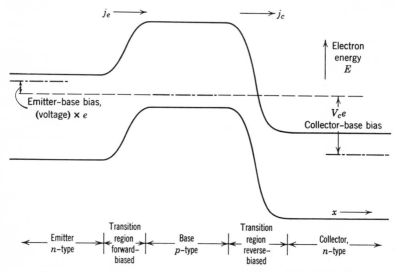

Figure 11.19   Energy level diagram for an *n-p-n* transistor biased as in Fig.11. 18.   Only electronic currents are shown.   (After Sproull)

the cathode and plate of the triode respectively.   The applied voltage between emitter and base has an effect similar to the applied voltage between cathode and grid in the triode.   The base current, like the grid, is small.   The capacitances between emitter and base and between base and collector limit the frequency response of the transistor.   The emitter-base and base-collector impedances are such that power gains of about 50 db are common.

11.10   Semiconducting Devices

Many applications of semiconducting devices exist in modern technology, and the number is increasing at a very rapid rate.   This chapter will be concluded with brief descriptions of a number of these applications.

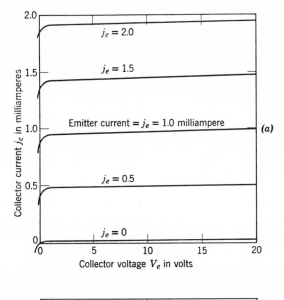

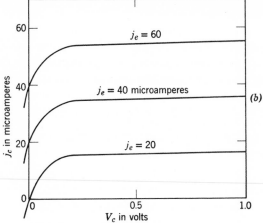

Figure 11.20 The collector current in an *n-p-n* transistor plotted as a function of collector voltage for various emitter currents. (After Shockley, Sparks, and Teal.)

Photocells. Photocells are devices that convert light intensity into an electrical signal. Semiconducting material may be used in photocells in two ways, either as a *photoconductive* solid as in CdS, in which the cell resistance is changed by the light intensity, or as a *photovoltaic* solid as in selenium, which produces a voltage dependent on the intensity of the incident radiation. Figure 11.21*a* and *b* illustrate the two uses.

The important performance criteria of photocells are the *quantum yield*, which is the number of charge carriers passing through the external circuit for one light quantum absorbed in the cell, and the *response* at different light wavelengths.

It has been shown over a wide range of frequencies in germanium and silicon that each photon absorbed will create one electron-hole pair. Quantum yields of about one are also found with other semiconductors used as photovoltaic cells. Quantum yields of orders of magnitude higher are possible, however, if the semiconductor is used as a photoconductor, a yield of 10,000 being attained for example, with cadmium sulfide.

The wavelength sensitivity for a number of important photocells is shown in Fig. 11.22. The wavelength range extends from about 2×10^{-7} m into the infrared at about 6×10^{-6} m. Because of the small energy transitions between impurity levels and the conduction band in extrinsic semiconductors, these materials give the best long wavelength sensitivity.

If the illumination produces electron-hole pairs close to a *p-n* junction—and in many cells such a junction is involved—the carriers diffuse to the junction. This is only possible without serious loss by recombination, if they are produced within a diffusion length of the barrier. There the electrons and holes are separated by the electrostatic field, the holes floating into the *p* region and the electrons sinking into the *n* region. In doing so they produce a voltage that lowers the junction barrier (as in forward bias). Lowering the barrier tends to produce a forward current in the junction, which affects the charge separation. A balance of these two effects creates an open-circuit voltage which will be less than the original barrier height, that is, less than the difference in Fermi level of the *n*- and *p*-type semiconductors. If the forward current is reduced, the open-circuit voltage increases up to the Fermi difference as a limit. The forward current is, of course, reduced by lowering the temperature, and thus the *p-n* junction will give higher output voltages at low temperaures.

One of the more exciting uses of the photovoltaic effect in *p-n* junctions is the *solar battery*. Solar energy produces the electron-hole pairs, the "battery" being an *n*-type silicon wafer with a surface region of *p*-type which must be made very thin to minimize recombination of the pairs before they reach the junction. The maximum theoretical efficiency of such cells is about 30 per cent.

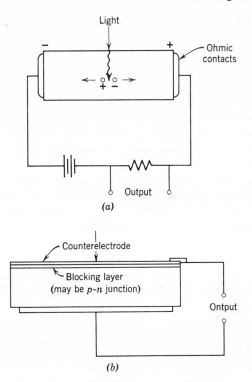

Figure 11.21   (a) A photoconductive cell with its basic circuit. Light photons produce electron-hole pairs or free carriers from impurity atoms. Variations in light intensity are recorded as voltage variations across the output. (b) A photovoltaic cell in which the light produces current carriers that give rise to a voltage across the blocking or barrier layer.

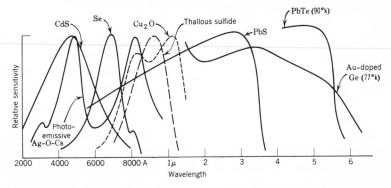

Figure 11.22 The sensitivity of some important photocells as a function of light wavelength. (After Dunlap)

Thermistors and Varistors.   *Thermistors* are semiconducting devices whose electrical resistance varies greatly with temperature. They have a wide variety of applications such as thermometers and temperature-control elements. If the temperature of the thermistor is kept constant, which will be reasonably true for small currents, the resistance is *ohmic*, that is, the voltage current characteristic obeys Ohm's Law. On the other hand, the strong temperature dependence of the resistance, which may be as high

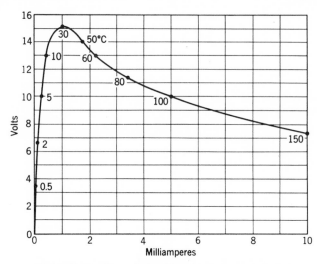

Figure 11.23   The relationship of voltage and current in a typical varistor. The numbers on the graph indicate the rise in temperature of the varistor due to the passage of the current. (After Becker, Green, and Pearson)

as 5 per cent per °K, can give rise to a nonlinear voltage current characteristic on which many applications of thermistors are based. Such a *nonohmic* element when used in electrical circuits is often called a *varistor*. Figure 11.23 shows a typical voltage-current varistor relation. The negative resistance shown in the graph at currents of more than 1 milliampere permits the use of varistor elements in amplifiers and oscillators. The sensitivity of the thermistor to the heat conductivity of its surroundings makes possible its use as a gas or liquid flowmeter, vacuum gauge, or manometer. The time of response will, of course, be affected by the physical size of the thermistor. Some of the smaller elements have been made with thermal time constants as small as 10^{-3} second.

An interesting use of nonohmic semiconducting elements is in lightning arresters. These are usually made of powdered silicon carbide in a casing of refractory material. Such protectors are connected in shunt across the electrical equipment to be protected. At the operating voltage of the electrical machinery the arrester passes little current, but it passes current very easily when a lightning surge at many times the operating voltage strikes the system.

Hall Devices. As a final example of the many uses of semiconducting devices in commercial practice, we will briefly describe the use of the Hall

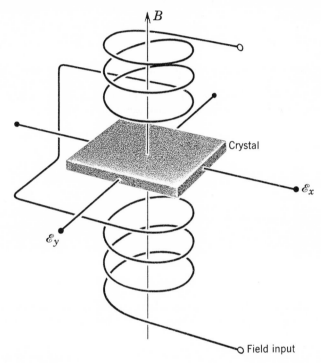

Figure 11.24 Gaussmeter and wattmeter applications of the Hall effect apparatus.

effect in semiconductors as a means of measuring quantities such as the magnitude of a magnetic field and the power in watts supplied to an electrical circuit. We recall from equation 11.20 that the Hall field $\mathscr{E}_y$ across a crystal is given as the product of the applied electric field $\mathscr{E}_x$, the magnetic induction B, and the mobility μ, that is,

$$\mathscr{E}_y = -B\mathscr{E}_x\mu$$

Figure 11.24 shows a circuit in which this effect can be employed for various practical measurements. If, for example, the value of B is to be measured in a *gaussmeter* application, $\mathscr{E}_x$ is supplied from a battery source, and $\mathscr{E}_y$

read on a meter gives the value of B. In another application as a *watt-meter*, the voltage drop in the electrical circuit is applied across a field coil giving rise to B, and the current of the circuit, or a known portion thereof, is passed through the Hall crystal. The product, which is proportional to the power consumed in the circuit, is then given by the Hall voltage across the crystal.

REFERENCES

A. J. Dekker, *Electrical Engineering Materials*, Prentice-Hall, Englewood Cliffs, N.J., 1959.
W. C. Dunlap, *An Introduction to Semiconductors*, John Wiley and Sons, New York, 1957
C. Kittel, *Introduction to Solid State Physics*, John Wiley and Sons, New York, 1956.
W. Shockley, *Electrons and Holes in Semiconductors*, D. Van Nostrand Company, Princeton, N.J., 1950.
E. Spenke, *Electronic Semiconductors*, McGraw-Hill Book Company, New York, 1958.
R. L. Sproull, *Modern Physics*, John Wiley and Sons, New York, 1956.

EXERCISES

1. Calculate the intrinsic conductivity σ at 300°K for germanium from the following data:
$$E_g = 0.72 \text{ eV}$$
$$\mu_n = 0.39 \text{ m}^2 \text{ V}^{-1} \text{ sec}^{-1}$$
$$\mu_p = 0.19 \text{ m}^2 \text{ V}^{-1} \text{ sec}^{-1}$$
Calculate also the dependence of conductivity on temperature about room temperature. Express the answer in mhos/m°K.

2. Calculate the position of the Fermi level E_F and the conductivity at 300°K for a germanium crystal containing 5×10^{22} arsenic atoms per cubic meter.

3. Calculate the position of the Fermi level and the conductivity at 300°K for a germanium crystal containing 10^{22} gallium atoms per cubic meter.

4. Calculate the position of the Fermi level and the conductivity at 300°K for a germanium crystal containing 5×10^{22} arsenic atoms per cubic meter and 10^{22} gallium atoms per cubic meter.

5. The resistivity of a doped silicon crystal is 9.27×10^{-3} ohm-m, and the Hall coefficient is 3.84×10^{-4} m³ coulomb⁻¹. Assuming that conduction is by a single type of charge carrier, calculate the density and mobility of the carrier.

6. Calculate the Hall voltage across the width of a semiconducting specimen from the following data:
Specimen dimensions: width 0.1 m, thickness 0.01 m. Field, applied perpendicular to both width and length has $B = 0.6$ weber m⁻²
Current flowing lengthwise $= 10 \text{ mA}$
Hall coefficient $= 3.84 \times 10^{-4}$ m³ coulomb⁻¹

7. For direct (i.e., without traps) recombination, an electron and hole must stay in the neighborhood (say within 1 Å) of each other for at least 10^{-8} sec. Assuming that the electron and hole have each an effective mass in the

particular application equal to that of the free electron and translation energies of room temperature thermal values, show that direct recombination is unlikely.

8. The saturation current of a *p-n* junction is 10^{-6} amp. For a temperature of 300°K, plot current vs. voltage from equation 12.26 for a voltage range of -5 to $+0.5$ volt. Also plot on log-log paper.

9. Calculate the applied voltages for currents across a *p-n* junction of 1 mA. Use the data:

Temperature	$= 300°K$
Conductivity on *n* side	$= 500$ mhos m^{-1}
Conductivity on *p* side	$= 2000$ mhos m^{-1}
Junction area	$= 10^{-6}$ m^2
Saturation current	$= 10^{-6}$ amp

10. A cadmium sulfide photodetector crystal is irradiated over a receiving area of 4×10^{-6} m^2 by light of wavelength 0.4×10^{-6} m and intensity 20 watts m^{-2}.

   (a) If the energy gap of cadmium sulfate is 2.4 eV, confirm that electron-hole pairs will be generated.

   (b) Assuming each quantum generates an electron-hole pair, calculate the number of pairs generated per second.

   (c) The increase in the density of electrons is given by the product (number of electrons produced per second) × (lifetime of the electron carriers). Calculate the increase in conductivity for an electron lifetime of 10^{-3} sec and an electron mobility of 10^{-2} m^2 V^{-1} sec.

12

Magnetism

In the past solids have been classified according to the magnitude of their magnetic properties into three groups, namely, *diamagnetic*, *paramagnetic*, and *ferromagnetic*. It is, however, also useful to differentiate among solids according to the temperature dependence of magnetic character. Then in fact eleven groups exist. In Section 12.1 we introduce the quantity *magnetic susceptibility*. This is the quantity that best characterizes the magnetic property of the atom and relates it to the macroscopic magnetic property of the solid. We will then show a table summarizing the different types of magnetic behavior in terms of susceptibility. The susceptibility relates three fundamental parameters **B**, **H**, and μ whose nature we will first discuss.

The Magnetic Induction or Flux Density B. A magnetic field of induction **B** exerts a force **dF** on an element dl of wire carrying a current placed in the field. The force is given by:

$$d\mathbf{F} = \mathbf{I} \times \mathbf{B}\, dl \qquad (12.1)$$

B is expressed in weber m^{-2}, **dF** in newtons, **I** in amps and dl in meters. Force **dF** is perpendicular to **I** and to **B** and is in the direction in which a right-handed screw advances when rotated from **I** to **B**.

The Magnetic Field Intensity H. Intensity **H** is defined so that the line integral of **H** along a closed curve is equal to the total current enclosed. That is,

$$\oint \mathbf{H} \cdot dl = I \qquad (12.2)$$

Thus **H** is expressed in amp m^{-1}. The relationship between **B** and **H** is

$$\mathbf{B} = \mu_0 \mu_r \mathbf{H} \qquad (12.3)$$

where μ_0 is the *permeability of free space* and equals $4\pi \times 10^{-7}$ weber m^{-1} amp^{-1}, and μ_r is the *relative permeability of the medium* in which **B** exists and is a pure number equal to unity for a vacuum.

Note that equation 12.3 implies a unique relationship between **B** and **H**.

The Magnetic Dipole Moment μ.   A magnetic dipole moment **μ**, which arises in ways that we will discuss, produces a magnetic field which at large distances is identical with that produced by a current loop. The moment **μ** is defined in terms of a planar loop of area A carrying a current I by the relation

$$\boldsymbol{\mu} = \mathbf{n}IA \qquad (12.4)$$

Here **n** is a unit vector in a direction normal to the loop.

In a solid the *total magnetic dipole moment per unit volume* is referred to as **M**.

12.1   Magnetic Susceptibility

We shall now discuss the relationship between **B**, **H**, and **M**. Suppose in Fig. 12.1 that a cylinder of material whose relative permeability is μ_r is placed in a magnetic field **H**. The magnetic induction **B** in the cylinder is given by equation 12.3.

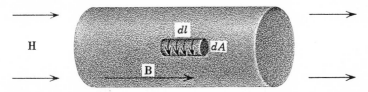

Figure 12.1   A cylinder of material of relative permeability μ_r in a magnetic field **H**. When a small cylinder of the material is removed, the magnetic induction inside the cavity falls and a current must be conceived to pass around the cavity walls to restore the induction inside to its former value. This current is shown by the circular arrows.

Now suppose that a small cylinder of length dl and cross-section dA is cut from the original cylinder. The magnetic induction inside the cylinder would change. It is possible, however, to conceive of a current, flowing around the cylinder walls, being introduced to keep the magnetic induction inside the cavity the same as it was before the material was removed.

Let us first calculate the magnitude of this current. The value of μ_r inside the cavity is unity. Thus if the subscript c refers to "inside the cavity," then in magnitudes

$$B_c = B$$

that is,

$$\mu_0 H_c = \mu_0 \mu_r H \qquad (12.5)$$

and hence

$$H_c - H = (\mu_r - 1)H$$

This increase in field $H_c - H$ inside the cavity can be produced by a current, according to equation 12.2, of magnitude I where

$$I = (\mu_r - 1)H \, dl \qquad (12.6)$$

Now, using equation 12.4, we deduce that the material that was removed from the cavity must have been contributing a magnetic dipole moment μ where the magnitude of μ is given by

$$\mu = (\mu_r - 1)H \, dl \, dA$$

The magnetic dipole moment per unit volume M is thus related to H by

$$M = (\mu_r - 1)H = \chi H \qquad (12.7)$$

where χ is called the *magnetic susceptibility*.

We shall now complete this section by classifying solids according to the magnitude and temperature dependence of magnetic susceptibility.

In Table 12.1 T_c the critical temperature, C the Curie constant, and θ the Curie temperature are each characteristic of the material considered.

12.2 Diamagnetism

An external magnetic field induces in all atoms and ions a diamagnetic moment equivalent to a negative susceptibility. This is often masked, however, by the permanent moments and positive susceptibility associated with the other classes of magnetism.

We will derive the magnetic susceptibility for a special case. Figure 12.2a shows an electron of charge $-e$ describing a circular orbit of radius r around a proton. The angular frequency of the electron is ω_0. From equation 12.4 the magnitude of the orbital magnetic dipole moment μ is given by

$$\mu = IA$$

$$= -\frac{e\omega_0}{2\pi}\pi r^2$$

that is,

$$\mu = -\tfrac{1}{2}er^2\omega_0 \qquad (12.8)$$

Table 12.1

TYPE	MAGNITUDE OF SUSCEPTIBILITY	TEMPERATURE DEPENDENCE	EXAMPLES
Diamagnetic	Small, negative Intermediate, negative	Independent Varies with field and temperature below 20°K (not discussed in text)	Organic materials, light elements, Alkali earths Bismuth
	Large, negative	Exists only below critical temperatures (See Section 10.11)	Superconducting metals
Paramagnetic	Small, positive	Independent	Alkali metals Transition metals
	Large, positive	$\chi = \dfrac{C}{T - \theta}$	Rare earths
Antiferromagnetic	Small, positive	When $T > T_N$; $\chi = \dfrac{C}{T + \theta}$ When $T < T_N$; $\chi \propto T$	Salts of transition elements
Ferromagnetic	Very large, positive	$T > T_c$; $\chi = \dfrac{C}{T - \theta}$ $T < T_c$; See Section 12.6	Some transition and rare earth metals
Ferrimagnetic	Very large, positive	$T > T_N$; $\chi = \dfrac{C}{T \pm \theta}$ $T < T_N$ See Section 12.10	Ferrites

Suppose now that the magnetic induction is increased from zero in Fig. 12.2*a* to a value B in Fig. 12.2*b*. As the flux ϕ is increasing then by Lenz's Law an *electric field* $\mathscr{E}$ is set up in the circular orbit such that

$$\oint \mathscr{E} \, dl = -\frac{d\phi}{dt} \tag{12.9}$$

where dl is an increment of the circular path of the electron. The electric field induces a current in the orbit, and the magnetic field associated with this current is in such a direction that it counteracts the increase $d\phi$. This is the meaning of the negative sign in equation 12.9.

Solving 12.9 for the complete orbit gives

$$\mathscr{E} = -\frac{1}{2\pi r} \cdot \frac{d\phi}{dt}$$

Since

$$B = \frac{\phi}{\pi r^2}$$

then

$$\mathscr{E} = -\frac{r}{2} \cdot \frac{dB}{dt} \tag{12.10}$$

While $\mathscr{E}$ is present, that is while B is changing, the electron will be subject to a force F of magnitude $-e\mathscr{E}$ which increases its angular momentum.

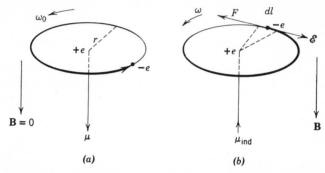

(a)   (b)

Figure 12.2   A simplified atom consisting of an electron circling a proton. The angular velocity ω_0 in the absence of a magnetic field is increased to ω when **B** is applied. The increase in angular velocity is associated with an induced magnetic moment μ_{ind} which is opposite in direction to **B** and thus is diamagnetic in character.

The increase in angular momentum $mr\,d\omega$ is given by

$$mr\,d\omega = F\,dt$$
$$= -e\mathscr{E}\cdot dt$$
$$= \frac{er}{2}\cdot dB$$

The new angular frequency of the electron in the presence of the magnetic induction B is given by integrating this last equation.

$$m\int_{\omega_0}^{\omega} d\omega = \frac{e}{2}\int_0^B dB$$

Thus

$$\omega = \omega_0 + \frac{e}{2m}\cdot B \tag{12.11}$$

The electron will retain this new frequency as long as **B** does not change. The term $e/2m \cdot B$ is called the *Larmor frequency*.

The change in frequency $e/2m \cdot B$ gives rise by equation 12.8 to a change in orbital magnetic dipole moment. The moment induced by B is thus given by

$$\mu_{\text{ind}} = (-\tfrac{1}{2}er^2)\left(\frac{e}{2m}B\right) = -\frac{e^2r^2}{4m} \cdot B \tag{12.12}$$

The direction of this induced moment is opposite to that of **B**.

An expression for the diamagnetic susceptibility can now be obtained from the definition of equation 12.7. The term r^2 can be identified as the mean square radius of the projection of the orbit on a plane perpendicular to **B**. For the atom of Fig. 12.2, $r^2 = x^2 + y^2$, and for an atom containing Z electrons where the distribution of charge is spherically symmetrical and of average radius $\bar{r}$, then

$$\bar{r}^2 = x^2 + y^2 + z^2 = \tfrac{2}{3}r^2$$

Thus when the foregoing treatment is extended to a solid containing N atoms per unit volume, each with Z electrons, we obtain for the dia-magnetic susceptibility χ, defined as the induced magnetic dipole moment per cubic meters per weber per square meters the expression

$$\chi = -NZ\frac{e^2}{6m}\bar{r}^2(\mu_0\mu_r) \tag{12.13}$$

Suppose $\bar{r}^2 \simeq 10^{-20}\ m^2$, $N \simeq 5 \times 10^{28}$, $Z = 10$, then $\chi \simeq 10^{-5}$. Table 8.2 gives the measured values of susceptibility of the elements. Diamagnetic susceptibilities are preceded by a negative sign.

12.3 Paramagnetism

Diamagnetism is an integral characteristic of all matter. The appearance of paramagnetism and the other types of magnetism is a result of the fact that many atoms have a permanent magnetic dipole moment which out-weighs the diamagnetic effect.

Permanent magnetic moments are the sum of three components, namely, (a) the *orbital* magnetic dipole moment of the electrons, (b) the *spin* magnetic dipole moment of the electrons, and (c) the *nuclear* spin magnetic moment.

The Orbital Magnetic Dipole Moment. In Fig. 12.2a we envisaged a single electron moving in orbit around a proton. The orbital magnetic dipole moment μ of the single electron was given by equation 12.8 as

$-\frac{1}{2}er^2\omega_0$. The orbital angular momentum of the electron is, of course, $mr^2\omega$. If we call this quantity $\mathbf{L}$, then

$$\boldsymbol{\mu} = \frac{-e}{2m} \cdot \mathbf{L} \qquad (12.14)$$

We have seen in Section 7.3 that orbital momenta are expressed in units of $h/2\pi$. An electron with orbital momentum of *one unit* will therefore have an orbital magnetic moment of $e/2m \cdot h/2\pi$. This unit quantity of magnetic dipole moment is called the *Bohr magneton* β and is of magnitude 9.27×10^{-24} amp m^2.

Also in Section 7.2 we saw that the orientation of the electron orbital momentum with respect to a magnetic field is limited so that the components of $\mathbf{L}$ in the field direction take the integral values l, $(l-1) \cdots -l$ when expressed in units of $h/2\pi$.

As a consequence, an s electron for which l is zero can have no orbital magnetic moment. A single p electron for which l is unity can have a moment. If, however, in a multielectron atom, all three p states corresponding to $m_l = 1$, $m_l = 0$ and $m_l = -1$ in the L shell are filled by electrons, the total magnetic moment of the p electrons would again be zero. In general, we can only expect a resultant orbital magnetic moment from electrons in incompletely filled shells.

The transition elements with Z equal to 21 to 28, 39 to 45, 58 to 41, and 89 to 92, have incomplete shells, and the *free* atoms of these elements do have permanent magnetic moments. If, however, these atoms are grouped together in a solid, interaction between the lattice atoms may prevent orientation of the orbital magnetic dipole moments of the individual atoms in a magnetic field. This is what happens in the first of the groups mentioned previously, namely, the iron group. The orbital magnetic moment is quenched. In the higher transition groups where the incomplete $4f$ shells that contribute to the orbital moments lie deep within the atom, the interaction with neighboring atoms is small. As a consequence, permanent orbital magnetic moments do exist in these solid elements.

The Spin Magnetic Dipole Moment of the Electrons. As discussed in Section 7.3, the electron has, in addition to its orbital angular momentum, an intrinsic spin angular momentum $\mathbf{L}_s$. The components of $\mathbf{L}_s$ along a field direction are given by $sh/2\pi$, where s the spin quantum number may take the values $\pm\frac{1}{2}$. Associated with each spin momentum is a *spin magnetic dipole moment*. We might expect, following the discussion of orbital moments, that the *spin magnetic* moment along the field direction would have components $s\beta$. In fact, however, these components are given by $gs\beta$ where the factor g is called the *Landé splitting factor*. Detailed discussion of g will not be given. For pure electron spin the value of g is exactly 2. For solid elements of the iron group where the magnetic moments arise from spin and the orbital moments are very small because of quenching, the measured magnetic moments give values of g very close to 2.

Nuclear Spin Magnetic Dipole Moment. The angular momentum associated with nuclear spin is also expressed in units of $h/2\pi$. The mass of the nucleus is of the order of one thousand times that of the electron, however. Thus the magnetic dipole moment associated with nuclear spin, a quantity called the *nuclear magneton*, is of the order of 10^{-3} Bohr magneton.

So far we have merely discussed the nature of the permanent moments that are associated with an atom. To compute the susceptibility we must make a calculation of the numbers of magnetic dipole moments which line

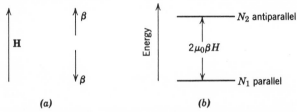

(a)   *(b)*

Figure 12.3   In the presence of a magnetic field **H** the two spin moments will align parallel and antiparallel to the field as in (*a*). The energy difference of the two configurations is shown in (*b*).

up parallel to an applied magnetic field. The magnitude of the susceptibility will be determined by the fractional number of magnetic dipole moments which line up in this way.

For simplicity, let us carry out the calculation for a system of atoms in which the magnetic dipole moments are due to pure electron spin. Let us further suppose that the spin moment of each atom does not interact with the moments of the other atoms.

We have seen that the spin moment of each simple atom is of magnitude $\pm\beta$ since here g just equals 2. This is equivalent to envisaging two possible spin moments, each of magnitude β, one lined parallel to a magnetic field and the other antiparallel. Now the energy of a magnetic moment in the presence of a magnetic field of induction B is given by the product of these quantities. Thus an energy difference exists between spin magnetic dipole moments parallel and antiparallel to the field, the magnitude of the energy difference being $2\beta B$. If no interaction exists between neighboring spin moments, the permeability is that of free space μ_0. The two spin energy levels are thus $+\mu_0\beta H$ and $-\mu_0\beta H$. This is summarized in Fig. 12.3. Let us suppose that in unit volume of the paramagnetic material that there is a total of N atoms and that the spin moments of N_1 atoms are parallel to the field and N_2 spin moments are antiparallel. The populations in each of the two energy levels are given by Boltzmann statistics. These populations are

$$\frac{N_1}{N} = \frac{e^{\mu_0\beta H/kT}}{e^{\mu_0\beta H/kT} + e^{-\mu_0\beta H/kT}} \tag{12.15}$$

and

$$\frac{N_2}{N} = \frac{e^{-\mu_0\beta H/kT}}{e^{\mu_0\beta H/kT} + e^{-\mu_0\beta H/kT}} \tag{12.16}$$

Also, $N = N_1 + N_2$, and the total magnetic moment per unit volume M is given by

$$M = (N_1 - N_2)\beta$$

Thus

$$M = N\beta \left[\frac{e^{\mu_0\beta H/kT} - e^{-\mu_0\beta H/kT}}{e^{\mu_0\beta H/kT} + e^{-\mu_0\beta H/kT}}\right] \tag{12.17}$$

This may be written more concisely as

$$M = N\beta \tanh \frac{\mu_0\beta H}{kT} \tag{12.18}$$

Fig. 12.4a shows a plot of $M/N\beta$ against $\mu_0\beta H/kT$ and Fig. 12.4b shows experimental measurements of the magnetic moments of the chromium, iron, and gadolinium ion for various field-temperature ratios. It is obvious that despite the many simplifications, equation 12.18 gives a good representation of the experimental results.

Let us examine the nature of the function given in equation 12.18 for two regions of $\mu_0\beta H/kT$.

When $\mu_0\beta H \ll kT$. This is the normal circumstance since even in a strong field of magnetic induction $\mu_0 H = 1$ weber m^{-2}, the value of $\mu_0\beta H \simeq 9 \times 10^{-24}$ joule, whereas at room temperature $kT \simeq 4 \times 10^{-21}$ joule. Under these circumstances

$$\tanh \frac{\mu_0\beta H}{kT} \simeq \frac{\mu_0\beta H}{kT}$$

$$M \simeq \frac{N\mu_0\beta^2 H}{kT}$$

and

$$\chi \simeq \frac{N\mu_0\beta^2}{kT} = \frac{C}{T} \tag{12.19}$$

The reciprocal dependence of χ and T is called *Curie's Law*. The Curie constant C is characteristic of the material. Figure 12.5 shows that Curie's Law is well obeyed in the case of copper potassium sulfate.

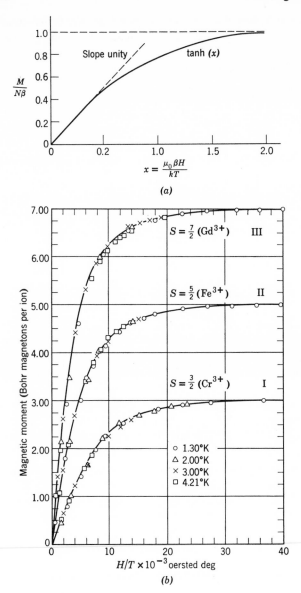

Figure 12.4 (a) Plot of $M/N\beta$ as a function of $\mu_0\beta H/kT$. (b) The magnetic moment vs. H/T for specimens of: I, potassium chromium alum; II, ferric ammonium alum; and III, gadolinium sulfate octohydrate. (After Henry)

For many paramagnetic substances, however, when the experimental values of χ are plotted against reciprocal temperature, the graph does not pass through the origin and the relationship reads $\chi = C/(T - \theta)$ where θ is also characteristic of the paramagnetic substance.

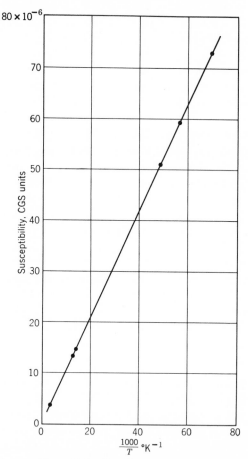

Figure 12.5   Plot of susceptibility per gram vs. reciprocal temperature for powdered $CuSO_4 \cdot K_2SO_4 \cdot 6H_2O$. (After Hupse)

Let us estimate the order of magnitude of the paramagnetic susceptibility of solids at room temperature. In mks units

$$N \simeq 10^{28}; \quad \beta \simeq 10^{-23}; \quad k \simeq 10^{-23}$$

and thus for $T \simeq 10^2$ the order of magnitude of χ is 10^{-3}. Table 8.2 shows measured susceptibility values.

The Special Case when $\mu_0 \beta H \gg kT$. This condition will apply only in the presence of strong fields at low temperatures. Then

$$\tanh (\mu_0 \beta H / kT) \simeq 1$$

and M approaches the saturation value of $N\beta$. This implies that every dipole moment of the material is lined up parallel to the magnetic field. Figure 12.4b shows that the condition can be achieved experimentally.

In the section discussing nuclear spin magnetic dipole moment, we noted that the nuclear magneton was of order $10^{-3}\beta$. Since the susceptibility χ depends on β^2, we would expect the susceptibility of a nuclear paramagnetic system to be smaller by a factor of 10^{-6} than that of an electronic paramagnetic system. This is experimentally found to be the case. It should be recalled also at this point that diamagnetic susceptibilities are of the order 10^{-5} m^{-3}. Thus in a system of permanent spin magnetic dipole moments the positive paramagnetic susceptibility will mask the diamagnetic and nuclear terms.

12.4　Electronic and Nuclear Spin Resonance

We have seen in Section 12.3 that the magnetic sublevels in an atom, characterized by the value of single electron spin, are separated by an energy difference of $2\mu_0\beta H$. In general, the energy difference is $g\mu_0\beta H$. Let us now suppose that electromagnetic radiation is supplied to a paramagnetic crystal at a frequency ν such that the following condition is fulfilled:

$$h\nu = g\mu_0\beta H \tag{12.20}$$

Here transitions between the magnetic sublevels are induced and energy is absorbed from the radiation source.

Figure 12.6 shows a simplified experimental setup to carry out studies of this nature. A static magnetic field H_y is applied in the direction indicated. The field H_x varies at the frequency ν, and the absorption of high frequency energy is measured in an associated circuit. Obviously either the magnitude of the static field H_y or the frequency ν may be varied to satisfy the resonance condition given by equation 12.20. For *electron spin resonance*, equation 12.20 simplifies to

$$\nu(Mc) = 3.52 \times 10^{-2}H \;(H \text{ in amperes m}^{-1}) \tag{12.21}$$

and for *proton spin resonance* (12.21) simplifies to

$$\nu(kc) = 5.35 \times 10^{-2}H \;(H \text{ in amperes}^{-1}) \tag{12.22}$$

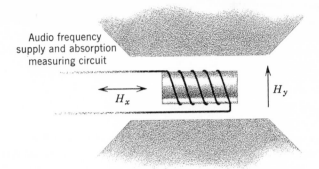

Figure 12.6   Apparatus to measure spin resonance in solids. The specimen is subjected to a field H_y and a high-frequency field H_x. Either H_y or the frequency of H_x may be varied.

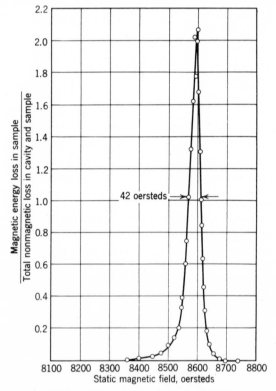

Figure 12.7   Electron spin resonance in an organic free radical compound at 24,446 mc sec^{-1}.   (After Holden)

Figure 12.7 shows electron spin resonance absorption in an organic compound. In this experiment the field was varied while the frequency remained constant. Spin resonance experimental techniques are now widely used in the study of solids and in the measurement and control of magnetic fields.

12.5 Ferromagnetism

The magnetic behavior of the three elements—iron, cobalt, and nickel—at the end of the first transition series is quite unique. Let us recall the

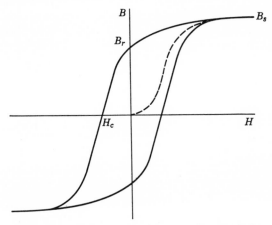

Figure 12.8 The hysteretic behavior of magnetic induction vs. field strength for a ferromagnetic solid. The dotted curve gives the initial behavior of an unmagnetized specimen.

magnetic characteristics of these elements and of the many ferromagnetic alloys which exist.

Ferromagnetic solids have very high values of susceptibility which are both field and temperature dependent. Above a certain temperature θ, which is characteristic of the particular substance, the temperature dependence of the susceptibility is similar to that of most paramagnetic solids, that is,

$$\chi = \frac{C}{T - \theta} \qquad (12.23)$$

At lower temperatures the dependence of *magnetization* M and the magnetic induction B on field strength H is shown by the familiar hysteresis curve of Fig. 12.8. The shape of the curve is dependent on the preparation and treatment of the ferromagnetic specimen. The value of M at high fields, corresponding to induction B_S, that is, the saturation magnetization M_S, depends only on the constitution and purity of the specimen. If the ratio of M_S at a particular temperature to the value at $0°K$ is plotted against the ratio of the temperature to the temperature θ at which ferromagnetism disappears, the plot of these reduced parameters is common for all ferromagnetic materials. This is shown in Fig. 12.9 for iron, cobalt, and nickel.

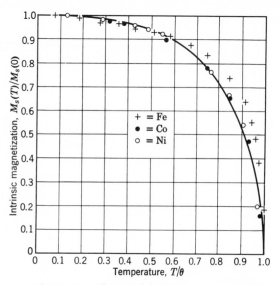

Figure 12.9   The ratio of the saturation magnetization at a particular temperature T to that at $0°K$ plotted against the ratio of the particular temperature T to that at which ferromagnetism disappears θ, for the metals iron, cobalt, and nickel. The full line shows the theoretical curve from Section 12.5.

These are some of the unique magnetic properties of ferromagnetic materials which a theory must attempt to explain.

In Section 12.3 on paramagnetic materials we saw that it was possible, at low temperatures and with strong magnetic fields, to produce saturation values of M. In ferromagnetic materials saturation magnetization is possible at ordinary temperatures and with small fields. Pierre Weiss in 1907 invented a concept to account for this behavior. He postulated the existence of an internal "molecular" field H_E which is proportional to the magnetization M. Thus

$$H_E = \lambda M \tag{12.24}$$

where λ is the *Weiss field constant*.

Weiss supposed this internal field to be the result of the cooperative interaction of neighboring dipoles. Let us at this point make a quick estimate of the magnitude of the interaction necessary to account for experimental values. In Fig. 12.8 the value of B_r at $H = 0$ for a typical magnet material is about 1 weber m^{-2}. Thus $M_r \simeq B_r/\mu_0 \simeq 10^6$ ampere m^{-1}. In most solids there are about 10^{29} atomic dipole moments per cubic meter each of moment β, which is of magnitude 10^{-23} ampere m^{-2}. Thus to obtain the measured value of M_r, the interaction must be such that *all the magnetic dipoles are aligned parallel* in the ferromagnetic material.

In the presence of an applied external magnetic field each dipole in a ferromagnetic material is subject to a total field of $H + \lambda M$. Let us again use the simplified model of Section 12.4 in which N spins per cubic meter line up parallel or antiparallel to the applied magnetic field. We simply replace H in equation 12.18 by the new total field $H + \lambda M$. Thus

$$M = N\beta \tanh \left[\frac{\mu_0 \beta}{kT} (H + \lambda M) \right] \tag{12.25}$$

Again as in the paramagnetic case we distinguish between two temperature regions.

1. At magnetizations well below saturation we have: where $\mu_0 \beta/kT \ll 1$, that is, the high temperature region, then $\tanh x \simeq x$, and equation 12.25 becomes

$$M = \frac{N\mu_0 \beta^2}{kT} (H + \lambda M) \tag{12.26}$$

The susceptibility χ is thus given by

$$\chi = \frac{M}{H} = \frac{N\mu_0 \beta^2/k}{T - N\mu_0 \beta^2 \lambda/k} = \frac{C}{T - \theta} \tag{12.27}$$

We have thus obtained an expression similar to the experimental relation of equation 12.23. Also from equation 12.27 the Curie constant

$$C = \frac{N\mu_0 \beta^2}{k} \tag{12.28}$$

and
$$\theta = \lambda C \tag{12.29}$$

The susceptibility of iron conforms to equation 12.27 at temperatures above a value of about 1000°K. The slope of the line of χ vs. $(T - \theta)^{-1}$ gives a value of C of about unity. Thus the Weiss field constant λ is of order 10^3 and corresponds to an extremely high value of internal field of induction about 10^3 webers m^{-2}. We will return later to a qualitative discussion of the nature of the dipole interaction that gives rise to this huge internal field.

2. Let us now consider the effect of the internal field in the *absence of an external field* and at lower temperatures. From equation 12.25 we have

$$M = N\beta \tanh \left(\frac{\lambda\mu_0\beta M}{kT}\right) \tag{12.30}$$

That is,

$$\frac{M}{M_s} = \tanh a \tag{12.31}$$

where $M_s = N\beta$ represents the saturation value of the magnetization, and

$$a = \left(\frac{\lambda\mu_0\beta M}{kT}\right)$$

Also from this expression for a we have

$$\frac{M}{M_s} = \left(\frac{kT}{N\lambda\mu_0\beta^2}\right) a$$

that is,

$$\frac{M}{M_s} = \frac{T}{\theta} a \tag{12.32}$$

since $\theta = \lambda N\mu_0\beta^2/k$ from equation 12.28. We now have two simultaneous equations for M/M_s as a function of a, which are plotted in Fig. 12.10.

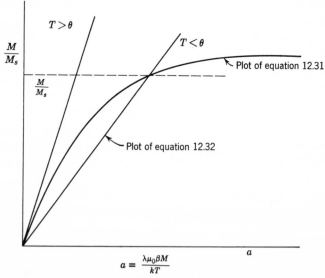

Figure 12.10 The graphical solution of the simultaneous equations 12.31 and 12.32. The point of intersection shows that intrinsic magnetization exists even in the absence of a field. This magnetization vanishes at $T > \theta$, since no crossing point of the curve is then possible.

For $T < \theta$ there are two solutions to the equations, one at zero magnetization and one at some finite value of M. Thus *at a sufficiently low value of temperature there can exist in a ferromagnetic solid a magnetization within the material, even in the absence of an external field.*

The values of M/M_s representing the points of intersection of (12.31) and (12.32) can be found for various values of T/θ. If M/M_s is plotted as a function of T/θ, the relation is shown by the full line of Fig. 12.9 in good agreement with the experimental values.

To explain the fact that even ferromagnetic materials are normally found in the demagnetized state, Weiss made his second postulate. He assumed the existence of small domains within which the ferromagnetic material is magnetized to saturation. The *direction of magnetization*, however, varies from domain to domain, and thus the *net macroscopic magnetization* may have values between zero and the saturation value. The following sections will contain further discussion of the two Weiss postulates.

12.6   The Internal Field: Exchange Interaction

We will first discuss in some more detail the nature of the magnetic dipole interaction which gives rise to the Weiss internal field. These ideas have been formulated by Heisenberg, Slater, and Stoner, subsequent to the introduction of the concept by Weiss, and they are not yet satisfactory.

We have seen in Section 12.5 that the induction of the Weiss internal field is of the order of 10^3 webers^{-2}. This value is about one thousand times as large as we would obtain on the assumption that the internal field is due to the *magnetic* interaction of the atomic dipoles. But electrostatic coulomb repulsion between two electrons is many orders of magnitude greater than the magnetic force between them that arises because of their spin magnetic moments. The source of the very large spin interaction found in ferromagnetic materials must therefore be sought in a spin-dependent electrostatic interaction. Quantum mechanics provides such an interaction— called the *exchange interaction.* Heisenberg considers that an interaction between near atomic neighbors in solids of certain of the transition elements results in the electron spins of the neighboring atoms being aligned.

Slater and Stoner have given an explanation on band theory, which will be followed in the ensuing discussion, iron being used as the example. In Fig. 8.21 we showed the band structure of iron with the narrow partially-filled $3d$ band and a broad overlapping $4s$. In Fig. 12.11a we again show the $3d$ band, this time separating the band into partial bands of positive and negative spin, each capable of holding five electrons. We will neglect the effect of the 4s band since this is not of major importance to the discussion. If the exchange interaction was not present, three of the six 3d electrons in iron would have spin $+\frac{1}{2}$ and three $-\frac{1}{2}$. Naturally without a preponderance of spin of one direction, the iron atom would have no spin magnetic moment. The exchange interaction causes the effect shown in Fig. 12.11b. In solid iron the total energy is lowered by making the maximum number of spins parallel. Thus five electrons go into $+\frac{1}{2}$ spin partial and one in the $-\frac{1}{2}$ spin partial. The Fermi energy is increased since the states now occupied at the top of the $+\frac{1}{2}$ band are of greater energy than

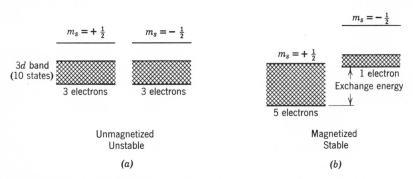

Figure 12.11   The partial 3d bands of iron shown with (a) three electrons in each band giving the unmagnetized state, and (b) with five electrons in one band and one electron in the other giving the magnetized state. The latter is stable for iron since the exchange energy lowers the total more than the Fermi energy raises it.

those vacated near the middle of the $-\frac{1}{2}$ band. The exchange energy, however, lowers the whole $+\frac{1}{2}$ band, and in iron this is the more important term. The magnetized state of Fig. 12.11b is therefore the one of lower total energy and thus the stable one.

If the outer unfilled band in a metal is much broader than we have pictured for iron, the magnetized state of Fig. 12.11b would be unstable. This is so because filling the $+\frac{1}{2}$ spin band, if it were very broad, would mean adding many electrons near the top and therefore of high energy. The increase in the Fermi energy term would then be greater than the decrease by the exchange energy.

A criterion for the appearance of ferromagnetism is therefore the width of the 3d band. Figure 12.12 shows the energy of magnetization—that is, the difference in energy between the magnetized and unmagnetized states—plotted as a function of the ratio of the interatomic spacings to the calculated radius of the 3d orbit. When the separation of the atoms is great, there is a small reduction of energy by the exchange effect. On the other hand, when the ratio becomes small, the 3d band is broadened, and the

Fermi energy term makes the magnetized state the unstable one. The magnitudes of band width and atomic spacing favor magnetization in the solids—iron, cobalt, and nickel. If the interatomic distance in a metal is altered by compound or alloy formation, the process might cause a metal that is not ferromagnetic to become so. In the Heusler alloys, which consist of aluminum, copper, and manganese, the effective interatomic distance.

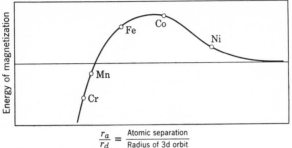

Figure 12.12 The energy of magnetization plotted as a function of the ratio of interatomic spacing to the radius of the 3d orbit. The magnetized state is stable for the elements iron, cobalt, and nickel.

for manganese is increased. The energy of magnetization in Fig. 12.12 is now positive, and the alloy is ferromagnetic within a certain composition range.

12.7   Domains

In Section 12.5 it was postulated that ferromagnetic materials contain small *domains* within which the material is magnetized to saturation, and the overall net magnetization is dependent on the degree to which the magnetic moments of the separate domains are aligned.

When a weak magnetic field is applied to a ferromagnetic specimen, domains that are favorably oriented with respect to the field grow at the expense of domains less favorably oriented. In stronger fields the directions of magnetization of the individual domains rotate toward the direction of the field. These two processes are pictured in Fig. 12.13, which also shows the resulting magnetization curve.

Direct evidence of domain structure is obtained from powder patterns. In this technique a drop of a colloidal suspension of finely divided ferromagnetic powder is allowed to spread over a prepared surface of the ferromagnetic material under investigation. The colloidal particles collect along the domain boundaries where strong magnetic fields exist. Photo-micrographs are then made of the powder pattern. Figure 12.14 shows such a pattern on a silicon–iron single crystal.

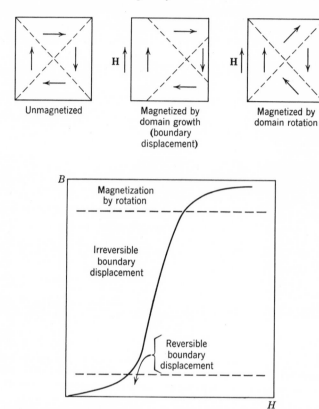

Figure 12.13   Magnetization by domain growth and by domain magnetic moment rotation. The associated stages in the magnetization curve are also shown.

Domain structure is brought about by three contributions to the total energy, namely, the *exchange energy, the anisotropy energy, and the magnetic energy*. We have already discussed the first of these and will now deal with the other two.

Crystalline Anisotropy.   It is found experimentally that the magnetic field required to magnetize a single ferromagnetic crystal depends on the direction of magnetization. Figure 12.15 shows magnetization curves for iron, nickel, and cobalt with the applied field directed along different crystallographic directions in the crystal. With iron, for example, it is evident that very much greater fields are required to produce magnetic saturation in the [111] direction than need be applied in the [100] direction. The difference in magnetic energy to produce saturation in an easy and hard direction is called the *anisotropy energy*. The energy difference E_K can be expressed for *cubic* crystals in terms of the constants K_1 and K_2, called the anisotropy constants, and the direction cosines α, β, and γ of the

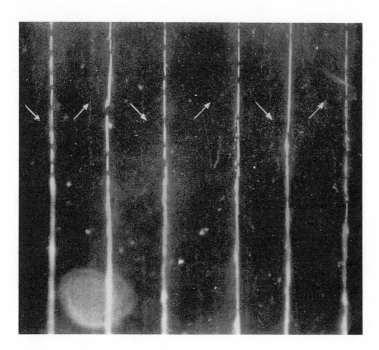

Figure 12.14 Domain walls in silicon-iron crystal. (After Williams, Bozorth, and Shockley)

magnetization direction, with respect to the cube axes. For example, in cubic crystals

$$E_K = K_1(\alpha^2\beta^2 + \beta^2\gamma^2 + \gamma^2\alpha^2) + K_2\alpha^2\beta^2\gamma^2 \qquad (12.33)$$

The anisotropy energy thus tends to make the magnetization of a domain line up parallel to an easy direction.

Magnetic Energy. The third energy term is the classical magnetostatic energy of a magnetic dipole in a magnetic field. In Section 12.3 we have already used the fact that the magnitude of the energy of a magnetic dipole μ in a field of magnetic induction B is given by the product of these quantities. In a ferromagnetic material of square cross section where the magnetic moment per unit volume is M_r the magnetic energy will therefore be of the order of $M_r B_r \simeq \mu_0 M_r{}^2 \simeq 10^6$ joule m^{-3}.

In Fig. 12.16a the exchange energy has established a single domain in a specimen of ferromagnetic material. The magnetic energy can, however

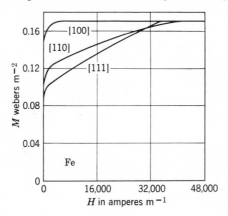

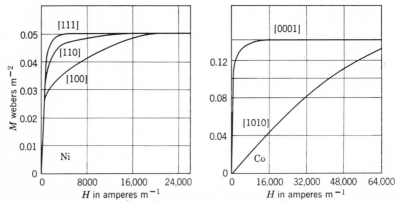

Figure 12.15   Magnetization curves for single crystals of iron, nickel, and cobalt. In iron, for example, the [100] and [111] are respectively the directions of easy and hard magnetization.

be reduced by dividing the specimen into two domains as in Fig. 12.16b. This subdivision process can be continued until the energy required to establish an additional interface, the *Bloch wall*, between domains is greater than the reduction in magnetic energy. The energy of the Bloch wall is about 10^{-3} joules m^{-2}, and in iron it is of the order of 100 atom spacings in thickness.

Figure 12.16*c* is an arrangement for which the magnetic energy is zero. The triangular prism domains are called *domains of closure*. Anisotropy energy will arise if the direction of magnetization in a domain of closure does not correspond to an easy direction of magnetization.

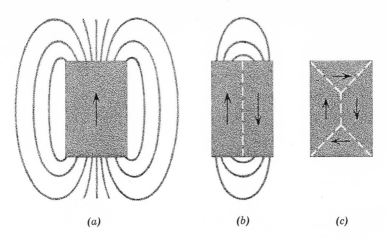

(*a*)   (*b*)   (*c*)

Figure 12.16 In (*a*) the exchange energy has established a single domain. In (*b*) the magnetic energy, which is roughly proportional to the spatial extension of the field, has been halved. In (*c*) the magnetic energy has been reduced to zero by the domains of closure.

The final domain pattern in a ferromagnetic crystal is thus determined by the pattern in which the sum total of exchange, anisotropy, and magnetic energy is a minimum.

12.8   Ferromagnetic Materials

In the introduction to ferromagnetism, we gave in Fig. 12.8 a representation of a *B*, *H* hysteresis loop. Starting with a virgin specimen, *B* varies *reversibly* with *H* for small fields (dotted line). Since there is no hysteresis in this region the *initial permeability* is defined in the same way as the permeability of a paramagnetic material, that is, as on page 297. As the applied field *H* is increased, *B* increases more rapidly and a *differential permeability* is defined as $1 + dM/dH$. The differential permeability increases at first with *H*. As *B* approaches its saturation value, the differential permeability then falls to unity. If the applied field is now reduced to zero, B_r, the *remanent induction*, remains and a reverse field $-H_c$, the *coercive force*, must be applied to reduce the induction to zero.

The coercive force varies over wide limits in ferromagnetic materials. For *permanent magnet materials* the coercive force should be high, whereas material used in transformers and in applications where the magnetic induction is rapidly varied should have low values of coercive force but high values of maximum permeability.

Table 12.3 shows some data on permanent magnet and high permeability materials.

Table 12.3

PERMANENT MAGNET MATERIALS	μ_r (weber m^{-2})	H_c (amp m^{-1})
Carbon steel	1	4,000
Alnico V	1.25	44,000

HIGH PERMEABILITY MATERIALS	$\mu_{r(\text{max})}$	B_s (weber m^{-2})	H_c (amp m^{-1})
Iron	5,000	2.1	80
4% Si–Fe	7,000	2.0	40
Mu metal	10^5	0.65	4
Supermalloy	8×10^5	0.8	0.16

The magnetic characteristics of ferromagnetic materials are determined by the ease with which the domain wall can move through the crystal. In *magnetically hard* material with high values of coercive force, the domain wall is restricted in its movement under the influence of a magnetizing field by the presence of (*a*) impurities, (*b*) stress, or (*c*) fine powder texture. *Magnetically soft* materials with low values of H_c and high permeability, on the other hand, should be highly purified, well annealed, correctly oriented for easy magnetization, and should be treated to remove other types of imperfection that would impede the movement of the Bloch walls.

12.9   Antiferromagnetism and Ferrimagnetism

To complete our discussion of the different kinds of magnetic behavior found in solid materials, we have yet to deal with the classes exhibiting *antiferromagnetism* and *ferrimagnetism*.

In Section 12.6 it was pointed out that the origin of the internal field in ferromagnetic materials was due to the exchange interaction that lined up neighboring spin moments in the solid. In some salts of the transition metals that contain ferromagnetic elements and that crystallize in a certain structure called the *spinel* structure, the spacing of the atoms is such that the *exchange interaction is negative*. Below a critical temperature, called

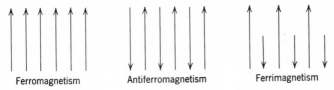

| Ferromagnetism | Antiferromagnetism | Ferrimagnetism |

Figure 12.17   Spin arrangements in ferromagnetic, antiferromagnetic, and ferrimagnetic materials.

the Néel temperature T_N, this can lead in such structures to *antiparallel* alignment of electron spins in neighboring atoms. If the two spin systems are balanced, the solid belongs to the *antiferromagnetic class* and, if unbalanced, to the *ferrimagnetic* class. Figure 12.17 shows the spin

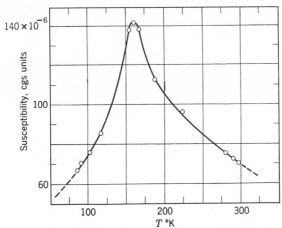

Figure 12.18   The magnetic susceptibility of MnO measured in a 5000 oersted field. The maximum is characteristic of antiferromagnetic solids. (After Bizette, Squire, and Tsai)

arrangements characteristic of ferromagnetism, antiferromagnetism, and ferrimagnetism, the temperature in each being below the critical temperature for spin disordering.

A typical antiferromagnetic solid is MnO. Figure 12.18 shows the magnetic susceptibility of MnO plotted as a function of temperature. The maximum is characteristic of antiferromagnetic behavior. In addition, above the temperature of the maximum, χ varies as $C/(T + \theta)$.

Let us consider in an antiferromagnetic material that the structure consists of two interpenetrating sublattices A and B in which all nearest neighbors of an A ion lie on sublattice B. The body-centered cubic structure is an example and for simplicity we shall use this. Figure 12.19 shows a unit cell with the spin directions of the ions marked by arrows. Following a procedure similar to that used to describe the internal field in ferromagnetics, let us introduce an expression for the internal field of the A ions, namely, H_A, and an expression for the internal field of the B ions,

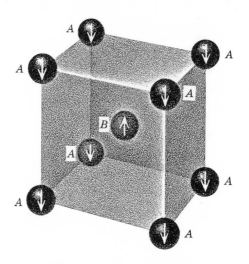

Figure 12.19 Body-centered unit cell with the spins of the A atoms oppositely directed to those of the B atoms.

namely, H_B. Since the magnetization M_A of the A ions is opposite to the internal field of the B ions, we have

$$H_A = H - \lambda M_B \qquad (12.34)$$

and $\qquad H_B = H - \lambda M_A$

Then as in equation 12.25 we have

$$M_A = N\beta \tanh\left[\frac{\mu_0\beta}{kT}(H - \lambda M_B)\right]$$

and $\qquad M_B = N\beta \tanh\left[\frac{\mu_0\beta}{kT}(H - \lambda M_A)\right] \qquad (12.35)$

Again at high temperatures tanh $[x] \simeq [x]$

and
$$M_A = N\beta^2 \frac{\mu_0}{kT} (H - \lambda M_B) \qquad (12.36)$$

$$M_B = N\beta^2 \frac{\mu_0}{kT} (H - \lambda M_A)$$

Adding gives

$$M = M_A + M_B = \frac{N\beta^2 \mu_0}{kT} (2H - \lambda M) \qquad (12.37)$$

Thus
$$\chi = \frac{M}{H} = \frac{2C}{T + \lambda_C} = \frac{2C}{T + \theta} \qquad (12.38)$$

where
$$C = N\beta^2 \mu_0 / k \quad \text{and} \quad \theta = \lambda C$$

The critical temperature above which these equations are valid is often called the *Néel temperature* T_N. The simple model has therefore accounted for the experimentally determined dependence of susceptibility on temperature above T_N.

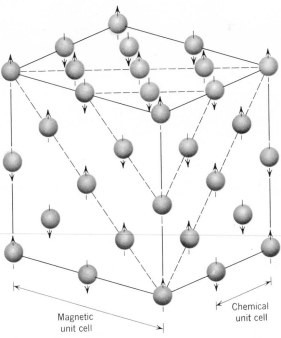

Figure 12.20 The MnO structure with the spin directions marked by arrows (from Shull, Strauser and Wollan)

Below T_N and with no externally applied field, it can be shown by an analysis similar to that used previously for the ferromagnetic case that spontaneous magnetization of the A lattice ions and B lattice ions can exist.

Figure 12.20 shows the MnO structure with the spin directions marked. The diagram shows that the chemical unit cell is just one-half the size of the magnetic unit cell. Diffraction studies by neutrons, which have magnetic moments, will differentiate between the presence of the magnetic cell below T_N and its absence by spin disordering above T_N. This has been shown in Fig. 2.14.

12.10   Ferrites

If the spin systems are unbalanced, ferrimagnetism results. The technically important solids exhibiting ferrimagnetism are the *ferrites*. The chemical formula for the ferrites is $MOFe_2O_3$ where M is a divalent metal ion such as manganese, cobalt, nickel, copper, magnesium, and iron, the best known ferrite being *magnetite* with the formula $FeO \cdot Fe_2O_3$.

The most technically important feature in ferrites is their high electrical resistivity, which makes them of use in high-frequency work. The resistivities of commercial ferrites like Ferroxcube 3 or Ferroxcube 4 are in excess of those of alloys like silicon–iron or permalloy by a factor of at least 10^6. This cuts down the eddy current losses in transformers at megacycle frequencies and in magnetic circuits using high-speed switching.

In Fig. 12.21 hysteresis loops of some typical ferrites are compared with those of iron and the high permeability alloy Mo permalloy. The rectangular nature of the ferrite hysteresis curves, coupled with the high resistivities discussed earlier, make the ferrites of interest to designers of digital computers and data-processing circuits. A necessary part of such circuits is an element which is stable in two configurations. The passage of a magnetizing current pulse through a primary winding on a ferrite core will leave a remanent magnetic flux ϕ_r in the core (see Fig. 12.21). The direction of the remanent magnetization will be dependent on the direction of the current pulse. The ferrite core will hold this remanent flux indefinitely without further power consumption. It can therefore function as a store for information in a binary code. Let us suppose that $-\phi_r$ represents "zero" and $+\phi_r$ represents "one."

This stored information must be readily accessible and identifiable. To achieve this the core is fitted with a secondary winding of, say, n turns. The integrated voltage pulse appearing at the secondary terminals during a flux change from ϕ_1 to ϕ_2 is then $n(\phi_2 - \phi_1)$. To read out the stored

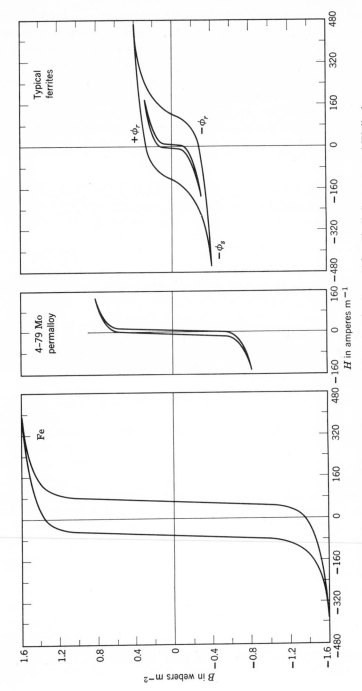

Figure 12.21   Hysteresis loops of iron, permalloy, and ferrites.   (After Shull, Strauser, and Wollan)

information, let us suppose that a negative current pulse is passed through the primary. If the duration of the pulse is sufficiently long to bring the ferrite core flux to $-\phi_s$, the voltage on the secondary for a remanent flux of $+\phi_r$ will be $n(\phi_r + \phi_s)$. If, on the other hand, the remanent flux is $-\phi_r$, the secondary voltage is $n(\phi_s - \phi_r)$. The greater voltage reads out as a "one" and the lesser as a "zero." It is now obvious that rectangular hysteresis loops give the best discrimination.

This is only one of a large number of technical uses of ferrites based on the physical properties we have discussed.

REFERENCES

L. F. Bates, *Modern Magnetism*, 3rd ed., Cambridge University Press, Cambridge, 1951.

F. Bitter, *Currents, Fields, and Particles*, John Wiley and Sons, New York, 1956.

R. M. Bozorth, *Ferromagnetism*, D. Van Nostrand Company Princeton, N.J., 1951.

J. L. Snoek, *New Developments in Ferromagnetic Materials*, 2nd ed., Elsevier, Amsterdam, 1949.

EXERCISES

1. A long straight wire carries a current of 10 amps. Calculate the magnetic induction B at a point in vacuum situated 2 m from the axis of the wire.

2. The magnetic susceptibility of copper is -0.5×10^{-5}. Calculate the magnetic moment per unit volume in copper when subjected to a field whose magnitude inside the copper is 10^4 amps m^{-1}.

3. Estimate the order of magnitude of the diamagnetic susceptibility of copper from equation 12.13. Use a value of 1 Å as the atomic radius and assume that only one electron per atom contributes.

4. A paramagnetic system of electric spin magnetic dipole moments is placed in an applied field of 10^5 amp m^{-1}. Calculate the average magnetic moment per dipole at 300°K and at 1°K. Also calculate the fractional number of spins which are parallel and antiparallel to the field.

5. Estimate the frequencies at which we would expect: (*a*) electron spin resonance in sodium with an applied field of 10^6 amps m^{-1}; (*b*) proton spin resonance in ferric nitrate solution with an applied field of 10^6 amps m^{-1}.

6. The Curie temperature of iron is 1043°K. Assume that iron atoms, when in the metallic form, have moments of two Bohr magnetons per atom. Iron is body-centered cubic with the lattice parameter $a = 2.86$ Å. Calculate: (*a*) the saturation magnetisation; (*b*) the Curie constant; (*c*) the Weiss field constant; (*d*) the magnitude of the internal field.

7. The ions in the molecule of magnetite are Fe^{+2}, Fe_2^{+3}, and O_4^{-2}, the subscripts giving the number per molecule. In the conventional unit cell, which is cubic with $a = 8.37$ Å, there are eight molecules. The Fe^{+3} magnetic moments cancel and the magnetisation is that produced by the Fe^{+2} ions alone. If the saturation magnetisation of magnetite is 5.2×10^5 amps m^{-1} calculate the moment per Fe^{+2} ion in Bohr magnetons.

13

The Properties of Dielectric Crystals

Dielectric crystals do not under normal circumstances transport electric charge and, as we have discussed before, this arises because of the large electron energy gap that exists between the valence and conduction bands. Impurities which may occur naturally or be deliberately added, however, may modify the insulating properties and impart a degree of conductivity to the dielectric. Furthermore, if the temperature is high enough so that for example in an alkali halide the ions can diffuse through the lattice, electrical charge transport results.

In a good insulator the electrons are tightly bound to the atoms of the solid, and electric fields, thermal excitation, or mechanical strain can merely displace them somewhat. In the same manner ions and molecules may be displaced. If a region which is positively charged is displaced with respect to a region negatively charged, a *local electric dipole* is produced and the process is called *polarization*. In many dielectrics, permanent electric dipoles exist naturally. Thermal energy can modify the directions of these permanent dipoles giving polarizations which are strongly temperature dependent. A lack of this temperature dependence of polarization is a strong indication that no permanent electric dipole exists. Crystals with permanent electric dipoles are called *polar* crystals and those without are called *nonpolar* crystals.

Although the physical nature of polarization in dielectric crystals is quite different from that of magnetization in magnetic solids, certain similarities exist in the mathematical descriptions of the two phenomena. We will, therefore, as in the chapter on magnetism, begin by defining three

327

dielectric quantities that correspond to the magnetic quantities **B**, **H**, and **μ**. We will then find a relationship between these quantities, thereby defining a new parameter, the *polarizability*. Just as the susceptibility in the discussion on magnetism related the atomic properties to macroscopic ones, so the polarizability relates the dielectric properties of the atom to those of the solid. The three dielectric quantities just referred to are the electric displacement **D**, the electric field strength $\mathscr{E}$, and the electric dipole moment **μ**.

The Electric Displacement or Flux Density D.   Gauss' theorem states that if a closed surface encloses a total electric charge ΣQ, the electric flux ϕ which emerges from the surface is given by

$$\phi = \Sigma Q \tag{13.1}$$

The total flux ϕ may be written as the surface integral $\iint \mathbf{D} \cdot d\mathbf{S}$ where **D** is the electric displacement or flux density in coulombs per square meter and $d\mathbf{S}$ is a surface element in square meters, represented by the outwardly directed vector $d\mathbf{S}$. Thus

$$\iint \mathbf{D} \cdot d\mathbf{S} = \sum Q \tag{13.2}$$

This is the definition of the electric displacement **D**.

The Electric Field Strength $\mathscr{E}$.   The *electric field strength* $\mathscr{E}$ is the force acting on unit charge placed in the field. $\mathscr{E}$ is related to the electric displacement by

$$\mathbf{D} = \epsilon_0 \epsilon_r \mathscr{E} \tag{13.3}$$

where ϵ_0 is called the *dielectric constant* or *permittivity* of a *vacuum* and ϵ_r is the *relative permittivity* of the medium through which the electric flux threads. The value of ϵ_0 in mks units is 8.854×10^{-12} farad m^{-1}, and ϵ_r is a dimensionless number which is equal to unity for a vacuum. The value of ϵ_r for a solid dielectric medium can be found experimentally in a relatively easy manner. It is the ratio of the capacitances of a parallel-plate condenser with and without the dielectric between the plates.

The Electric Dipole Moment μ.   The electric dipole moment is defined in the following way. Suppose that a system of charges $Q_1, Q_2, Q_3, \ldots, Q_i$ exists at vectors $\mathbf{r}_1, \mathbf{r}_2, \mathbf{r}_3, \ldots, \mathbf{r}_i$ from the origin of a coordinate system. The overall net charge of the system is zero. Then the *total electric dipole moment* of the system is given by

$$\boldsymbol{\mu} = \sum_i Q_i \mathbf{r}_i \tag{13.4}$$

The units in which **μ** is expressed are coulomb meters. The *dipole moment per unit volume* is called the *polarization* **P** of a dielectric medium and is expressed in coulomb m^{-2}.

13.1   Electric Polarization P and Polarizability α

We will now discuss the relationships which exist between the three quantities $\mathbf{D}$, $\mathscr{E}$, and μ.

Let us suppose that a slab of homogeneous isotropic dielectric material is placed as in Fig. 13.1a between two parallel plates and that an electric voltage is applied across the plates so that the electric field has a value $\mathscr{E}$. The electric displacement $\mathbf{D}$ from equation 13.3 is $\epsilon_0\epsilon_r\mathscr{E}$.

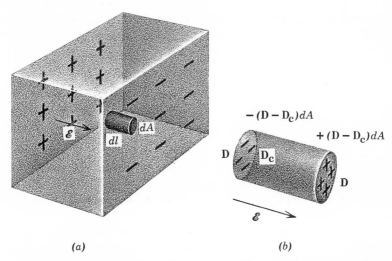

(a)   (b)

Figure 13.1   (a) A dielectric material with an applied electric field $\mathscr{E}$. (b) When a volume element is removed, charges $\pm(\mathbf{D} - \mathbf{D_c})\, dA$ must be placed as shown to keep the field strength in the cavity at the original value.

Suppose now that a small cylinder of area dA and length dl is removed from the dielectric as shown in the diagram. To produce a field inside the cavity equal to what existed before the material of the cavity was removed necessitates a reduction in electric displacement inside the cavity. In fact if $\mathbf{D_c}$ is the electric displacement "inside the cavity," the relationship between the original $\mathbf{D}$ and the new $\mathbf{D_c}$ must be

$$\mathbf{D_c}/\epsilon_0 = \mathbf{D}/\epsilon_0\epsilon_r = \mathscr{E} \tag{13.5}$$

The electric displacement may be reduced, according to equation 13.2, by reducing the sum of the electric charges on the end faces of the cavity. By placing a negative charge, as in Fig. 13.1b, of $(\mathbf{D} - \mathbf{D_c})\, dA$ on one end face and a positive charge of the same magnitude on the opposite end, the electric displacement is reduced from $\mathbf{D}$ to $\mathbf{D_c}$. The field in the cavity is thus maintained at the original value of $\mathscr{E}$. Now positive and negative charges on the respective ends of the small cylindrical cavity correspond according to equation 13.4 to an electric dipole moment from left to right in the figure, that is in the same direction as $\mathscr{E}$. The magnitude of the dipole moment is given by

$$\mu = (\mathbf{D} - \mathbf{D_c})\,dA\,dl \tag{13.6}$$

We can thus conclude that to maintain an electric field inside a dielectric unchanged when a portion of the dielectric is removed necessitates providing the vacant portion with an electric dipole moment. It would appear therefore that the portion of dielectric material before removal must have carried an electric dipole moment.

Per unit volume the dipole moment is $(\mathbf{D} - \mathbf{D_c})$. That is $\mathbf{P}$, the polarization is given by

$$\mathbf{P} = \mathbf{D} - \mathbf{D_c}$$

and from equation 13.5 this becomes

$$\mathbf{P} = \epsilon_0 \mathscr{E}(\epsilon_r - 1) \tag{13.7}$$

This relationship obviously applies to dielectric materials in which the polarization is produced by the applied field. If polarization exists in zero field, as it does in the ferroelectric materials, a unique relationship does not exist between $\mathbf{P}$ and $\mathscr{E}$. In fact, just as in the ferromagnetic materials, hysteretic behavior is observed.

We are now in a position to relate the macroscopic quantity ϵ_r to the quantity that characterizes the polarization of an individual atom or molecule. Before doing so, however, we should look more closely into the detailed nature of the electric field. The value of $\mathscr{E}$ thus far in the discussion has been an average value over a volume element large in comparison with molecular volumes.

Suppose that the field which the molecule actually experiences is a local field $\mathscr{E}_{\mathrm{Loc}}$. Then it is customary to write the induced molecular dipole moment as μ_{m} where

$$\mu_{\mathrm{m}} = \alpha \mathscr{E}_{\mathrm{Loc}} \tag{13.8}$$

and α is called the polarizability of the molecule and describes the ease of polarization. If there are N_d dipoles per unit volume, then

$$\mathbf{P} = N_d \mu_{\mathrm{m}} = N_d \alpha \mathscr{E}_{\mathrm{Loc}} \tag{13.9}$$

It now follows from equation 13.7 that

$$\epsilon_r - 1 = \frac{\mathbf{P}}{\epsilon_0 \mathscr{E}} = \frac{N_d \alpha \mathscr{E}_{\mathrm{Loc}}}{\mathscr{E}} \tag{13.10}$$

This equation relates the experimentally observed quantity ϵ_r to the molecular quantity α. It is important to first calculate the magnitude of the local field which the molecule experiences.

13.2 The Local Electric Field

The local electric field which acts on any particular molecule can be regarded as made up of four parts.

$$\mathscr{E}_{\text{Loc}} = \mathscr{E}_0 + \mathscr{E}_1 + \mathscr{E}_2 + \mathscr{E}_3 \tag{13.11}$$

where $\mathscr{E}_0$ is the externally applied electric field, and $\mathscr{E}_1$ is the depolarization field that results from polarization charges *on the outer surface of the specimen.*

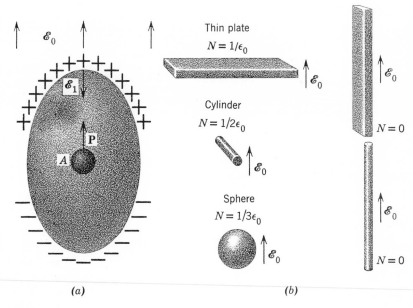

(a)   (b)

Figure 13.2 (a) The depolarization field $\mathscr{E}_1$ due to the induced charges on the surface of an ellipsoid placed in the electric field $\mathscr{E}_0$. (b) The values of N, the depolarization factor, for dielectric specimens of various shapes placed in a field $\mathscr{E}_0$.

To give a meaning to the components $\mathscr{E}_1$ and $\mathscr{E}_2$, first imagine a small sphere of dielectric material removed from around the site of the molecule A, as in Fig. 13.2. The *Lorentz field*, $\mathscr{E}_2$, is then the field due to the polarization charges on the inside of the spherical cavity. If the radius of the sphere is considerably greater than that of the molecule then the remainder of the dielectric around the sphere can be treated on a macroscopic basis. Thus both $\mathscr{E}_1$ and $\mathscr{E}_2$ are treated on this basis, their magnitudes being calculated from equations 13.2 and 13.3 where integration over the outer surface gives $\mathscr{E}_1$ and integration over the surface of the spherical cavity gives $\mathscr{E}_2$. The *field of the adjacent dipoles*, $\mathscr{E}_3$, is the field due to the molecules within the spherical cavity, and this summation must be made on a microscopic

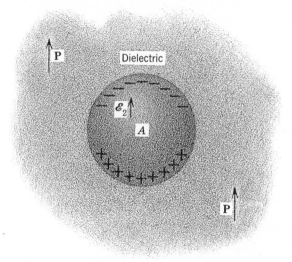

Figure 13.3   A small sphere in a dielectric of polarization **P** is subject to a depolarization or Lorentz field $\mathscr{E}_2$. The induced electric charges giving rise to $\mathscr{E}_2$ are shown.

basis. The field components will now be discussed separately and in some more detail.

The Depolarization Factor.   A dielectric specimen of simple geometry such as the sphere, cylinder, or ellipsoid or revolution when placed in a uniform electric field $\mathscr{E}_0$ becomes uniformly polarized. The charges that are induced on the surface reduce the field strength inside the surface from the value $\mathscr{E}_0$. The reduction in field, that is, $\mathscr{E}_1$, is proportional to the polarization, the constant of proportionality N being known as the *depolarization factor N* and dependent on the specimen geometry.

We have, therefore, that

$$\mathscr{E}_1 = -N\mathbf{P} \qquad (13.12)$$

Figure 13.2*a* shows the depolarization field $\mathscr{E}_1$ which arises when a dielectric specimen of ellipsoidal shape is placed in a uniform field $\mathscr{E}_0$. Figure 13.2*b* gives the values of N for other geometries.

The Lorentz Field. The induced charges that cause the Lorentz field $\mathscr{E}_2$ are shown in Fig. 13.3. These charges are opposite in sign to those that appear on an outside surface. It is possible to show that the inside field at A is the same whether A is at the center of the spherical cavity or not. The magnitude of this field is given by

$$\mathscr{E}_2 = \frac{\mathbf{P}}{3\epsilon_0} \tag{13.13}$$

Note that the factor $\frac{1}{3}\epsilon_0$ also appears in Fig. 13.2 as the depolarization factor for a sphere.

Field of Adjacent Dipoles. The field $\mathscr{E}_3$, which is caused by the dipoles within the cavity, must be computed microscopically and will depend on the crystal structure. The calculation is complex. If the environment of the molecule A is cubic, however, it can be shown that $\mathscr{E}_3$ has the value zero. Although this is always true for a pure element, in a solid cubic compound like barium titanate the symmetry of the oxygen atoms is not cubic, and a contribution to the local field from these atoms does exist.

13.3 Polarizability

Thus far we have related the measurable relative permittivity ϵ_r to the polarizability α and have also indicated how the local field, to which the molecule is exposed is calculated. In this section the mechanisms by which the polarizability may arise are discussed.

The total polarizability of an atom or ion consists of three parts, namely, the electronic, ionic, and orientational polarizability.

Electronic Polarizability. Suppose in Fig. 13.4a that an atom is represented by a positive nucleus surrounded by a negative electron cloud. If a static electric field $\mathscr{E}$ is applied in the directions shown in Figs. 13.4b and 13.4c, the field tends to displace the center of gravity of the electrons away from coincidence with the nucleus. The displacement force is counteracted by the attraction of the nucleus and the actual magnitude of the displacement is small. For instance, a field of say 30 kV m^{-1} will displace the center of gravity of the electrons by about 10^{-17} m. The formula that gives the displacement d in terms of the atomic radius R, the electronic charge e, and number of electrons Z is

$$d = \frac{4\pi\epsilon_0 R^3}{Ze} \mathscr{E} \tag{13.14}$$

This equation is a simple consequence of Coulomb's Law of attraction between electrical charges.

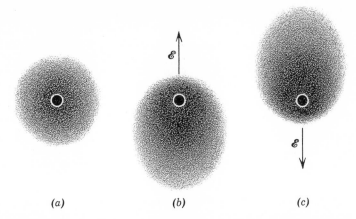

(a)   (b)   (c)

Figure 13.4 (*a*) An atom represented by a positive nucleus (black dot) surrounded by a negative electron cloud. In (*b*) and (*c*) the center of gravity of the electron cloud is displaced from coincidence with the nucleus by an electric field.

The two electric charges $+Ze$ and $-Ze$, now displaced by distance d, constitute an induced electron dipole moment μ_e where

$$\mu_e = Ze \cdot d = 4\pi\epsilon_0 R^3 \cdot \mathscr{E} \tag{13.15}$$

The dipole moment μ_e is also linked to the electric field $\mathscr{E}$ by the definition of *electronic polarizability* α_e, since

$$\mu_e = \alpha_e \mathscr{E} \tag{13.16}$$

Ionic Polarizability. In molecules an electric field may also displace the individual ions or molecules with respect to one another, thus changing the bond angles or interatomic distances. This is pictured in Fig. 13.5.

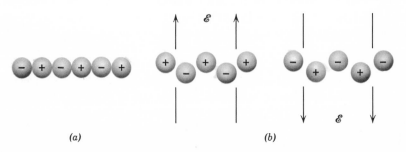

(a)   (b)

Figure 13.5 (*a*) Positive and negative ions in a dielectric. (*b*) The ions are displaced with respect to one another by an electric field.

Again dipole moments are induced by the field, the *ionic dipole* moment being given by

$$\mu_a = \alpha_a \mathscr{E}.$$ (13.17)

where α_a is the *ionic polarizability*.

Orientational Polarizability. Some molecules such as water and alcohol exhibit permanent dipole moments. In the liquid form each electric dipole moment is free to rotate. Thus in a static electric field the dipoles tend to line up in the direction of the field. Thermal energy, however, tends to make the distribution of dipole orientations a random one. The orientational polarizability α_0 depends on the fractional number of electric dipoles lined up at any temperature.

The calculation of orientational polarizability α_0 follows closely the method used to obtain the magnetic susceptibility of a paramagnetic solid in equation 12.20. Once again a Curie Law of temperature dependence is found, namely,

$$\alpha_0 = \frac{C\mu_0^2}{T}$$ (13.18)

where μ_0 is the permanent dipole moment and T the temperature; C is the Curie constant. This equation applies only to polar materials in which the dipole moments are free to rotate with ease into the direction of minimum energy. Whereas this is true in gases and liquids, it is seldom true in solids.

Later in this chapter we will discuss a class of substance—the ferro-electrics—where the dipoles become completely aligned over regions in the crystal. The ions of ferroelectric crystals are bound together by Coulomb forces (ionic bond), unlike the molecules we discuss in this section, and the mechanism of dipolar saturation is quite different.

13.4 Polarizability in Alternating Fields

If the dielectric material is exposed to an alternating electric field, the total polarizability α depends on the ability of the dipoles to reverse their alignment with each reversal of field. The time associated with a disturbed system in reaching its equilibrium configuration is called its *relaxation time*. The reciprocal of the relaxation time is the *relaxation frequency*. Thus if the frequency of the applied electric field is much higher than that of the relaxation frequency of the dipole system, the dipoles cannot reverse fast enough, and the particular polarizability mechanism does not apply. The relaxation frequencies differ for each of the three polarizability mechanisms we have discussed.

If the total polarizability of a dielectric is measured as a function of frequency, there are found to be three frequency ranges over which α, although having a different value in each range, is essentially constant. This statement ignores resonances in complicated structures. Figure 13.6 shows the contributions to the total polarizability and the frequency ranges over which the separate mechanisms are operative. It is often possible to evaluate the separate contributions.

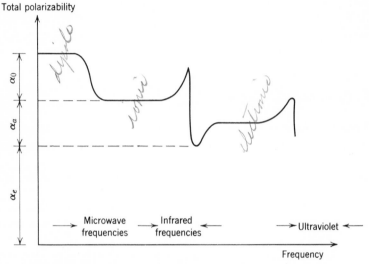

Figure 13.6   The total polarizability of a dielectric as a function of frequency. The frequency limits of the different components are described.

In a dielectric material such as diamond, which is composed of one kind of atom, the electronic polarizability is the only component present. The deformation of the electron cloud around the nucleus by an alternating field can follow the field at frequencies up to the optical range (10^{15} cps). High-frequency measurements of dielectric constant are made by simply measuring the index of refraction n with light of a known wavelength. Then, according to Maxwell's theory of electromagnetic waves for materials with a magnetic permeability equal to that of a vacuum, we have

$$\epsilon_r = n^2 \tag{13.19}$$

In ionic crystals such as the alkali halides, the heavy positive and negative ions cannot follow rapid field variations. Consequently at optical frequencies, only the electronic polarizability are measured. If such measurements are followed by a measurement of dielectric constant with a static electric field, both the ionic and electronic polarizabilities may be deduced.

Thus for ionic crystals: At optical frequencies, $\epsilon_r = 1 + N\alpha_e \mathscr{E}_{\text{Loc}}/\mathscr{E}$; and with a static field, $\epsilon_r = 1 + N(\alpha_e + \alpha_a)\mathscr{E}_{\text{Loc}}/\mathscr{E}$.

Measured values of ϵ_r for sodium chloride are respectively 2.25 and 5.62.

Although we have indicated in a qualitative way the reason for the three levels of polarizability in Fig. 13.6, we have said nothing about the rather complicated behavior at the frequencies separating the three levels. This behavior is concerned with the application of an alternating field at a frequency close to that of the relaxation frequency of the particular type of dipole system. The subject of dipole relaxation and the energy losses in dielectrics associated with relaxation will not be discussed; the reader is referred to the bibliography at the end of this chapter.

13.5 Ferroelectric Crystals

The polarization of a ferroelectric crystal is dependent on the history of the crystal. Figure 13.7 shows the relationship between polarization

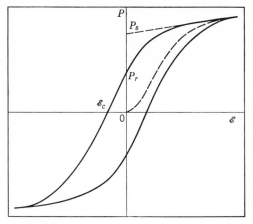

Figure 13.7 The hysteretic relationship between electric field and polarization for a ferroelectric crystal. The dotted curve from the origin shows the initial behavior.

and field for a ferroelectric crystal. In a nonpolarized specimen the polarization first rises rapidly with applied field to a value above which the dependence is linear. Linear extrapolation to zero field gives P_s, the saturation or spontaneous polarization. On subsequently reducing the field to zero a *remanent polarization P_r* remains. The negative field to reduce the polarization to zero is called the *coercive field* and is represented by $\mathscr{E}_c$. Ferroelectric crystals, like ferromagnetics, have Curie temperatures and a Curie-Weiss dependence of polarization with temperature. They also reveal domain structure. The similarity in nomenclature used to describe ferroelectric and ferromagnetic phenomena is, however, somewhat misleading as the fundamental processes are quite different.

At temperatures below the ferroelectric Curie temperature, where the polarization is a function of field strength, it is obviously impossible to

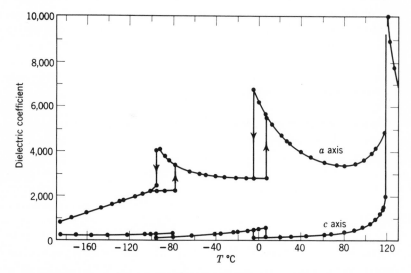

Figure 13.8   The initial relative dielectric coefficient of barium titanate plotted as a function of temperature. The arrows refer to the direction in which the temperature is changing. (After Merz)

apply equation 13.7 directly. This equation was developed on the assumption that ϵ_r was independent of $\mathscr{E}$. We can, however, define a *differential relative permittivity* from the slope of the polarization versus field strength curve. That is, from

$$\epsilon_0(\epsilon_r - 1) = \frac{dP}{d\mathscr{E}} \qquad (13.20)$$

The simplest of the ferroelectric crystals are the titanates of which the best known is ceramic barium titanate $BaTiO_3$. The dielectric constant defined by equation 13.20 at the *origin of the P vs. $\mathscr{E}$ curve* is shown in Fig. 13.8 as a function of temperature. As can be seen, there are anomolies in the dielectric constant at the temperatures of 120°C, 0°C, and −100°C.

At temperatures above 120°C, which is the Curie temperature, the dielectric constant of barium titanate varies with temperature according to a Curie-Weiss Law, namely

$$\epsilon_r = \frac{C}{T - \theta} \qquad (13.21)$$

where C is a constant and θ is the Curie temperature characteristic of the particular ferroelectric crystal.

Below 120°C, barium titanate is spontaneously polarized. The spontaneous polarization is associated with a displacement of charge, corresponding to a lattice expansion in the direction of polarization. Thus at the Curie temperature and also at the other two transition temperatures, structural changes in the crystal take place. The Curie temperature structural change reduces the polarization to zero and at the other two transition temperatures changes in the direction of spontaneous polarization take place.

Free energy differences exist between the barium titanate structures below and above each of the transition temperatures. Energy is required to drive the structure from one form to another. As a consequence the dielectric constant, which is dependent on the structure, measured with the temperature increasing does not follow the same path when the temperature is decreasing. Loops occur at each of the transition temperatures as shown in Fig. 13.8.

Let us now look more closely into the nature of the spontaneous dipole moment in barium titanate. The crystal structure is called *perovoskite* after the name of the prototype calcium titanate. The structure above the Curie temperature is shown in Fig. 13.9. It is cubic with each of the titanium Ti^{4+} ions surrounded by six oxygen O^{2-} ions in an octahedral configuration. At temperatures above 120°C, the TiO_6 octahedron is symmetrical and the center of gravity of the negative charges coincides with that of the positive charges. The net dipole moment is therefore zero. As the temperature falls through the Curie temperature, the titanium and barium ions move with respect to the oxygen ions so that a dipole moment results. From neutron diffraction studies it is now known that the O' and O'' type oxygen ions (see Fig. 13.9) move in the same direction whereas the Ti and Ba ions move in the opposite direction. The titanium ions move considerably further than the barium ions. The distance that the titanium ion moves with respect to the oxygen ion can be roughly computed from the known value of the saturation polarization P_s of barium titanate.

The lattice constant of $BaTiO_3$ is 4×10^{-10} m and the saturation polarization P_s is 0.16 coulomb m^{-2}. There is one titanium ion per unit cell carrying a charge of $4e$. If it is assumed that the dipole moment is due to the displacement d of the titanium ion only, the dipole moment per unit cell is

$$4e \times d = 0.16 \times (4 \times 10^{-10})^3 \simeq 10^{-29}$$

Thus
$$d \simeq 1.6 \times 10^{-11} \text{ m.}$$

We have assumed that the spontaneous polarization below the Curie temperature is due largely to the strong interaction between the Ti and O′

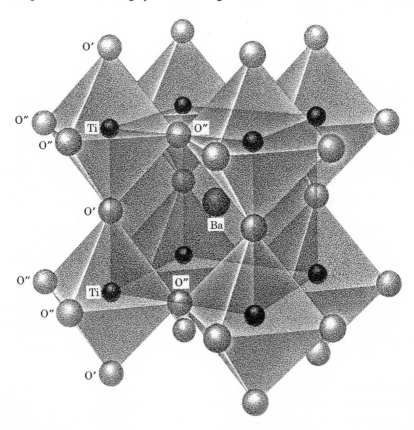

Figure 13.9   The structure of barium titanate above the Curie temperature. (After Kittel)

ions. The buildup process of polarization is cumulative and is called the *polarization catastrophe*. This means that the polarization of the Ti ions increases the local field at the O′ ion sites, which increases the polarization of the O′ ions and which in turn increases the polarization of the Ti ions.

13.6 Domain Structure in Ferroelectric Crystals

In our discussion of ferromagnetism it was shown that the concept of domains magnetized in different directions enabled us to account for the possibility of a net magnetization of zero, even if each domain is spontaneously magnetized. A similar concept is used to account for net polarizations of zero in ferroelectric crystals below the Curie temperature.

Figure 13.10 Wedge-shaped laminar domains in barium titanate. (After Forsbergh)

We have seen that the cubic structure of barium titanate just above the Curie temperature becomes slightly tetragonal as the temperature falls. The polar direction in the crystal is the c axis of the tetragonal cell which coincided with one of the former cube axes. Often in a specimen crystal the tetragonal axes of different regions correspond with different cube directions. This means that different regions have different directions of spontaneous polarization. These different regions are called *domains*.

The index of refraction of barium titanate parallel to the tetragonal c axis differs from the index at right angles to the c axis. Since the crystal is transparent to ordinary light, it is possible to send polarized light through a specimen plate and view the emergent light with an analyzer. The domains then show up as dark and light bands. Figure 13.10 shows wedge-shaped laminar domains in barium titanate rendered visible by this technique. It is found that the *domain wall*, unlike the magnetic domain wall, is only a few atomic spacings thick.

Another difference between ferroelectric and ferromagnetic domains concerns the growth process. The growth of ferroelectric domains is brought about by the formation of a great number of new antiparallel domains of thickness about one micron. If an external electric field is applied in a direction that tends to reverse the polarization in a domain, these narrow spikes grow out from the edges of the specimen plate. There is little or no sideways growth. The number of spikes nucleated is dependent on the magnitude of the applied field.

13.7 Piezoelectricity

We have seen that an applied electric field, in inducing an electric dipole moment in a dielectric, displaces ions relative to each other. The structural

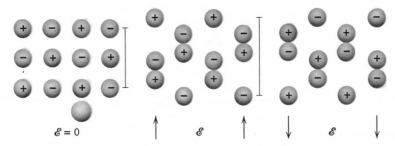

Figure 13.11   Electrostriction. Displacement of the ions by the applied electric field increases the dimension of the crystal in the field direction.

dimensions of the crystal have been changed by the applied field. Figure 13.11 shows an ion array with and without an applied field. The dimensions of the crystal have increased in the field direction. This physical property is called *electrostriction*.

Now let us consider the effect on the polarization of changing the dimensions of the crystal by means of a *mechanical strain*. We consider two kinds of crystals, namely those with a *center of symmetry* and those without. First a word about the nature of a center of symmetry. If the unit cell of a dielectric is such that we can draw from a central point a vector to one charged ion, and on drawing an equal and opposite vector from the point we also find a similar ion, then the structure has a center of symmetry at the central point. Of the thirty-two crystal classes which exist in nature (point groups) twelve have a center of symmetry.

We will now consider the effect of mechanically changing the spacing in very simple two-dimensional ion arrays with and without centers of symmetry.

Array with a Center of Symmetry. Figure 13.12a shows an array of ions in which the position of the ion A is obviously a center of symmetry.

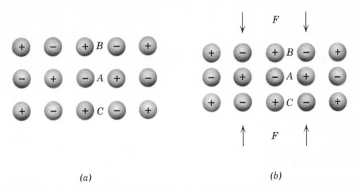

(a)   (b)

Figure 13.12   (a) Ionic structure with a center of symmetry. (b) Structure compressed by force. No net change in polarization.

In Fig. 13.12b the array has been compressed by a mechanical force. Ion B has been moved closer to ion A thus decreasing the BA dipole moment. However atom C has also been moved closer to atom A also decreasing the CA dipole moment by the same amount and moreover in the opposite direction to the decrease in the BA moment. Thus no net change in polarization results from mechanical deformation of a crystal with a center of symmetry.

Array without a Center of Symmetry. Figure 13.13a shows a very simple two-dimensional array of ions with no center of symmetry. A compressive force is applied to this array in 13.13b and a tensile force in 13.13c. The total electric dipole moment has been decreased in b and increased in c. Materials that exhibit this phenomenon are called *piezoelectric*. Piezoelectric behavior in dielectric crystals can be put to a number of uses of which a few will be mentioned.

A piezoelectric crystal will vibrate naturally in several mechanical modes, the frequencies of vibration being dependent on the dimensions of the specimen and the elastic constants of the material. If the crystal is placed between electrodes and an alternating voltage at one of the resonant frequencies is applied, the amplitude of oscillation will build up at this frequency. The stability of the oscillator system will be controlled by the constancy of the elastic constants of the crystal. Specially cut quartz disks are generally used for this purpose, the stability being particularly high since the coefficient of thermal expansion of quartz is very low. The use of quartz crystal oscillators in electronic circuitry is already very great.

Another application of piezoelectric oscillators lies in the conversion of mechanical pulses into electrical ones, and vice versa. The crystal is here used as a *transducer*. Acoustic pulses are used in underwater search and

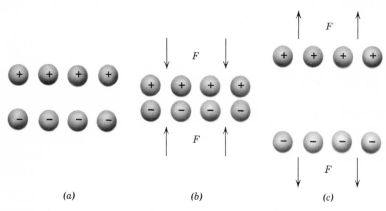

Figure 13.13 (*a*) Ionic structure with no center of symmetry. (*b*) Structure compressed. Polarization decreased. (*c*) Structure extended. Polarization increased.

other applications. In almost all such cases the acoustic pulses are produced by piezoelectric transducers shock excited by electric fields.

A final application lies in the use of piezoelectric materials as delay lines. If an electrical signal is converted into an acoustic one, at one end of a quartz rod, the signal will pass along the rod as an acoustic wave. It will travel in the quartz with the appropriate *sound velocity*. On reaching the end of the rod the acoustic wave may be picked off as an electrical signal. The initial electrical signal has been delayed, a requirement often found in communication devices.

13.8 Optical Absorption

So far in our discussion of a dielectric crystal we have chosen to regard such a crystal as possessing the simplest possible electron band structure, that is, one with a filled valence band separated by a gap of several electron volts from an unfilled conduction band. As we might expect from the previous discussion of impurity energy levels in semiconductors, this simple picture does not apply to all dielectric crystals. In the remainder of this chapter we will investigate the physical properties that arise in dielectric solids because of local energy levels between the valence and conduction bands. Perhaps the most striking of these properties is that of optical absorption, and we will therefore begin by reminding the reader of what is meant by this term.

If light of intensity I_0 is incident on a crystal and in the course of transmission through a distance x of the solid the intensity falls to a value I, the *optical absorption constant A* is given by the equation

$$I = I_0 e^{-Ax} \tag{13.22}$$

If the incident light consists of photons of energy less than that necessary to excite an electron between its own level and a higher one, no absorption occurs and A has the value zero. In the discussion of semiconductors we have already seen that electron-hole pairs are formed if the energy is greater than the energy gap between the valence and conduction bands. In such a case optical absorption would, of course, occur. Usually, however, absorption occurs because of electron excitation between intermediate levels, and several kinds of these levels will now be discussed.

13.9   Exciton, Impurity, and Defect Levels

Since an electron and a hole have an attraction for one another, given by their Coulomb interaction, it is possible for them to be held together in stable bound states rather like the proton and electron in a hydrogen atom. The photon energy to produce one of those stable states will be less than that necessary to entirely separate the electron and hole, that is, less than the energy gap of the dielectric. These stable states are called *exciton states*.

Suppose that the energy of one of the exciton states when referred to the top of the valence band is E_n. Then, as in the hydrogen atom, E_n is inversely proportional to the square of the appropriate quantum number n; that is,

$$E_n \propto \frac{1}{n^2} \tag{13.23}$$

In addition, if light irradiates the dielectric crystal, we would expect the electron and hole to be completely separated and absorption to take place, with high values of A, at frequencies given by

$$h\nu = E_g - E_n \tag{13.24}$$

Figure 13.14 shows a photometer record of optical transmission through Cu_2O at 4.2°K. The dips in the record are at the light frequencies where exciton absorption takes place. From the measured values of ν and equation 13.24, the values of E_n may be calculated. It is then seen that equation 13.23 is obeyed for $n = 2, 3, 4,$ and 5.

The exciton is, of course, neutral and therefore cannot carry an electric charge through the crystal. Nor is it affected by an electric field. It should be appreciated, however, that the exciton is a property of the whole lattice

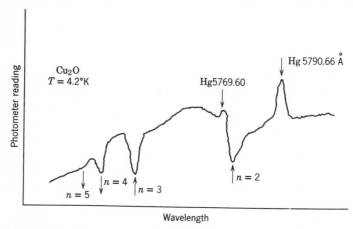

Figure 13.14   Transmission through Cu_2O at 4.2°K. The absorption is high at the wavelengths of the exciton series. The mercury lines are included for calibration. (After Apfel and Hadley)

of the crystal, and can transfer energy from one point to another. The exciton is not localized in position in the crystal as in the case of an impurity energy level.

Exciton levels often occur at energy values of about 0.8 of the energy gap. Lower values of energy are to be found associated with impurity levels in dielectric crystals. The mechanism of optical absorption of light by impurity levels is again given by an equation like (13.24) where E_n would be the impurity level. Levels are also found in crystals associated with lattice defects. The color changes found in crystals after irradiation by X-rays or neutrons are associated with defect levels. Naturally, if selective absorption at energy levels is present the crystal will be colored. If the dielectric crystal contains no impurity or defect levels, it will be transparent to visible light since the exciton levels we have discussed give absorption in the ultraviolet.

Often the absorption of light by electron transfer between levels is followed by the re-emission of light as the electron falls back to a lower level. This property of a solid is called *luminescence*. The time delay between absorption and re-emission serves to classify luminescent materials into two classes. If the time is less than about 10^{-8} sec, the material is classed as *fluorescent*, if longer than 10^{-8} sec, it is classed *phosphorescent*. Sometimes *phosphorescence* lasts up to several hours. Commercially useful phosphorescent materials are called *phosphors*.

13.10 Phosphors

Typical phosphors include zinc sulfide, zinc oxide, cadmium sulfide, and the organic materials anthracene, stilbene, and camphor. These

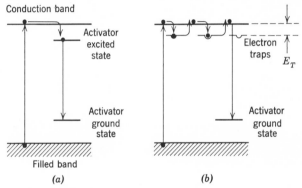

Figure 13.15   Energy band structure of two types of phosphor.

substances are perhaps better classed as semiconductors, since the impurity electron energy levels on which their phosphorescent nature depends are similar to the energy levels in extrinsic semiconductors, and the valence conduction gap is often not very wide. Often the chemical impurities or *activators*, as they are called, are deliberately added.

The energy band structure for two types of phosphor are shown in Fig. 13.15a and b. The process of phosphorescence may be generally considered as taking place in three stages: (a) absorption of incident energy, (b) the transfer and storage of this energy, and (c) the conversion of the energy into emitted light. Let us suppose that an incident light photon (or energetic electron or nuclear particle) is absorbed and produces an electron in the conduction band and a hole in the valence band. After a certain time the electron may be trapped in the activated state of the activator as in Fig. 13.15a or in another level independent of the activator as in 13.15b. The time that the electron stays in either trap before being thermally excited back into the conduction band is dependent on the factor $e^{-E_T/kT}$ where E_T is the *depth of the trap* or the energy difference between the trap and the bottom of the conduction band. An electron jump from the excited state of the activator to the ground state of the activator is usually very rapid. Thus an electron trapped in the excited

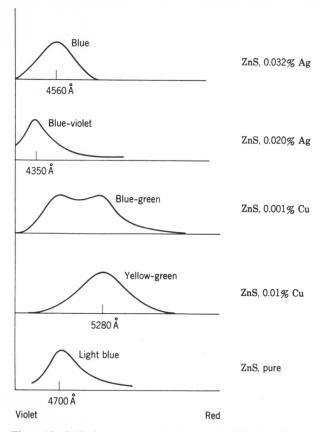

Figure 13.16   Emission bands of various zinc sulfide phosphors. (After Leverenz).

state will usually go down to the ground state in a very short time. The longer times between the incident radiation and the emitted radiation will therefore depend on the number of traps of the type shown in Fig. 13.15*b*. Often the electron can be trapped and reexcited into the conduction band many times before it finally falls to the ground state, emitting light.

Since the energy transition to the ground state is always less than the energy gap E_g, it follows that the wavelength of light emitted is always longer than that absorbed. The color of the light emitted depends, of course, on the activation levels present. Figure 13.16 shows emission bands in various zinc sulfide phosphors with added activators.

It might be surprising that the phosphorescent emission shown in Fig. 13.16 is in the form of bands of wavelengths and not as line spectra, since the activation levels we have talked about are sharply defined. Band emission occurs because the energy of the electron, as it sits momentarily in the activator trap, varies with the thermal motion of the trap. The

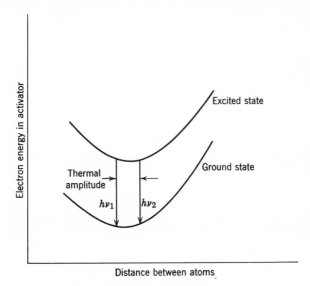

Figure 13.17 Dependence of energy in activator level on distance between neighboring atoms.

dependence of the energy in the activator level on distance between atoms is shown in Fig. 13.17. Transitions between excited and ground state may therefore lie between $h\nu_1$ and $h\nu_2$, depending on the phase of the thermal vibration. Since many electrons are held in many traps, the emitted light is therefore broadened into a band of wavelengths by the dependence of wavelength on the phase of the traps' thermal motion.

13.11 The Optical Laser

To conclude this chapter we will discuss a new phenomenon, *laser operation*, which, like luminescence, depends on the presence of localized energy levels in dielectric solids. We will illustrate the principles of this phenomenon with reference to a specific solid—ruby. Laser action was first reported in ruby by Mainian in 1960, and both technique and theory have since been extensively developed.

Ruby is aluminum oxide in which a few aluminum atoms have been replaced by chromium atoms, that is, Cr^{3+} in Al_2O_3. Ordinarily, of course, the electrons of the chromium atom are in their ground or lowest energy states. If the chromium atom is irradiated by green light, some of these electrons are excited into one or other of two excited states of chromium. No excitation into the conduction band is possible because of the large

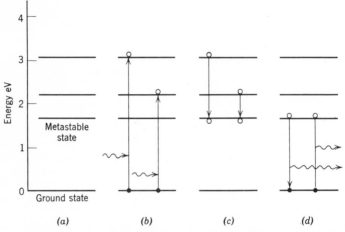

Figure 13.18   (a) Excited levels of chromium atom. (b) Atoms being excited by photons into higher states. (c) Excited atoms fall to metastable state. (c) Fall from metastable to ground state. Emission of photons.

energy gap. To make the distinction clear between this case and that in semiconduction, we will henceforth talk of the chromium *atom* being excited. The excited levels of chromium are shown in Fig. 13.18a and atoms being excited into the two states are shown in 13.18b. Normally at this point the excited chromium atoms would fall to a metastable state as shown in Fig. 13.18c and from there to the ground state, emitting in Fig. 13.18d fluorescent radiation in the red.

Suppose, however, that the chromium atoms, while in the metastable state, are bathed in light of a frequency similar to that which they are about to emit. In such a circumstance the atoms are *stimulated* to make the last transition much earlier than they would spontaneously. This stimulated emission in contrast to spontaneous emission distinguishes laser action from fluorescence.

The laser apparatus is shown in Fig. 13.19. A ruby rod of a specific size, with the end faces polished and half silvered, is placed near an electronic flash tube. The flash tube provides broad band pumping light. Up to a certain flash intensity ordinary fluorescence results. Above this critical intensity, however, laser action commences, and a powerful beam of red light flashes out from the ends of the ruby rod. This red light lasts for about 5×10^{-4} second and has the enormous power output of more than 10^4 watts over a beam of cross-sectional area 10^{-4} m. The emitted band is within a wavelength interval of about 0.02 Å. The beam from the end face of the ruby rod has an angular spread of less than one degree.

The two striking features of the laser are the amplification of light intensity and the narrow range of wavelengths emitted. The first of these

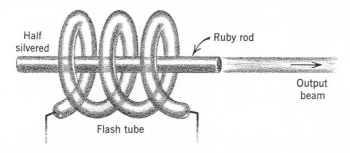

Figure 13.19   Ruby laser apparatus.

features is discussed with the help of Fig. 13.20. Figure 13.20*a* shows the ruby rod with the circles depicting the chromium atoms. Pumping light from the sides has excited a number of the atoms. The excited atoms are shown as open circles and the ground state atoms as filled circles. When an excited atom spontaneously emits a photon, shown by the arrow, in *b*, parallel to the axis of the crystal rod, this photon may stimulate a second atom to emit a second photon. Photons not parallel to the axis pass out of the crystal. The stimulation process is continued as in *c* while the photons are reflected back and forth between the half-silvered ends. The greatly amplified beam passes out through the end of the crystal.

The second feature—that of narrow range of emitted wavelengths—is a function of what is called the *coherence* of the emitted radiation. Normally, photons from different atoms in a solid are emitted completely at random. The wave associated with the photon from one atom is unlikely to be in phase with the wave from another atom. The beam of emitted light is *incoherent*. The difference in phase broadens the emitted spectral line. We have seen this before in fluorescence and it is, of course, the same effect which produces side bands in a modulated carrier wave in radio broadcasting. Now in stimulated emission the excited chromium atoms are

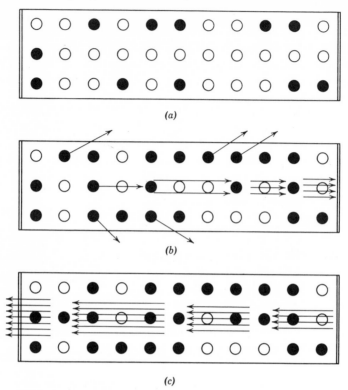

Figure 13.20   (*a*) Ruby rod with half-silvered ends. Open circles are excited chromium atoms. Filled circles are chromium atoms in ground state. (*b*) Arrows show photons emitted when excited atoms fall to ground state. The photons may stimulate other excited atoms with increasing photon emission. (*c*) After further stimulation the photons pass through the end of the ruby crystal.

made to emit practically simultaneously. The waves from these atoms are almost in phase and the beam of light is *coherent*. This gives a narrow spectral emission.

The list of potential applications of lasers includes uses in communication, chemical reaction control, amplification of weak light signals, and many others.

REFERENCES

A. J. Dekker, *Electrical Engineering Materials*, Prentice Hall, Englewood Cliffs, N.J., 1959.

C. Kittel, *Introduction to Solid State Physics*, John Wiley and Sons, New York, 1962.

A. Von Hippel, *Dielectric Materials and Applications*, John Wiley and Sons, New York, 1954.

R. L. Sproull, *Modern Physics*, John Wiley and Sons, New York, 1956.

EXERCISES

1. Calculate the electric dipole moments of the following charge configurations. (*a*) Charges of $+1$ microcoulombs are located at the points $(0, 0)$, $(1, 0)$ and $(2, 0)$ and charges of -1 microcoulombs are located at $(4, 0)$ $(5, 0)$ and $(6, 0)$. The number referring to meters. (*b*) Charges of $+3$ microcoulombs at $(0, 0)$; $+6$ microcoulombs at $(1, 1)$; -3 microcoulombs at $(1, 0)$; and -6 microcoulombs at $(0, 1)$.

2. A charge of Q coulombs is distributed homogeneously throughout the volume of a sphere of radius R meters. The sphere is in vacuum. Find the electric displacement D and the electric field strength $\mathscr{E}$ as a function of the distance from the center of the sphere.

3. Two square parallel plates of side 0.1 m are separated by a sulfur ($\epsilon_r = 4.0$) slab 0.01 m thick and are connected to a 200-volt battery. (*a*) What is the capacitance of this capacitor? (*b*) What is the charge on the plates? (*c*) What is the induced electric dipole moment per unit volume of dielectric? (*d*) What is the electric field strength in the sulfur?

4. The relative permittivity of argon at 0°C and 1 atmosphere pressure is 1.000435. Calculate the polarizability of the argon atom.

5. A long narrow cylindrical rod is composed of atoms each with polarizability 10^{-40} farad m^2. The solid contains 5×10^{28} atoms per cubic meter. An electric field is applied parallel to the length of the rod. Calculate the ratio of local to applied field.

6. The resonant frequency of a piezoelectric quartz crystal given by

$$f_0 = \frac{1}{2b} \sqrt{E/\rho}$$

where b is the dimension that determines the mode of oscillation of the crystal, E is Youngs Modulus, and ρ the density of quartz. Calculate useful sizes of crystal for oscillators in the kilocycle and megacycle ranges. For quartz, $E = 10^{10} \, n \, m^{-2}$; $\rho = 2500$ kg m^{-3}.

7. The fractional number of electrons released per second from traps in a particular phosphor is equal to $10^8 \, e^{-E_T/kT}$. If the intensity of phosphorescent light drops to half the value at the time of excitation in 0.02 second at 300°K, calculate the depth of trap E_T in electron volts. What is the time interval to half intensity at -50°C?

Appendix

A.I The Physical Constants

Speed of light	$c = 2.998 \times 10^8$ m sec^{-1}
Electronic charge	$e = 1.602 \times 10^{-19}$ coulomb
Electronic rest mass	$m = 9.108 \times 10^{-31}$ kg
Proton rest mass	$m = 1.672 \times 10^{-27}$ kg
Planck's constant	$h = 6.625 \times 10^{-34}$ joule sec
Boltzmann's constant	$k = 1.380 \times 10^{-23}$ joule deg^{-1}
	$= 8.616 \times 10^{-5}$ eV deg^{-1}
Gas constant	$R = 8.317 \times 10^3$ joule (kg mole)$^{-1}$ deg^{-1}
Avogadro's number	$N = 6.025 \times 10^{26}$ (kg mole)$^{-1}$
Bohr magneton	$\beta = 9.273 \times 10^{-24}$ amp m^2
Permittivity of free space	$\epsilon_0 = 8.854 \times 10^{-12}$ farad m^{-1}
Permeability of free space	$\mu_0 = 4\pi \times 10^{-7}$ henry m^{-1}

A.2 Conversion Factors

eV–joule conversion	1 eV $= 1.602 \times 10^{-19}$ joule
Magnetic induction conversion	1 gauss $= 10^{-4}$ weber m^{-2}
Magnetic field conversion	1 oersted $= 7.96$ amps m^{-1}
Magnetic suceptibilitys conversion	To convert susceptibility in cgs units to susceptibility in mks units, multiply by 4π.

Answers to Exercises

Chapter I

2. 7920 kg m^{-3}
   8990 kg m^{-3}
   7180 kg m^{-3}
   3530 kg m^{-3}
4. Coordinates $\frac{1}{2} \frac{1}{2}$ 0
   $r = 0.154R$ where R is radius of atom.
   Coordinates $\frac{1}{2} \frac{1}{4}$ 0
   $r = 0.291R$ where R is radius of atom.
5. (a) 1.73×10^{19} atoms per square meter
   (b) 1.77×10^{19} atoms per square meter
       1.09×10^{19} atoms per square meter
   (c) 1.63×10^{19} atoms per square meter

Chapter 2

1. (a) 3.85×10^{-10} m
   (b) 2.52×10^{-10} m
   (c) 0.41×10^{-10} m
2. (a) 2.3 m
   (b) 2.9×10^{-6} m
3. 6.23×10^{26} atoms per kg atomic weight.
4. 20.0×10^{-6} °K^{-1}
5. 3.304 Å

Chapter 3

1. fav. fav. fav.
   fav. fav. res.
   fav. fav. fav.
   fav. fav. fav.
   res. res. res.

357

2. 1, 2   1, 2   1, 1
   1, 2   1, 2   1, 1
   1, 2   1, 3   1, 4
   1, 2   1, 3   1, 4
   1, 2   1, 3   1, 3
   0, 3   1, 4   1, 3

3. 10^{15} hours

4. Interstitial.

5. Approximately 88 per cent nickel
   70 per cent nickel
   24 per cent nickel
   0.37 kg solid

6. 76 per cent α in eutectic
   (a) Liquid phase.
   (b) Liquid and β phases of which 53 per cent is β.
   (c) Eutectic microconstituent of which 28 per cent is α.

7. Method similar to that of exercise 6.

9. $K_0 \simeq 0.5$ and from Fig. 3.11.
   Ultimately purity is approximately 10^{-5} per cent by weight of copper. In approximately 13 passes.

Chapter 4

1. (a) $\dfrac{N!}{(N-n)!\,n!}$

   (b) $\dfrac{N'!}{(N'-n)!\,n!}$
   $\simeq 10^{31}$

2. $6 \times 10^{-7}\,\text{m}^2\,\text{sec}^{-1}$
   $6 \times 10^{-27}\,\text{m}^2\,\text{sec}^{-1}$

4. At 100°C, $D_V: D_M: D_R = 10^{27}: 10^{18}: 1$
   At 500°C, $D_V: D_M: D_R = 10^{13}: 10^{8.5}: 1$

5. D_2 $2 \times 10^{-28.5}\,\text{m}^2\,\text{sec}^{-1}$
   D_2 (volume) $0.72 \times 10^{-36.5}\,\text{m}^2\,\text{sec}^{-1}$
   D_2 (grain boundary) $0.14 \times 10^{-19.5}\,\text{m}^2\,\text{sec}^{-1}$

Chapter 5

1. $\sigma_1 + \sigma_2 = -\dfrac{E}{\nu}\left(\dfrac{d_s - d_u}{d_u}\right)$

if d_s and d_u is the spacing of atomic planes lying parallel to the surface in the stressed and unstressed condition respectively.
(511) plane.

2. 2×10^6 n m^{-2}
4. 13.1 Å
5. 137 calories
6. 0.83 min

Chapter 6

1. Radius: 1.07×10^{-4} m
   Pitch: 6.72×10^{-4} m
   Frequency: 1.4×10^{10} sec
2. 2.38×10^{17} sec^{-1}
3. 1.24×10^4 volts
4. 0.11 Å
5. 5.05×10^{-15} m
6. 5.47 Å
7. 1.3 per cent
8. (a) Energy difference: 10.92×10^{-19} joules
      Wavelength: 1840 Å
   (b) Energy difference: 27.30×10^{-35} joules
      Wavelength: 7.29×10^8 m

Chapter 7

1. 1.97×10^6 m sec^{-1}
2. Energy: -2.42×10^{-19} joule
   Angular momentum: 1.49×10^{-34} kg m^2 sec^{-1}
   $\qquad\qquad\qquad\qquad 2.58 \times 10^{-34}$ kg m^2 sec^{-1}
   Wavelength: 1030 Å
3. Momentum: 1.10×10^{-24} kg m sec^{-1}
   Energy: 6.63×10^{-19} joule
4. $\pm \kappa_x \pm 2\kappa_y = \dfrac{\pi}{a} 5, \pm 2\kappa_x \pm \kappa_y = \dfrac{\pi}{a} 5, \pm \kappa_x \pm \kappa_y = \dfrac{\pi}{a} 2$
5. $\pm \kappa_x \pm \kappa_y = \dfrac{\pi}{a} 2, \pm \kappa_x \pm \kappa_z = \dfrac{\pi}{a} 2, \pm \kappa_y \pm \kappa_z = \dfrac{\pi}{a} 2$
6. Surface is hexagonal with faces parallel to those of conventional unit cell. The dimensions of the zone are inversely proportional to those of the cell.

Chapter 8

1. 1260 °K
2. 0.684 eV, 25 per cent
3. 2.8×10^{-9}

4. Wavelength: 1.38 Å
   Potential difference: 8950 volts
5. 0.97×10^{-18} joule
6. 2.9×10^{-9} newtons
7. 5.1×10^{23}
8. Fermi energy: 4.67 eV
   Fermi temperature: 54,200 °K

Chapter 9

1. 2760 Å
2. Current: 4.40×10^{-7} amp m^{-2}
   Potential: 0.48 volt
4. 0.54 μa
5. Current: 0.585 μa
   Change in ϕ: 0.015 eV
6. 0.08 volt
7. 1.51×10^2, 0.63 per cent

Chapter 10

1. 2.02×10^6 m sec^{-1}
2. 5.31×10^{-8} m
3. 2.54×10^{28} m^{-3}
4. $m^*/m = 0.755$
5. 4.6×10^2 joule m^{-2} sec^{-1} (deg m^{-1})$^{-1}$
6. 150 amps

Chapter 11

1. 2.33 mhos m^{-1}
   0.11 mho m^{-1} °K^{-1}
2. $E_g - E_F = 0.16$ eV
   3120 mhos m^{-1}
3. $E_F = 0.20$ eV
   304 mhos m^{-1}
4. Carry out calculation with 4×10^{22} donors.
5. 1.6×10^{22} carriers m^{-3}
   0.04 m^2 volt sec^{-1}
6. 2.3×10^{-4} volt
9. 0.18 volt

10. (a) $hv = 3.1\,\text{eV}$, Gap $= 2.4\,\text{eV}$
(b) 16.1×10^{13}
(c) $\Delta\sigma = 2.6 \times 10^{-10}\,\text{mho m}^{-1}$

Chapter 12

1. $B = \dfrac{\mu_0\mu_r I}{2\pi a} = 10^{-6}\,\text{webers m}^{-2}$
2. $-0.05\,\text{amp m}^{-1}$
3. $\simeq -5 \times 10^{-6}$
4. At $300°\text{K}$: $2.4 \times 10^{-27}\,\text{amp m}^2$
At $1°\text{K}$: $7.2 \times 10^{-25}\,\text{amp m}^2$
At $300\,°\text{K}$: fraction <0.01 per cent
At $1\,°\text{K}$: fraction 54 per cent
5. (a) $35{,}200\,\text{Mc sec}^{-1}$
(b) $53.5\,\text{Mc sec}^{-1}$
6. (a) $15.8 \times 10^5\,\text{amps m}^{-1}$
(b) 0.66
(c) 1580
(d) $3140\,\text{webers m}^{-2}$
7. 4β

Chapter 13

1. (a) $12\,\mu\text{Cm}$ in $-x$ direction
(b) $3\,\mu\text{Cm}$ in x direction
2. $r < R$: $\mathbf{D} = Qr/4\pi R^3$: $\mathscr{E} = Qr/4\pi\epsilon_0 R^3$
$r > R$: $\mathbf{D} = Q/4\pi r^2$: $\mathscr{E} = Q/4\pi\epsilon_0 r^2$
3. (a) $35.4 \times 10^{-12}\,\text{farad}$
(b) $7.08 \times 10^{-9}\,\text{coulomb}$ on each plate
(c) $5.31 \times 10^{-7}\,\text{C m}^{-2}$
(d) $2 \times 10^4\,\text{V m}^{-1}$
4. $1.43 \times 10^{-40}\,\text{farad m}^{-2}$
5. $\mathscr{E}_{\text{Loc}}/\mathscr{E} = 1.23$
6. $1\,\text{kc sec}^{-1}$: $1\,\text{m}$
$10\,\text{kc sec}^{-1}$: $0.1\,\text{m}$
$1\,\text{Mc sec}^{-1}$: $10^{-3}\,\text{m}$
$10\,\text{Mc sec}^{-1}$: $10^{-4}\,\text{m}$
7. $0.38\,\text{eV}$
$1.7\,\text{sec}$

Index